Formula One MATHS

A2

Catherine Berry ● **Margaret Bland**
Sophie Goldie ● **Terry Heard**
Leonie Turner ● **Brandon Wilshaw**

SERIES EDITOR: **Roger Porkess**

HODDER
EDUCATION
AN HACHETTE UK COMPANY

Introduction

This book is designed for Year 7 students and is the first in a series covering Key Stage 3 Mathematics. It contains a considerable amount of enrichment material, designed to interest and challenge talented students. Each textbook in the series is accompanied by an extensive Teacher's Resource including additional material. This allows the series to be used with the full ability range of students.

The series builds on the National Numeracy Strategy in primary schools and its extension into Key Stage 3. It is designed to support the style of teaching and the lesson framework to which students will be accustomed.

This book is presented as a series of double-page spreads, each of which is designed to be a teaching unit. The left-hand page covers the material to be taught and the right-hand page provides examples for the students to work through. Each chapter ends with a review exercise covering all its content. Further worksheets, tests and ICT materials are provided in the Teacher's Resource.

An important feature of the left-hand pages is the Tasks, which are printed in boxes. These are intended to be carried out by the student in mid-lesson. Their aim is twofold: in the first place they give the students practice on what they have just been taught, allowing them to consolidate their understanding. However, the tasks then extend the ideas and raise questions, setting the agenda for the later part of the lesson. Further guidance on the Tasks is available in the Teacher's Resource.

Another key feature of the left-hand pages is the Discussion Points. These are designed to help teachers engage their students in whole class discussion. Teachers should see the ? as an opportunity and an invitation.

Several other symbols and instructions are used in this book, which are explained on the 'How to use this book' page for students opposite. The ⌨ symbol indicates to the teacher that there is additional ICT material directly linked to that unit of work. This is referenced in the teaching notes for that unit in the Teacher's Resource.

The order of the 27 chapters in this book ensures that the subject is developed logically, at each stage building on previous knowledge. The Teacher's Resource includes a Scheme of Work based on this order. However, teachers are of course free to vary the order to meet their own circumstances and needs.

This book includes a number of questions from Junior Mathematical Olympiad (JMO) papers and we are grateful to the United Kingdom Mathematics Trust for permission to use them. These questions require careful thought and some mathematical ingenuity. Particular emphasis is placed on the quality of explanation that accompanies the answers. Further information on the UKMT can be found on www.ukmt.org.uk.

This series stems from a partnership between Hodder and Stoughton Educational and Mathematics in Education and Industry (MEI).

The authors would like to thank all those who helped in preparing this book, particularly Nick Lord who contributed many good ideas and Pat Perkins who was the source of some of the paper folding questions. They would also like to thank those involved with the writing of materials for the accompanying Teacher's Resource.

Roger Porkess   2002
Series Editor

How to use this book

 This symbol means that you will need to think carefully about a point. Your teacher may ask you to join in a discussion about it.

 This symbol next to a question means that you are allowed (and indeed expected) to use your calculator for this question.

 This symbol means exactly the opposite – you are not allowed to use your calculator for this question.

 This is a warning sign. It is used where a common mistake, or misunderstanding, is being described. It is also used to identify questions which are slightly more difficult or which require a little more thought.

It should be read as 'caution'.

 This is the ICT symbol. It should alert your teacher to the fact that there is some additional material in the accompanying Teacher's Resource using ICT for this unit of work.

Each chapter of work in this book is divided into a series of double page spreads – or units of work. The left-hand page is the teaching page, and the right-hand page involves an exercise and sometimes additional activities or investigations to do with that topic.

You will also come across the following features in the units of work:

Task

The tasks give you the opportunity to work alone, in pairs or in small groups on an activity in the lesson. It gives you the chance to practise what you have just been taught, and to discuss ideas and raise questions about the topic.

Do the right thing!

These boxes give you a set of step-by-step instructions on how to carry out a particular technique in maths, usually to do with shape work.

JMO Question

These problems are from some recent Junior Mathematical Olympiad (JMO) papers. The use of calculators and measuring instruments is not allowed and you must accompany your answers with clear explanations and proofs.

Contents

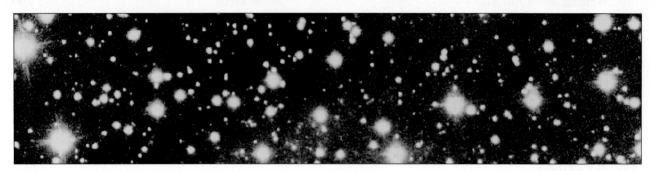

There are 100 000 000 000 stars in our galaxy.

? **How do you say 100 000 000 000 in words?**

The scientific or mathematical way of writing 100 000 000 000 is 10^{11}.
10^{11} means $10 \times 10 \times 10 \times 10 \times 10 \times 10 \times 10 \times 10 \times 10 \times 10 \times 10$.

Say this as '10 to the power of 11'.

? **How many noughts are there in 100 000 000 000?**
What is the connection between the power of ten and the number of noughts?

Task

Copy and complete the table below.

Name	Number	Power of ten	Example
ten	10	10^1	ten fingers
hundred	100	10^2	hundred years in a century
thousand	1000	10^3	
ten thousand	1 0000	10^4	
hundred thousand	100 000	10^5	
million	100 000 0	10^6	
billion	1 000 000 000	10^9	
trillion	1 000 000 000 000	10^{12}	

? **Look at the powers of ten for the numbers thousand, million and billion.**
What do you notice?

? **How many noughts are there in ten billion?**
Write the number 100 000 000 in words.

Look at the number 673 802.

673 802

This 6 represents 600 000. It is in the 100 000s column.

8 is in the 100s column. It represents 800.

? **How do you say 673 802 in words?**
In large numbers the digits are grouped in threes. Why?

Exercise

1 Write as a power of ten:
(a) 100
(b) 100 000
(c) 10 000 000 000
(d) 10 000 000 000 000 000.

2 Write in figures:
(a) ten thousand
(b) one hundred thousand
(c) ten million.

3 Choose the larger number from each of the following pairs of numbers:
(a) 10^4 and one thousand
(b) 100 000 and 10^6
(c) ten billion and 10^9.

4 In 1352 the 3 is in the 100s column. It represents 300.
For each of the following numbers say which column the 3 is in, and how much it represents.
(a) 732
(b) 3179
(c) 65 382
(d) 738 924
(e) 3 768 772
(f) 384 200 789
(g) 38 567 486
(h) 67 824 253

5 Write the following numbers in figures.

(a) Four thousand two hundred and sixty five.
(b) Five hundred thousand, six hundred and eighty seven.
(c) Eight million, two hundred and seven thousand, three hundred and ninety five.
(d) Seven billion, six hundred and twenty thousand, four hundred and nineteen.

6 Write these numbers in words.
(a) 6574
(b) 12 876
(c) 675 004
(d) 3 450 672
(e) 27 102 005

7 Elisabeth has lived one million hours. Guess how old she is. Now use your calculator to work out her age to the nearest year, and see how near your guess was.

Activity 1
In a school there are 10 English teachers.
Each teacher has to mark 100 pupils' work.
Each pupil writes 10 essays. Each essay is 10 pages long.
Each page contains 1000 words.
How many words, in total, are read by all the English teachers?

Activity 2
(a) The British meaning of the word 'billion' has chang[ed]
50 years. Find out about this.
(b) Find the meaning of these words: quadrillion, m[i]
googol, googolplex.

Using large numbers

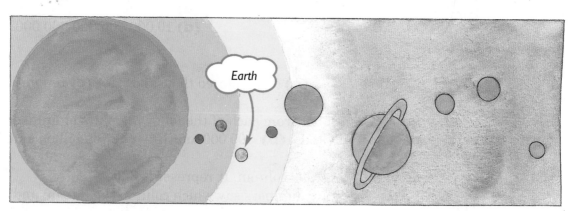

Light travels 300 000 000 metres every second.
It takes 500 seconds for light to travel from the sun to earth.

150 000 000 000

 What is the distance between the sun and the earth?

Calculations like this can be done easily when you know how to deal with numbers containing lots of noughts.

Task

Copy and complete the multiplication table given right.

×	10	100	20	30	200	300	1000	4000
2	20	200	40	60	400	600	2000	8000
5	50	500	100	150	1000	1500	5000	20000
7	70	700	140	210	1400	2100	7000	28000
12	120	1200	2					
20								
22								
200								

 Work out 330 × 200 000.
Explain how to do this in your head.

Dividing by numbers containing lots of noughts can often be done in your head.

$200 \div 10$
$20\emptyset \div 1\emptyset = 20$

To divide by 10, remove a nought.

$6300 \div 300$
$63\emptyset\emptyset \div 3\emptyset\emptyset = 21$

To divide 6300 by 300, divide by 100 by removing 2 noughts. Then divide 63 by 3.

Write down the answer to 4 800 000 ÷ 200.
in how you got your answer.

Exercise

You may need to know the following to work out some of the questions below.

   1 Speed = distance ÷ time
   2 Distance = speed × time
   3 Time = distance ÷ speed

1 Write down the answers to the following:

  (a) 40 × 20   **(b)** 120 × 40   **(c)** 60 × 700
  (d) 700 × 8000   **(e)** 1300 × 30 000   **(f)** 1300 × 40

2 Work these out in your head.

  (a) 500 ÷ 10   **(b)** 360 ÷ 20   **(c)** 360 ÷ 30
  (d) 1000 ÷ 50   **(e)** 427 000 ÷ 700   **(f)** 10 800 ÷ 900

3 The distance around the earth at the equator is about 24 000 miles.
The earth turns round once every day (24 hours).

Shetland Isles

  (a) How fast is a person travelling because of the
       earth's rotation when standing on the equator?

At latitude 60° north, the distance around the
earth parallel to the equator is about 12 000 miles.
The Shetland Isles are at latitude 60° north.

  (b) How fast is somebody standing in the Shetlands
       travelling?

4 A light year is the distance that light travels in a year. The speed of light
is 300 000 000 metres every second.
  (a) How far does light travel in 1 minute?
  (b) How far does light travel in 1 hour?
  (c) How far does light travel in a year? (This is the length of a light year.)

5 The distance from the earth to the nearest star (apart from the Sun) is
about 43 trillion kilometres. How many light years is this?

Activity

  1 A red blood cell lives for 4 months.
    It travels 1 metre every minute.
    How far does it travel in its lifetime?

  2 There are 126 million cells in the retina of the human eye.
    A typical cell contains 1 billion molecules of fat.
    How many molecules of fat in the retina of the human eye?

  3 Venus is 110 million kilometres from the sun.
    How many metres is this?
    How long will it take for light from the sun to reach Venus?

The metric system

The best is yet to come...

For just £23K on the road –
you get the car of your dreams and a lot more besides...

GLOBAL

? How much does the car cost?

? The K stands for *kilo*. Where else have you seen the prefix *kilo*?

In the *metric system* of measures, length can be measured in *centi*metres.

? What does the prefix *centi* tell you?
Weight can be measured in *milligrams*. What does *milli* mean?

Task

Copy and complete the table below for the metric system of measures.

Prefix	Size	How the prefix is used
giga	$\times 10^9$ (or 1 000 000 000)	
mega		
kilo		1 kilogram = 1000 grams
hecto		1 hectare = 100 ares
deca		
Basic unit	$\times 1$	*Metre, litre, gram, are*
deci		
centi	$\times \frac{1}{100}$	1 centimetre = $\frac{1}{100}$ of a metre or 100 cm = 1 metre
milli		
micro		
nano		

1 are = 100 square metres

? What fraction of a second is a nanosecond? How many decimetres in a metre?

Length is usually measured in kilometres (km), metres (m), centimetres (cm) and millimetres (mm).

? From the measurements below match any that are equal in length.

200 cm	5 km	1.5 m	2 m	0.65 m	5000 m	1 500 cm	150 cm
6.5 cm	65 cm	0.002 km	500 000 cm	650 mm	1 500 mm	65 mm	

Exercise

1 The volume of bottles of liquid is given in litres, centilitres (cl) or millilitres (ml). From the measurements opposite, select any volumes that are equivalent.

> 330 ml   70 cl   20 cl   33 cl
> 200 cl   1.5 litres   50 cl
> 0.7 litre   2 litres   3300 ml
> 0.5 litre   1500 ml   3.3 litres
> 200 ml   500 ml

2 Fill in the blank spaces in the following sentences.
(a) There are _____ centimetres in a metre.
(b) A _____ metre is $\frac{1}{100}$th of a metre.
(c) There are 1 000 _____ grams in a gram.
(d) A kilolitre is _____ litres.
(e) A megawatt is _____ watts.
(f) There are 1 000 milliamps in _____.
(g) To change from metres to millimetres multiply by _____.
(h) A volume in centilitres can be changed into litres by _____ by 100.
(i) The prefix _____ means 10 of the basic unit.
(j) A giga-unit is _____ × the basic unit.

(Amps and watts are used when measuring electricity.)

3 3 litres is the same as 300 cl and 3000 ml.
Write each of the measurements below in two different ways.
(a) 5 grams   **(b)** 7 metres   **(c)** 35 centimetres
(d) 70 centilitres   **(e)** 2 kilometres   **(f)** 0.8 kilograms

4 Write the following in order, smallest first.

0.5 m,   35.9 cm, $\frac{1}{1000}$ of a kilometre,   512 mm

5 **(a)** Given that 1 tera-unit = 1000 giga-units and 1 pico-unit = $\frac{1}{1000}$ nano-unit, extend your copy of the table on the opposite page.
(b) Is 1 light year more or less than 1 terametre?
(c) How many picoseconds are there in 1 terasecond?

Activity   The size of a computer's memory is measured in bytes.
A kilobyte is 1024 bytes (not 1000 bytes).
Find out why.

How many bytes are there in a megabyte?
How many in a gigabyte?

The answers are not 1 000 000 and 1 000 000 000 but they are near to these numbers.

Finishing off

Now that you have finished this chapter you should:

- be able to write large numbers in words and figures
- know how to write powers of ten
- know how big 1 million, 1 billion and 1 trillion are
- be able to multiply and divide large numbers that end in noughts
- understand the meaning of the prefixes used in the metric system of measures.

Review exercise

1 Place the following numbers in ascending order of size:

45 678   40 × 1000 10^5 54 678 10^4 1 million.

2 Write in words the numbers contained in each of the sentences below.
 (a) Jupiter is 778 300 000 km from the sun.
 (b) Greenland has an area of 2 175 000 square kilometres.
 (c) Everest is 8848 metres high.
 (d) The age of the dinosaurs lasted for 167 000 000 years.
 (e) There are 31 536 000 seconds in a year.
 (f) An accurate value for light speed is 299 792 500 metres per second.

3 Write these numbers in figures.
 (a) One million two hundred and fifty thousand, seven hundred and twenty six.
 (b) Ten billion three hundred and fifty three million, seven hundred and five thousand and twenty four.

4 Work out:
 (a) 200 × 300   **(b)** 32 000 × 200   **(c)** 2400 × 30
 (d) 800 ÷ 40   **(e)** 24 000 ÷ 800   **(f)** 36 000 000 ÷ 1200.

5 Take the orbits of the planets around the Sun to be circular.
 (a) As they move around the Sun, what is the farthest apart that the Earth and Mars can be?
 (b) What is the closest that Earth and Mars can be?

Planet	Distance from the sun in km
Earth	149 600 000
Mars	227 900 000
Saturn	1 427 000 000

 (c) What are the greatest and least separations of Mars and Saturn?
 (d) Are the orbits really circular?

6 A square of dots is made like this:

(a) How many dots is this?

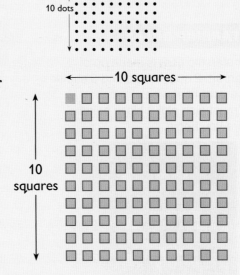

A larger square is made from smaller squares, like this:

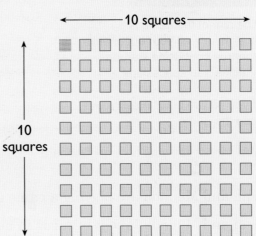

(b) What is the total number of dots in this square?

These new squares are now arranged to form an even larger square, like this:

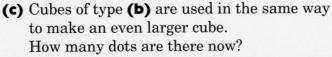

(c) How many dots are there now?

7 **(a)** A cube of dots is made like this. How many dots are there?

(b) A larger cube measuring 10 cubes by 10 cubes by 10 cubes is made from smaller cubes of the type shown in **(a)**. What is the total number of dots in the larger cube?

(c) Cubes of type **(b)** are used in the same way to make an even larger cube. How many dots are there now?

(d) This process is repeated. Write down the number of dots at the 4th, 5th and 6th stages. At what stage does the number of dots first exceed one googol (10^{100})?

STARSHIP RULES

Your starship fleet is made up of
1 starport, 2 spaceships and 3 shuttles.
Place your fleet wisely!
You must also plot 2 black holes
before you begin.

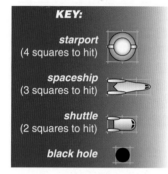

KEY:

starport
(4 squares to hit)

spaceship
(3 squares to hit)

shuttle
(2 squares to hit)

black hole

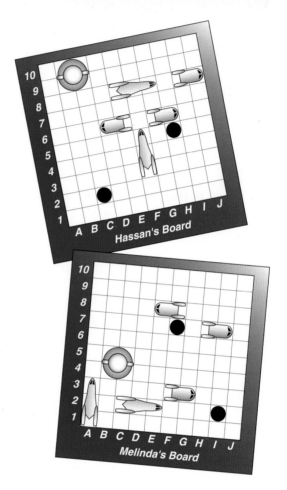

Hassan's Board

Melinda's Board

❶ The aim of the game is
to eliminate all your opponent's
squares containing starports,
shuttles and spaceships.

❷ If you hit two black holes you
lose the game.

❸ You cannot see your opponent's board.

Hassan and Melinda are playing a game of Starships.

Hassan and Melinda take it in turns to name a square to eliminate on the other's board.

Hassan goes first and chooses square C5. He hits parts of a starport.

Go along to C   Then go up 5

To choose a square the letter is always given first, and then the number of squares up.

? What other squares should Hassan hit to completely eliminate the starport?
Which 2 squares contain black holes on Melinda's board?
What is contained in square D6 on Hassan's board?

Task

Play your own game of Starships with a partner.

Exercise

1 The diagram shows part of a seating plan in an aeroplane.

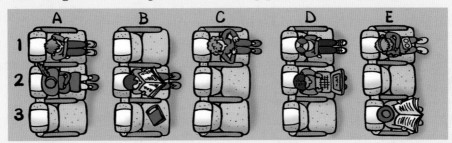

(a) What colour hair has the person in seat B2?
(b) What is the man in seat D2 doing?
(c) Which seats are empty?
(d) In which seats are people wearing hats sitting?

2 Here is a map of Skull Island. Blackbeard and his pirate crew are using the map to try to find the buried treasure.

(a) The pirates want to land on the island. In which square should they leave their ship?
(b) In which squares are the dangerous rocks?
(c) What is in square B4?
(d) Where on the island is there quick sand?
(e) Where would you be if you were at the following squares:
    (i) E7   **(ii)** D5   **(iii)** A6?
(f) In which square is the treasure?
(g) Write down which squares the pirates should pass through to reach the treasure safely.

Activity   Find out how chess or draughts games are recorded.
        Play one of these games with a friend, writing down each move.

The National Grid

Many road atlases use the **National Grid** to describe positions of places.

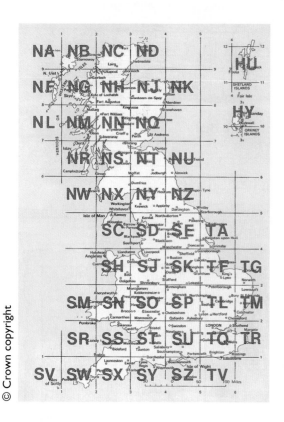

© Crown copyright

This is a grid of squares over a map of Great Britain. The squares are 100 km across.

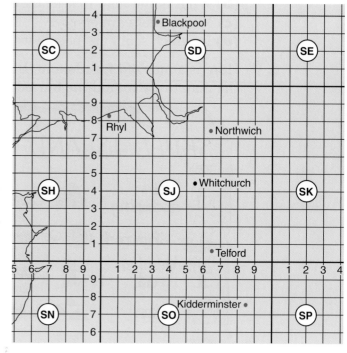

Each large square is divided into small squares. The position of Whitchurch is described as SJ54.

Task

1 Write down the positions of the following places:
Northwich, Telford, Rhyl, Blackpool, Kidderminster.
2 Explain how the system works.

3 How wide is each small square?
4 How many small squares are there in each large square?
5 How *accurate* is a grid reference such as SJ54?

A two figure National Grid reference gives the approximate position of anywhere in Britain.

? **Can you give an approximate position for your school?**
Which large National Grid square is it in?

Exercise

Here is a map of part of Scotland showing National Grid squares.

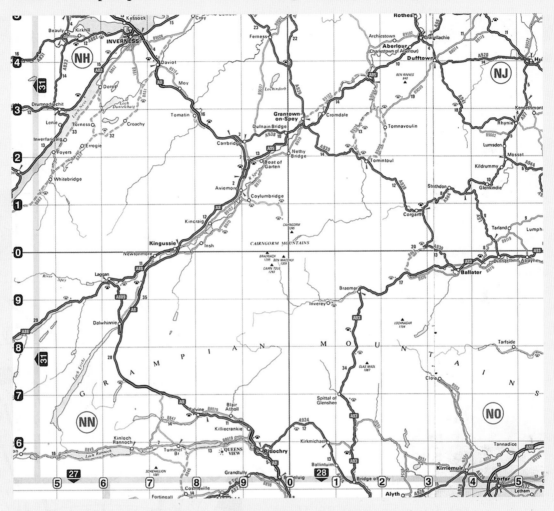

1   Give the National Grid references of these places:
     (a) Grantown-on-Spey   **(b)** Inverness   **(c)** Aberlour   **(d)** Ballater

2   Write down the names of the places with these National Grid references:
     (a) NH70   **(b)** NN68   **(c)** NJ11   **(d)** NO47   **(e)** NJ22

3   Write down the National Grid references of Kildrummy, Glenkindie and
     Mossat. (They are in square NJ.)
     What is the problem? What is the solution?
     Explain how Kildrummy could be given the four figure reference NJ4618.
     Give the four figure references of Glenkindie and Mossat.

Investigation   Six figure references give even greater accuracy.
                     Explain how these work.
                     Two houses have identical six figure National Grid references.
                     What is the greatest possible distance between these houses?

Finishing off

Now that you have finished this chapter you should be able to:

- describe the position of a square systematically
- use map referencing
- understand seating plans, etc.

Review exercise

1 Sally is rearranging her bedroom.
She draws a plan of her room.
Each square represents 1 square metre.

(a) What is in square B2?

(b) What is in square C3?

(c) In which squares is her bed?

(d) Where is Sally's desk?

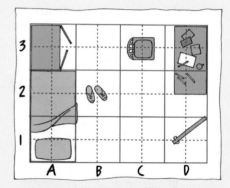

2 Here is the seating plan of
a cinema.

(a) How many seats are
there in row C?

(b) How many seats are there
between the two aisles in
row D?

(c) Jenny has seat E8. How
many rows are there in
front of her?

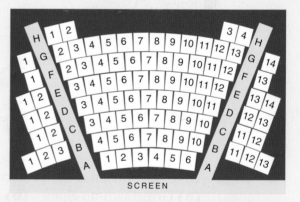

SCREEN

(d) Matt has seat F5. How many seats are there between him and the
nearer aisle?

(e) Alison has seat A1. Charlie has seat A6. How many seats are there
between them in that row?

(f) Write down the seats where you can sit with no-one next to you.

(g) Find the pairs of seats where two people can sit by themselves.

3 The village church and the village inn are joined by a straight road (all in
the same National Grid square). They are in the centres of the squares
with these grid references:

Church: 432135,   Inn: 432128.

(a) What is the direction from the church to the inn?

(b) How far is the inn from the church?

4 This map is part of the London A–Z. Underground stations are represented by red circles with blue strips.

(a) Charing Cross underground station is given in the index as 2A 52. Explain how the referencing system works.

(b) Give the names and references of the other underground stations on this map.

(c) In which squares will you find:
 (i) Downing Street
 (ii) Strand
 (iii) The Houses of Parliament.

5 Here is a **spreadsheet** from a computer screen. Each rectangle is called a **cell**.

	A	B	C	D	E	F	G	H	I
1									
2		34		56		45			
3		25		5		5			
4		25		965		0			
5		91		34		3			
6		10000		32		1			
7									
8	TOTALS	10175		1092		54			
9									

D8 = SUM(D1:D6)

Microsoft Excel - Formula One Maths.xls

(a) What number is in cell B3?

(b) What number is in cell D5?

(c) In which cell is the word TOTALS?

(d) Why does the reference D8 appear above the grid?

(e) Above the grid you can see =SUM(D1:D6). Can you explain this?

(f) Where can you find 34 + 25 + 25 + 91 + 10 000 on the grid?

(g) Write down the references of the cells which contain *even* numbers.

FILM OF THE WEEK

Crimson Tide (PG) (1995) ★★★★

Starring: Gene Hackman, Denzel Washington
Don't miss this exciting submarine drama.
Running time: 135 minutes

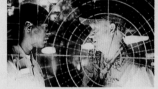

Tatjana has two video tapes, each of 180 minutes.

On the first she has two episodes of 'Neighbours', each 25 minutes long. On the second she has recorded 'Champions of Nature', which is 30 minutes long.

 Can she record 'Crimson Tide' on either tape without wiping out her earlier recordings?

Task

Tatjana wants to record all the programmes listed below. What is the smallest number of video tapes she can use (180 minutes on each) and which programmes should she put on each tape?

The Flintstones	25 mins	Charlie Brown	30 mins	The Waltons	1 hr
From Earth to Moon	1 hr 35 mins	Storm Forces	25 mins	High School High	45 mins
The Simpsons	30 mins	Tom and Jerry	10 mins	Hercules	55 mins
Finian's Rainbow	2 hrs 15 mins	Dappledown	30 mins		

Task

In one very strange cricket match all 11 batsmen's scores are consecutive numbers.

1 What is the smallest total they could have scored?

2 What are the scores of the batsmen if the total is

   (a) 121 runs   **(b)** 374 runs   **(c)** 616 runs?

3 Could the total be   **(a)** 84 runs   **(b)** 95 runs?

Exercise

1 The table shows distances, in miles, between towns in Britain.

Bristol							
36	Gloucester						
213	178	Leeds					
172	137	44	Manchester				
233	211	172	185	Norwich			
145	110	74	71	119	Nottingham		
220	191	24	71	181	87	York	
120	102	198	202	116	131	211	London

Find the distances travelled on the following journeys.
(a) Bristol to Gloucester then Gloucester to Nottingham.
(b) Leeds to Manchester then Manchester to Nottingham.
(c) Nottingham to Norwich then Norwich to London.
(d) Bristol to Gloucester then Gloucester to Nottingham then Nottingham to York.
(e) York to Leeds then Leeds to Nottingham then Nottingham to London.
(f) London to Norwich then Norwich to Nottingham then Nottingham to Manchester.

2 England need 132 runs to win a game of cricket.
How many more must be scored at each stage if:
(a) one opening batsman gets 24
(b) the first two batsmen get 53 altogether
(c) the first three batsmen get 76 altogether
(d) the first six batsmen get 105 altogether
(e) the first nine batsmen get 128 altogether?

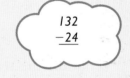

3 **(a)** Tatjana's father needs to saw pieces of wood to the following sizes:

(i) 700 mm	**(ii)** 140 mm	**(iii)** 806 mm
(iv) 693 mm	**(v)** 715 mm	**(vi)** 932 mm.

In each case work out how much wood he has left if he takes a new piece of wood 1 m long (1000 mm) each time.

(b) If Tatjana's father starts with 1 m pieces of wood, but also uses up any left-over pieces, what is the smallest number of 1 m pieces he would need to use to cut all the pieces in part **(a)**?

JMO Question

The numbers from 1 to 7 inclusive are to be placed, one per square, in the diagram on the right so that the totals of the three numbers in the horizontal row and each of the two columns are the same.

In how many different ways can this be done if the numbers 1 and 2 must be in the positions shown?

Short multiplication and division

Leicester City in Transfer Scoop

Leicester City have signed soccer aces Roberto Luigi and Guiseppe Maldini. At 18 million Euros each, this is seen as the buy of the decade.

Numbers are grouped in threes from the units digit.

1 thousand	=	1000	(3 noughts)	1 million	=	1 000 000 (6 noughts)
4 thousand	=	4000		3 million	=	3 000 000
65 thousand	=	65 000		17 million	=	17 000 000

Task

Match these numbers and words correctly.

12 000 000

C forty thousand

D seventy-six million

A two thousand   2000   5000

40 000   **E** twelve million   **B** five thousand   76 000 000

? **What did the transfer fees for these two players cost Leicester City in pounds (£s)?**

Cost of players = 2 × 18 000 000 Euros
                = 36 000 000 Euros.

> 2 × 18 = 36
> 2 × 18 000 000 = 36 000 000

The exchange rate, at the time, was 3 Euros = £2.
So to change Euros to £s multiply by 2, then divide the answer by 3.

36 000 000 × 2 = 72 000 000

> 36 × 2 = 72
> 36 000 000 × 2 = 72 000 000

72 000 000 ÷ 3 = 24 000 000

Total cost of transfer fees = £24 000 000.

> 72 ÷ 3 = 24
> 72 000 000 ÷ 3 = 24 000 000

? **Each player is paid £40 000 a week. How much is this per year?**

Each player = £40 000 × 52 per year
            = £2 080 000 per year.
Total wages for Luigi and Maldini = 2 × £2 080 000 per year
                                  = £4 160 000 per year.

> There are 52 weeks in a year.
> 4 × 52 = 208
> 40 000 × 52 = 2 080 000

Exercise

1 Tickets for the section behind the goal at a football match cost £12 each. Find the total cost of
(a) 5 tickets bought by five friends
(b) 50 tickets bought by a coach party
(c) 5 000 tickets bought by home fans.

2 The local theatre is showing *Swan Lake*.
Here are the ticket prices.

What is the total cost of tickets for:
(a) a couple if they sit
  (i) in section A
  (ii) in section B
(b) a family of five if they sit
  (i) in section B   (ii) in section C

(c) a small coach party of twenty people if they sit
  (i) in section A
  (ii) in section C

(d) a large coach party of fifty people if they sit
  (i) in section C
  (ii) in section D.

The Touring Ballet Company present
——— SWAN LAKE ———
27 December - 20 January
Ticket Prices:
Section A (Balcony) £8 each
Section B (Upper Circle) £11 each
Section C (Dress Circle) £14 each
Section D (Stalls) £17 each
Avonford Theatre A_T

3 In these multiplications each letter represents a missing digit.
Find these missing digits. Hint: Find B first, then D, then A and C.

(a)
```
   A 7 B
 ×     3
 ───────
 C 4 D 5
```

(b)
```
   E 6 4
 ×     F
 ───────
 6 1 G 2
```

(c)
```
   H I J K
 ×       7
 ─────────
 3 6 7 2 9
```

4 Change the following to £s using the method shown on the opposite page.
(a) 15 Euros
(b) 18 Euros
(c) 270 Euros
(d) 4800 Euros
(e) 540 Euros
(f) 324 000 Euros

5 A coach party of forty people visit the following places in London.
How much is the cost per person for each outing if the total cost is:
(a) Madame Tussaud's   £480
(b) Buckingham Palace   £1400
(c) West End Show   £960
(d) Chelsea versus Arsenal football match   £600.

6 In these divisions each letter represents a missing digit.
Find these missing digits.

(a)
```
    L M 5
 3 )9 7 N
```

(b)
```
      5 3 8
 P )4 Q 4 R
```

(c)
```
      6 5 3
 7 )S T U V
```

Investigation Devise quick methods for multiplying a number by
(a) 25   (b) 99   (c) 1001.
Explain why your methods work.

Long multiplication and more division

The Patel family are taking a 16-day holiday costing £128 per day. How much is this altogether?

Fly to the Rockies

Canada Travel

Cruise to Alaska

Spectacular mountains, ice-scapes, glaciers, SNOW, SNOW, SNOW...

You need to calculate: £128 × 16

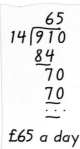

? **Look at the calculation. Explain in simple words how you do it.**

$128 \times 10 = 1280$
$128 \times 6 = 768$

$$\begin{array}{r} 128 \\ \times\ 16 \\ \hline 1280 \\ 768 \\ \hline 2048 \end{array}$$

Total cost of holiday: £2048

They look at another holiday. It is £910 for 14 days.
Rita works out how much this is per day.

? **Explain, step by step, what Rita has done.**

$$\begin{array}{r} 65 \\ 14\overline{\smash)910} \\ 84 \\ \hline 70 \\ 70 \\ \hline \cdots \end{array}$$

£65 a day

Rough Work

$\begin{array}{r} 14 \\ \times 5 \\ \hline 70 \end{array}$ $\begin{array}{r} 14 \\ \times 7 \\ \hline 98 \end{array}$

$\begin{array}{r} 14 \\ \times 6 \\ \hline 84 \end{array}$

Task

Copy and complete this crossnumber.

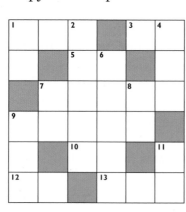

Across
1 12 × 12
3 225 ÷ 5
5 330 ÷ 15
7 672 × 60 add 3
9 479 × 21
10 361 ÷ 19
12 512 ÷ 8
13 49 × 9

Down
1 391 ÷ 23
2 One more than 60 × 700
4 19 × 27
6 11 797 × 2
7 800 ÷ 20
8 319 ÷ 11
9 14 × 14
11 612 ÷ 12

Their next holiday is to Nassau and will cost £3545 altogether.
There are four people in the family, so how much is this each?
You need to calculate: £3545 ÷ 4

? **Explain, step by step, how you would do this without a calculator.**

Exercise

1 How much would it cost in the currency given to stay for 17 days at the following places:
  (a) £65 per day
  (b) 187 Euros per day
  (c) 97 dollars per day
  (d) 238 Euros per day.

2 How much would a newspaper girl earn in a year if she was paid:
  (a) £7 per week
  (b) £16 per week
  (c) £23 per week
  (d) £14 per week?

3 The cost of a ferry journey from Hull to Amsterdam is £26 for one person. What is the total cost for:
  (a) 35 people
  (b) 48 people
  (c) 53 people?

4 How much is the cost per day of each of the following holidays?
  (a) an 11-day Ski holiday in the Alps for £1 375
  (b) a 16-day holiday in Canada for £2 048
  (c) a 14-day Greek Island cruise for £1 386
  (d) a 28-day Andes trek for £1 484.

Activity

An earlier way of multiplying was used in India in the 12th century, and reached Italy 200 years later.
Compare this example of 128×16 with the working opposite.

> *It is called gelosia multiplication because the grid it uses looks like a window grating (gelosia in Italian).*

1 Write one number along the top of the rectangle, and the other down the side. Divide the rectangle into blocks and then divide each block as shown.

2 Now multiply the top line by 1

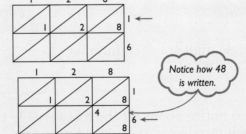

3 and then the bottom line by 6.

> *Notice how 48 is written.*

4 Add diagonally. When necessary carry into the next diagonal.

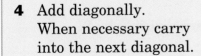
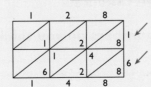

5 Answer 2048.

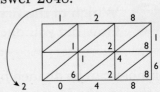

Now try these multiplications by this method:
(a) 23×12
(b) 428×35
(c) 7968×429
(d) 8004×405.

List some advantages and disadvantages of *gelosia* multiplication.

Multiples and divisibility tests

Mr. X Becomes Lottery Millionaire for a Second Time

Mr. X, who does not wish to be named for security reasons, became a multi-millionaire for the second time last night. He says the secret is to select at least one multiple of three in every line.

? **What is a multiple?**
How can you easily identify one?

Sometimes you only need to look at the end of the number.

All even numbers are divisible by 2.
714 is an even number as it ends with a 4.
865 is not an even number because it does not end with 0, or 2, or 4, or 6, or 8.

Even numbers all end in 0, or 2, or 4, or 6, or 8.

All numbers ending with a 5 or 0 are divisible by 5.

So 4635 can be divided exactly by 5, but 4636 cannot.

Task

How does Mr X decide which numbers to select?

1 Divide these numbers into two groups; **(a)** those divisible by 3
(b) those not divisible by 3.

11   36   1042   2139   4096
507   2087   4086   7125

2 Add the single digits of each number in the first group (a).

36
$3 + 6 = 9$

3 What do you notice about all the answers? Is this also true if you add the single digits of each number in the second group (b)?

? **Which of the first group of numbers do you think are divisible by 9?**
How did you decide?

A number can be divided by 4 *exactly*, if 4 goes exactly into the **last two digits**. e.g. 1732 is a multiple of 4 because 4 goes exactly into 32.

4 will go into any number of hundreds, so we only need to know if 4 will go into the tens and units.

There is a similar test for divisibility by 8, but the **last three digits** must be looked at in this case. Unfortunately, there is no easy test for divisibility by 7.

Exercise

1 Which of the following numbers can be divided by 5?

203   735   920
661   805   40 300

2 Which of the following numbers are divisible by 3?

83   257   4196
102   1 137   200 736

3 Which of the following numbers are divisible by 9?

108   7135   103 284
243   8226

4 If a number can be divided exactly by 2 AND by 3, then it can be divided exactly by 6.

This is because 6 = 2 × 3

Which of these numbers are multiples of 6?

105   1734   7814
306   2871

5 Which of these numbers are multiples of 4?

124   4082   11 335
421   4096

6 Which of the following numbers are multiples of 8?

4084   11 335
4096   11 336

7 Find the smallest number which must be added to
(a) 222 222 to make it divisible by 4
(b) 529 267 to make it divisible by 5
(c) 402 213 to make it divisible by 9.

8 Find the remainder in these divisions, but without actually dividing.
(a) 32 855 ÷ 3
(b) 41 768 ÷ 5
(c) 938 197 ÷ 8

Why the divisibility tests work

 How do you do a divisibility test?

You look at the end few numbers.

That's not always true. Sometimes you add them all up.

Sort the tests for the divisibility by 2, 3, 4, 5, 8, 9 and 10 into these two types.

In the Exercise you will meet a third type of test (for divisibility by 11).

 What is 100 ÷ 4? What is 700 ÷ 4?
How do you know that 700, 1300 and 25 700 are all divisible by 4?

Explain how you know (without dividing) that 724 is divisible by 4 but 742 is not.

Explain why the test for divisibility by 4 works.

Look at why the test for divisibility by 3 works for the number 3852.

$$3852 = 3 \times 1000 + 8 \times 100 + 5 \times 10 + 2$$
$$= (3 \times 999 + 3) + (8 \times 99 + 8) + (5 \times 9 + 5) + 2$$
$$= (3 \times 999 + 8 \times 99 + 5 \times 9) + (3 + 8 + 5 + 2)$$

Every number can be written in terms of powers of 10 like this.

1000 = 999 + 1, 100 = 99 + 1 and 10 = 9 + 1

999, 99 and 9 are all divisible by 3, so this is divisible by 3.

This is the sum of the digits.

Since $3 + 8 + 5 + 2 = 18$, which is divisible by 3, it follows that 3852 is divisible by 3.

 Explain all the steps in this example.

Write out a similar explanation for testing 43 726 for divisibility by 3.

 Explain why the test for divisibility by 3 works.

Exercise

1 Explain why the test for divisibility by 8 works.

2 Explain why the test for divisibility by 9 works.

3 Devise tests for divisibility by **(a)** 6 **(b)** 15.

4 Devise a test for divisibility by 36.

Investigation **Testing for divisibility by 11**

1 Tom spots a pattern in some multiples of 11:

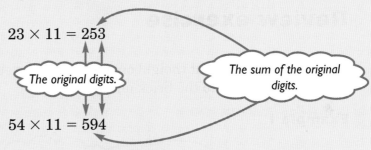

$$23 \times 11 = 253$$

The original digits.

The sum of the original digits.

$$54 \times 11 = 594$$

Explain why this happens.
Jenny points out that this does not work for 47×11 or 68×11.
Explain how to adapt the pattern in these cases.

2 Without doing any division, decide which of these are divisible by 11:
(a) 438 **(b)** 275 **(c)** 825 **(d)** 439 **(e)** 902.

3 The hundreds, tens and units digits of a 3-digit number are H, T, U respectively. Complete this statement:
'The number is divisible by 11 if $H - T + U = \ldots$ or $\ldots$.'

4 Work out 352×11, 791×11, 229×11 and 831×11.
If the thousands, hundreds, tens and units digits of the answers are M, H, T, U respectively, work out
$M - H + T - U$ each time.
What do you notice?
Devise a test for dividing a 4-digit number by 11.

5 How can you test larger numbers for divisibility by 11?

JMO Question Suppose you know that the middle two digits of a 4-digit integer N are '12' in that order and that N is an exact multiple of 15.

Determine all the different possibilities for the integer N.
(You must explain clearly why your list is complete.)

Finishing off

Now that you have finished this chapter you should be able to:

● add numbers up to 1000
● subtract numbers less than 1000
● write numbers in words and figures
● do long and short multiplication
● do short division (or successive short divisions)
● know about multiples and tests for divisibility

Review exercise

1 Add two adjacent (neighbouring) bricks together to obtain the number which goes into the brick on top.

Example 1

Example 2

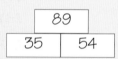

(a)

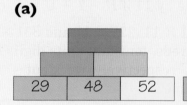

(b)

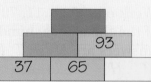

(c)

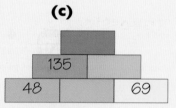

(d)

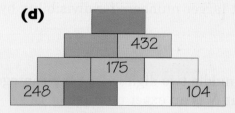

(e)

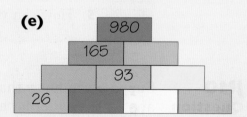

2 Use the fact that $2664 \div 72 = 37$ to find the answers to the following questions:

(a) $2664 \div 37 =$ (b) $2664 \div 74 =$

(c) $2664 \div 36 =$ (d) $2664 \div 9 =$

(e) $37 \times 72 =$ (f) $37 \times 36 =$

(g) $370 \times 36 =$ (h) $37\,000 \times 18 =$

3 Use the fact that $2080 \div 32 = 65$ to find the answers to the following questions:

(a) $2080 \div 65 =$ (b) $2080 \div 16 =$

(c) $32 \times 65 =$ (d) $64 \times 65 =$

(e) $20\,800 \div 64 =$ (f) $2\,080\,000 \div 64 =$

4 Which of the numbers

9 150 625	99 999	4 855 851	7 272 727

(a) is divisible by 9

(b) is divisible by 11

(c) is divisible by 99?

5 Find the missing digits to make each of these statements true. If there is more than one possible answer list them all.

(a) $23\,95\boxed{?}$ is divisible by 4

(b) $11\,\boxed{?}45$ is divisible by 3

(c) $275\,\boxed{?}34$ is divisible by 9

(d) $84\,2\boxed{?}6$ is divisible by 8

(e) $\boxed{?}6\,768$ is divisible by 11.

Investigation   Check that 51 238 is divisible by 11. Write down eleven more 5-digit numbers which have the same five digits (1, 2, 3, 5, 8) and are also divisible by 11.

Activity   **Speed test**

See how quickly you can answer these.

1	$25 + 60 + 18 =$	**11**	$327 \times 63 =$
2	$41 + 173 + 68 =$	**12**	$516 \times 88 =$
3	$514 + 307 + 266 =$	**13**	$210 \div 6 =$
4	$399 + 28 + 514 =$	**14**	$2891 \div 7 =$
5	$19 - 8 =$	**15**	$832 \div 8 =$
6	$65 - 32 =$	**16**	$832 \div 16 =$
7	$236 - 197 =$	**17**	$27 \times 8 =$
8	$1050 - 688 =$	**18**	$27 \times 16 =$
9	$403 \times 6 =$	**19**	$1764 \div 9 =$
10	$589 \times 7 =$	**20**	$1764 \div 36 =$

Types of angle

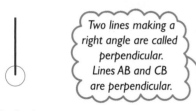

*Two lines making a right angle are called **perpendicular**. Lines AB and CB are perpendicular.*

The corners of a square are right angles.

This angle can be written ∠ABC or AB̂C or just ∠B.

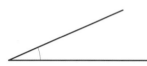

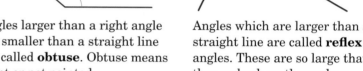

A **whole turn**.

A **quarter of a turn**.

A **straight line**.

Angles which are smaller than a right angle are called **acute** angles. Acute means sharp.

Angles larger than a right angle but smaller than a straight line are called **obtuse**. Obtuse means blunt or not pointed.

Angles which are larger than a straight line are called **reflex** angles. These are so large that they go back on themselves.

Task

? Which angle is the smallest? Which angle is the largest?

Write down the angles in order of size, smallest to largest.

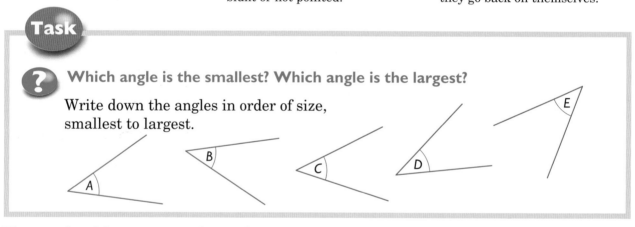

You *may* be able to arrange the angles in the correct order just by looking at them. To be sure you need to *measure* them using a protractor.

" Do the right thing!

The protractor is placed over the angle and the size of the angle is shown on the scale on the outside edge. Angles are measured in **degrees**. This angle is 42°.

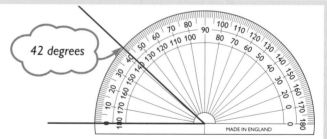

42 degrees

? Why are there two sets of numbers round the protractor? How do you know which set to use?

? How many degrees are there
(a) in a right angle?   (b) on a straight line?   (c) in a whole turn?

? How would you use a protractor to measure an obtuse angle?

Exercise

Before you start this Exercise, bring your vocabulary up to date.

- A flat surface is called a **plane**. This page is part of a plane.
- A line goes on for ever across a plane, in both directions.
- A small part of a line, like AB, is called a **line segment**.
- Two lines **intersect** at a **point** and angles are formed.

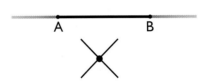

1 Write down which of these angles are acute, which are obtuse and which are reflex.

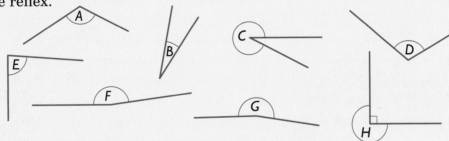

It is important to be accurate when measuring angles.
The centre of the protractor must be on the centre of the angle.
The start line must be lined up *exactly* over one of the angle lines.
Your eyes must be directly over the protractor when reading the scale.

2 Measure angles *A* to *E* on the opposite page and write them down in order of size.

3 Write down the size of these angles.

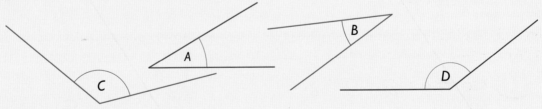

4 Write down the size of these angles.

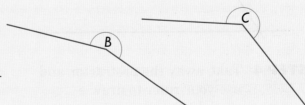

Investigation   Draw a large triangle.
Measure the angles inside it and write them down. Add up the three angles.
Repeat this for two other triangles. What do you notice?

Drawing angles

Do the right thing!

Protractors can be used to draw angles very accurately.

Following these steps to draw an angle of *exactly* 57°.
Use a sharp pencil.
Keep your eyes over your drawing.

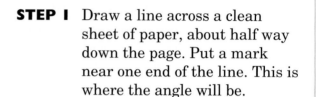

STEP 1 Draw a line across a clean sheet of paper, about half way down the page. Put a mark near one end of the line. This is where the angle will be.

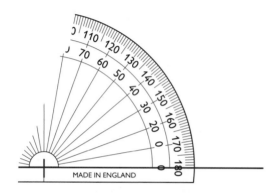

STEP 2 Put the centre of the protractor on the mark with the start line of the protractor over the line you have drawn.

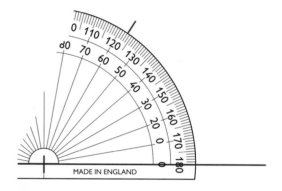

STEP 3 Draw a mark on the paper next to 57°.

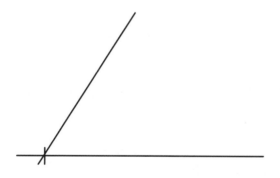

STEP 4 Take away the protractor and use your ruler to draw a straight line through the two marks.

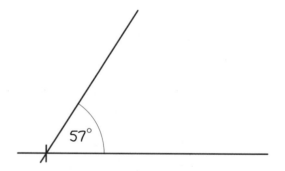

STEP 5 Draw the arc and label the angle.

? How do you use a protractor to draw a reflex angle?

Exercise

1 Follow the 5 steps given opposite to draw each of these angles.
Be as neat and as accurate as possible.

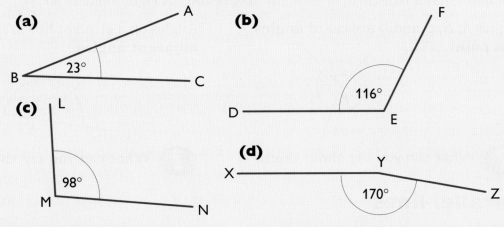

(e) An angle of 86°   **(f)** An angle of 163°

2 Make an accurate drawing of this reflex angle of 207°.
You have to do a calculation to draw the correct smaller angle with your protractor.

This angle is
$360° - 207° = 153°.$

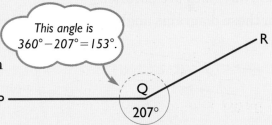

3 Use the method in Question 2 to draw and label these reflex angles.
Write down the calculation next to each one.
(a) 200°   **(b)** 243°   **(c)** 270°   **(d)** 315°

4 Draw a triangle ABC in which AB = 9 cm, angle $A = 50°$ and AC = 5 cm.
Measure angles B and C.

5 Draw a triangle XYZ in which YZ = 8 cm, angle $Y = 34°$ and angle $Z = 41°$.
Measure angle X.

6 Through how many degrees does **(a)** the minute hand, and
(b) the hour hand of a clock turn in 12 minutes?
Make an accurate drawing showing the hands of a clock at
12 minutes past 7 o'clock.

Angle calculations

From your work on page 28 you know that **there are 360 degrees in a whole turn.**
It follows that a half-turn, or straight line, is 180°. A right angle is 90°.

Angles *A*, *B*, *C* and *D* are called **angles at a point**.

Angles on a straight line are called **adjacent angles**.

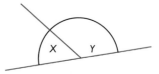

 What can you say about them?

 What can you say about X and Y?

Parallel lines

When two lines are always the same distance apart
(equidistant) they are **parallel**.
Railway lines are parallel.
In these diagrams angles are made where lines **intersect**.

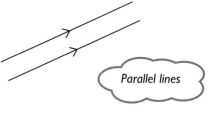

Parallel lines

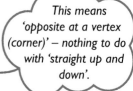

This means 'opposite at a vertex (corner)' – nothing to do with 'straight up and down'.

Corresponding angles   *Alternate angles*   *Vertically opposite angles*

 Using this diagram, name
  (a) four pairs of corresponding
      angles
  (b) two pairs of alternate angles
  (c) four pairs of vertically opposite
      angles.

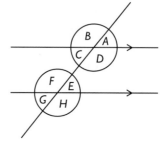

 Task

  1 Use a ruler and **set square** to draw a pair of parallel lines.

   How does this work?

  2 Draw another straight line which intersects both parallel
      lines.
  3 Measure a pair of corresponding angles and write them
      down.
  4 Measure a pair of alternate angles and write them down
  5 Measure a pair of opposite angles and write them down.
  6 Write down what you notice each time.

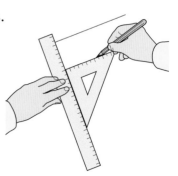

Exercise

The angle facts on the opposite page enable you to solve angle *problems*.

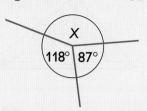

Example   What is angle *X*?

The angles round a point add up to 360°.
118° + 87° = 205°
So *X* = 360° − 205°
X = **155°**.

1   Find the value of each lettered angle in these diagrams:
For each one write down the angle fact(s) that you use.

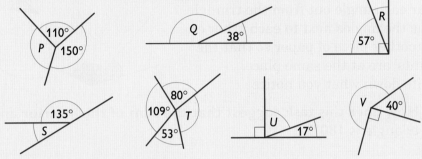

2   Make a *sketch* copy of each of these diagrams.
For each one calculate the lettered angles and write down your reasons.

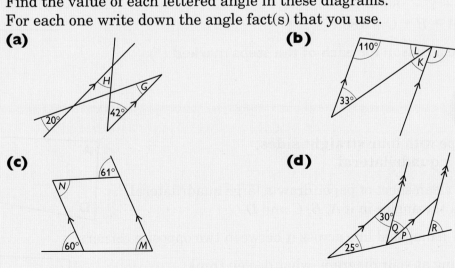

3   Find the value of each lettered angle in these diagrams.
For each one write down the angle fact(s) that you use.

(a)

(b)

(c)

(d)

Angles in a triangle

The angles inside a shape are called **interior angles**.
The investigation on page 29 shows you that
the interior angles of a triangle add up to 180°.

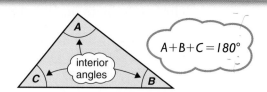

Task

1 Draw any large triangle on a piece of paper. Mark each angle and shade each one with a different colour.

2 Tear each angle out from the triangle. Glue the angles next to each other on to another piece of paper so that the 'points' are at the same place. Write down what you notice

 How does this task suggest that the sum of the interior angles of a triangle is 180°?

Your investigation on page 29 and the Task above both use particular triangles. Your results cannot be exact even if you measure very carefully. But you can be certain that

the interior angles of *every* triangle add up to *exactly* 180°

because of the following geometrical proof.

Draw the line through one vertex (corner) of the triangle which is parallel to the opposite side.

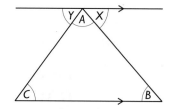

Then $X = B$ (*) and $Y = C$ (*).
But $A + X + Y = 180°$ (*)
Therefore $A + B + C = 180°$.

 Give a reason for each of the steps marked (*).

Task

Any shape with **four straight sides** is called a **quadrilateral**.

1 On a clean sheet of paper draw a large quadrilateral. Label the angles in it A, B, C and D.

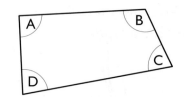

2 Draw a diagonal line across it between two opposite corners.

3 Looking at your diagram, what do you think the angles A, B, C and D add up to? Write down a reason for your answer.

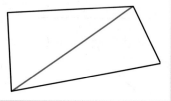

4 Now check your answer by measuring angles A, B, C and D.

Exercise

1 Find the value of each unknown angle in these diagrams:

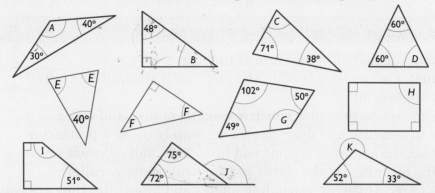

2 Find the value of each lettered angle in these diagrams.
Write down your reasons.

(a)

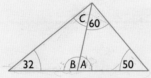

(b)

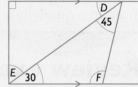

(c)

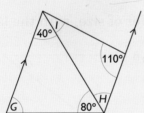

(d)

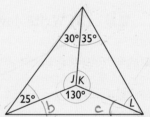

3 Find the sum of the interior
angles of every
(a) pentagon (five sides)
(b) hexagon (six sides).

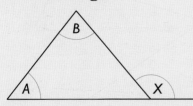

*Hint: use the diagonals
through one corner
to divide them
into triangles.*

Investigation

In this diagram angle *X* is called an
exterior angle.

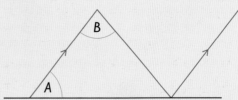

A and *B* are the two *opposite* interior angles.

1 Copy this diagram:

2 Use it to show how an exterior angle
of a triangle is related to the two
opposite interior angles.
Explain your reasoning.

Finishing off

Now that you have finished this chapter you should:

- know that an angle is a measure of turning
- know that a whole turn is 360°, the angle on a straight line is 180° and a right angle is 90°
- be able to recognise angles which are acute, obtuse and reflex
- be able to measure and draw angles accurately using a protractor
- know that the angles at a point add up to 360° and adjacent angles add up to 180°
- know the meanings of the words perpendicular and parallel
- be able to recognise corresponding angles and know that they are equal
- be able to recognise alternate angles and know that they are equal
- know that the angles inside a triangle add up to 180°, and those in a quadrilateral to 360°.

Review exercise

1 **(a)** Write down these angles in order of size, with the largest first.

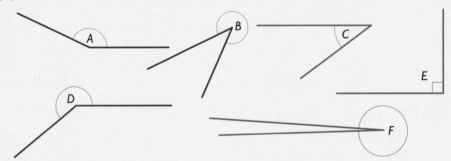

(b) Write down which of the above angles are
   (i) obtuse   **(ii)** reflex   **(iii)** acute.

2 Write down the size of these angles.
Measure them as accurately as you can.

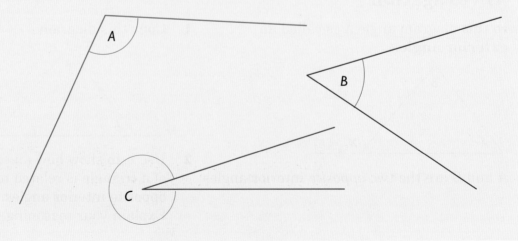

3 Make accurate drawings of these angles and label them.
   (a) 28°   **(b)** 146°   **(c)** 324°   **(d)** 265°

4 Write down the following angles in order of size, with the smallest first.

| 53° | An obtuse angle | A straight line | 240° | A right angle | 3° | 300° |

5 Find the value of the lettered angles in these diagrams:

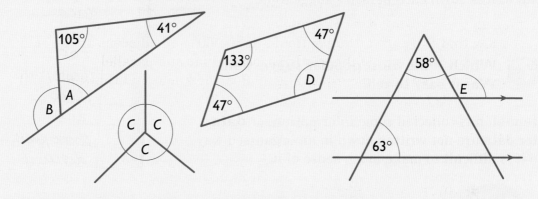

What can you say about the sides of the quadrilateral?

Investigation

(a) The angle sum of a quadrilateral is 360°.

Investigate the truth of the statement above for these quadrilaterals.
These are all possible shapes formed by four jointed rods.

(i)    **(ii)**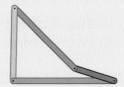

(iii)    **(iv)**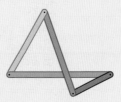

(b) If you think the statement is true give a proof.
If not, find some other true general statement about the angles of that sort of quadrilateral.

Hannah is organising an end-of-year event for her year group.

She decides to ask everyone in her class what they would like to do.

She writes down each person's suggestion.

disco	ice skating
theme park	disco
disco	zoo
cinema	theme park
zoo	disco
theme park	ice skating
disco	theme park
zoo	cinema
theme park	ice skating
disco	disco

? **Which is the most popular suggestion? Was it easy to tell?**

Hannah has collected some information, or **data**. Her data are not written down in an organised way, so it is difficult to make much sense of it.

Task

Collect data from everyone in your class to find out what they would like to do for an end-of-year event.

Try to record your data in a way which makes it easy to see which are the most popular suggestions.

? **What different ways have people in your class recorded this data? Which ways are most useful?**

One way of collecting data is to use a **tally chart**.
Here is Hannah's data recorded in a tally chart.

ACTIVITY	TALLY	FREQUENCY
Disco	IIII II	7
Theme park	IIII	5
Cinema	II	2
zoo	III	3
Ice skating	III	3
	TOTAL	20

Frequency means the number of people.

*This is sometimes called a **frequency table**.*

? **What does each line in the tally column mean?
What does IIII mean?
How many people has Hannah asked in her survey?
Which activity is the most popular?**

Exercise

1. Jason is doing a survey about the traffic passing his house during the morning rush-hour.
He notes down each type of vehicle that he sees.
Here are Jason's results:

car	car	car	lorry	car	bicycle	bicycle
van	car	car	car	car	bus	car
lorry	car	car	motorbike	bus	car	car
car	car	lorry	van	car	car	
car	car	bus	bicycle	car	car	
car	car	motorbike	lorry	lorry	lorry	
bicycle	car	car	car	lorry	lorry	

   (a) Make a tally chart to show Jason's results.
   (b) How many vehicles did Jason see altogether?
   (c) What was the most common vehicle?

2. Maddy is making a patchwork quilt.
She is copying this design.
Make a tally chart to show how many squares of each colour Maddy needs.

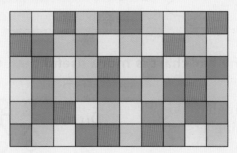

3. Mark throws a die 30 times.
Here are the scores he gets:

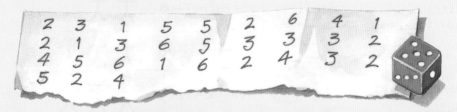

2	3	1	5	5	2	6	4	1
2	1	3	6	5	3	3	3	2
4	5	6	1	6	2	4	3	2
5	2	4						

   (a) Make a tally chart to show Mark's results.
   (b) Which number came up most often?
   (c) Do you think the same number would come up most often if Mark threw the die another 30 times?

Investigation

1. Find a book and count the number of letters in each word for 50 words. Record your data in a tally chart.
2. Repeat part 1 using a different type of book.
3. Which book do you think has longer words on the whole? Why do you think this is?

Pictograms and bar charts

Here are the results of Hannah's survey again.
They are shown in a **frequency table**.

Activity	Disco	Theme park	Cinema	Zoo	Ice-skating
Frequency	7	5	2	3	3

Hannah wants to show her data in
a graph or chart.
She draws this **bar chart**.

Bar chart to show what
people would like to do

*Make sure you always label the axes
and give the chart a title.*

? **Do you think the bar chart is more useful than the tally chart?**

Another way that Hannah could
show her data is by using a
pictogram like this:

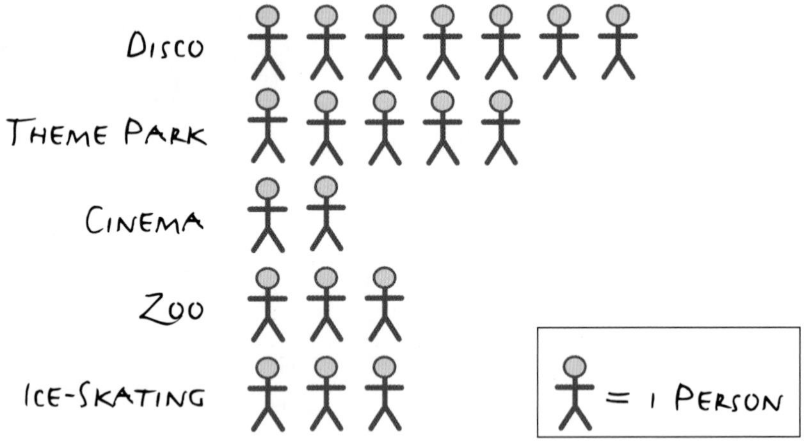

DISCO

THEME PARK

CINEMA

ZOO

ICE-SKATING

= 1 PERSON

*You can use any symbol you like
for the picture.*

Task

Look back to the data you collected for the last lesson.

Draw a bar chart and a pictogram to illustrate your data.

Make a poster to show your work.

? **Which do you think shows the data better, the pictogram or the bar chart?**
Which is easier to draw?

Exercise

1 Joe works at the village shop. He wants to know how many pints of each type of milk he should order.
This pictogram shows the number of pints of each type of milk that Joe sells one morning.

(a) What does the symbol (mean?
(b) How many pints of each type of milk did Joe sell?
(c) How many pints of milk did Joe sell altogether?
(d) Draw a bar chart to show this data.

2 Lisa has drawn a bar chart to show how the people in her class travel to school.

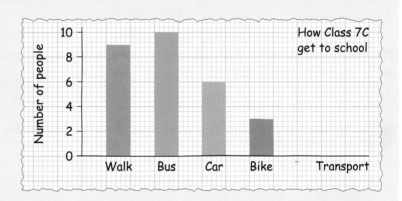

(a) What is the most popular way to get to school in Lisa's class?
(b) How many people walk to school?
(c) How many people come to school by bus or car?
(d) How many people are there in Lisa's class?
(e) Draw a pictogram to show this data.

3 Jack is doing a survey to find out the most popular terrestrial TV channel.
This frequency table shows his results.

Channel	BBC1	BBC2	ITV	C4	C5
Frequency	8	5	7	4	1

(a) Draw a pictogram to illustrate this data.
(b) Draw a bar chart to illustrate this data.
(c) Which way of displaying the data do you think is better? Why?

Pie charts

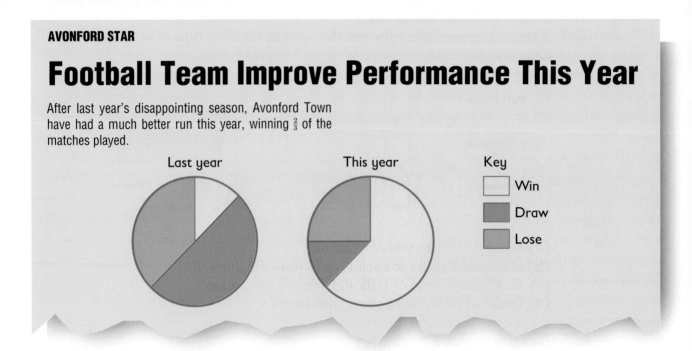

AVONFORD STAR

Football Team Improve Performance This Year

After last year's disappointing season, Avonford Town have had a much better run this year, winning $\frac{2}{3}$ of the matches played.

Last year   This year   Key

☐ Win

▨ Draw

▨ Lose

The diagrams used in the *Avonford Star* report shown above are called pie charts.

The yellow section in each chart shows the number of wins. In the chart for last year, the yellow section is 45° or $\frac{1}{8}$ of the circle. This means that the team won $\frac{1}{8}$ of their matches.

 What fractions of the matches did the team win, lose and draw this year?

 Task

Copy the table opposite.

Decide what fraction of the matches Avonford Town won, lost and drew in each year and fill in the 'Fraction' column of the table.
The team played 32 matches last year and 40 matches this year. Use this to fill in the 'Number of matches' column.

Draw two bar charts to illustrate these data.

		Fraction	No. of Matches
Last Year	Won	$\frac{1}{8}$	
	Lost		
	Drew		
This Year	Won		
	Lost		
	Drew		

? **Does a pie chart have any advantages over a bar chart or a pictogram?**

? **What fractions correspond to pie chart angles of**
(a) 90°   (b) 180°   (c) 60°   (d) 120°   (e) 30°?

Exercise

1 This pie chart shows the favourite sports of a group of children.

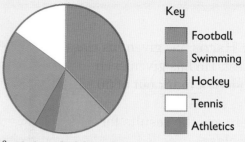

Key
- Football
- Swimming
- Hockey
- Tennis
- Athletics

(a) What is the most popular sport?

(b) Which two sports are equally popular?

(c) Which is the least popular sport?

(d) Which sport is preferred by about $\frac{3}{8}$ of the children?

2 Look at the two football team's improvement pie charts on the opposite page. Now work out the angle at the centre of the circle for each of the slices.

3 Ellie kept a record of the weather for several weeks in the summer. On half of the days it was sunny, on $\frac{1}{8}$ of the days it rained, and the rest of the time it was cloudy.

Ellie also kept a record of the weather for the same amount of weeks in the autumn. On $\frac{1}{3}$ of the days it rained, $\frac{1}{4}$ of the days it was sunny, and the rest of the time it was cloudy.

Draw two pie charts to show this information. Work out the angle of the 'cloudy' slice in each pie chart.

4 Stuart has carried out a survey to find out how people get to school. He has surveyed three classes: 7P, 7Q and 7R.

CLASS	7P	7Q	7R
WALK	14	10	9
BUS	10	8	12
CAR	4	3	6
BIKE	2	7	4
TOTAL	30	28	31

Here are the three pie charts that Stuart has drawn, but without a key and now they are mixed up.

Decide which pie chart is for each class, and make a key.

A   B   C

Investigation Find out how to use ICT to draw a pie chart.

Grouping data

Mr Harris has given his class a test. He has given each student a mark out of 50.

Here are the results for his class.

32	38	43	21	30	46	29	35
37	42	27	25	33	32	16	48
39	37	26	19	40	23	35	34
8	24	35	39	41	36		

Mr Harris is going to give each student a grade.
He wants to make a tally chart to show his results.

 What problem will there be with making a tally chart of these data?

Mr Harris can solve the problem by using **grouped data**.
This means that he will collect the data in groups.
Each group will be given a different grade.
Here is Mr Harris' tally chart.

Grade	Mark	Tally	Frequency
E	1–10	I	1
D	11–20	II	2
C	21–30	HHT III	8
B	31–40	HHT HHT IIII	14
A	41–50	HHT	5
		Total	30

 What other ways could Mr Harris have grouped the data?

 Task

Ask everyone in your class to measure his or her handspan in millimetres.
Collect the results using a grouped tally chart.
Compare your results with the rest of the class.

 Has everyone grouped the data in the same way?
Which way do you think is best?

You can draw bar charts, pictograms and pie charts using grouped data.

Here is a bar chart to show Mr Harris' data.

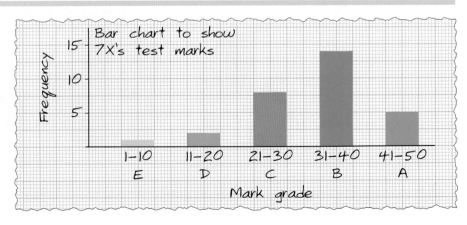

Exercise

1 Zoe has measured the heights of everyone in her class.
She has measured to the nearest centimetre. Here are her results.

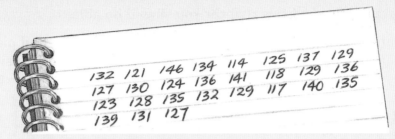

132 121 146 134 114 125 137 129
127 130 124 136 141 118 129 136
123 128 135 132 129 117 140 135
139 131 127

(a) Copy and complete this tally chart.

Height (cm)	Tally	Frequency
110–119		
120–129		

(b) Draw a bar chart for Zoe's data.

2 Matt works at a swimming pool. He is doing a survey to find out what age groups use the swimming pool most.
He writes down the ages of all the people who visit the pool one morning. Here are his results.

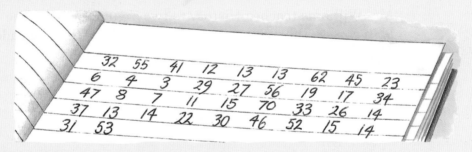

32 55 41 12 13 13 62 45 23
6 4 3 29 27 56 19 17 34
47 8 7 11 15 70 33 26 14
37 13 14 22 30 46 52 15 14
31 53

(a) Make a tally chart using groups 0–9, 10–19, and so on.
(b) Draw a bar chart.
(c) How many people visited the pool that morning?
(d) Which age group used it the most?

3 Sarah keeps a record of her scores when she plays her new computer game. Here are her scores for the first few weeks.

```
 17   55   82  134  168  143  182  174
240  113  194   98  257  322  286  301
126  264  228  319  160  200  258  320
          247  281  177  346
```

(a) Make a tally chart using groups 0–49, 50–99, 100–149, and so on.
(b) Draw a bar chart.
(c) What do you think the bar chart will look like after another few weeks?

Finishing off

When you have finished this chapter you should be able to:

- collect and organise data using a tally chart
- draw bar charts and pictograms
- understand pie charts
- group data using a tally chart.

Review exercise

1 Sonia helps in the school tuck shop. One day she keeps a record of what drinks she has sold. Here is her list.

(a) Make a tally chart.
(b) How many drinks did Sonia sell altogether?
(c) Draw a pictogram to illustrate the data.

Cola Lemon Coffee Cola Orange
Tea Tea Cola Lemon Coffee
Cola Cola Cola Lemon Orange
Tea Cola Tea Orange Coffee
Tea Cola Lemon Cola Lemon
Orange Tea Cola

2 Mrs Williams teaches History to two Year 7 classes. One day she gives both classes the same test. She gives each student a grade A, B, C, D or E. Mrs Williams draws this bar chart to show the results.

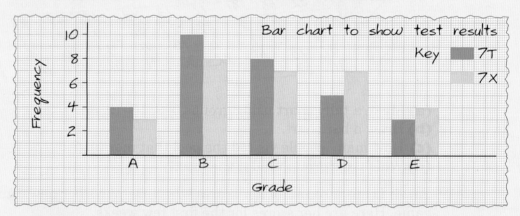

(a) Copy and complete this table.

Grade	A	B	C	D	E
Frequency for 7T	4				
Frequency for 7X	3				

(b) How many students are there in Class 7T?
(c) How many students are there in Class 7X?
(d) Which class do you think did better in the test?

3 This pie chart shows the different types of pets owned by a group of children.

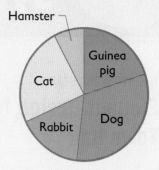

(a) What fraction of the children own cats?
(b) What pet is owned by about $\frac{1}{3}$ of the children?
(c) Write the pets in order of popularity, starting with the most popular.

4 A skating rink keeps a record of the number of visitors it has every day during the month of July.
The numbers are written on this calendar.

JULY						
Mon	Tues	Weds	Thurs	Fri	Sat	Sun
		1 73	2 52	3 121	4 324	5 286
6 35	7 67	8 112	9 89	10 95	11 274	12 239
13 93	14 104	15 78	16 115	17 127	18 310	19 262
20 48	21 83	22 306	23 283	24 259	25 261	26 249
27 250	28 315	29 352	30 296	31 245		

(a) Why are there more visitors on Saturdays and Sundays?
(b) What day do you think the school summer holidays began?
(c) Make a grouped tally chart using groups 0–49, 50–99, and so on.
(d) Draw a bar chart to illustrate the data.

5 A travel company keeps a record of how many ski holiday bookings are made in one year to the five countries it has on offer. Anika was preparing to draw a pie chart. She has got this far with the calculations, but had to stop to attend to a customer.

	Frequency	Angle of slice
France	25	100°
Switzerland	23	
Austria	20	
Italy		64°
Scotland		

Finish the table for her and draw the pie chart.

How many bookings were there in total?

Activity   Draw a pie chart to show how your lesson time at school is divided between the subjects you take.

Elegant Design for New Town Hall

The design for Avonford's new Town Hall was revealed today.

Here is an architect's drawing of the front view.

Task

Look at the Town Hall and write down the answers to these questions.

1 How many ground floor windows are there?

2 How many 1st floor windows are there?

3 How many flagpoles are there?

4 How many chimneys are there?

 Sometimes there is an odd number of features, sometimes even. Why is this?

The Town Hall is **symmetrical**. Many buildings are designed like this.

If you stand a mirror on the centre of the drawing, in line with the flagpole, the Town Hall will look exactly the same in the mirror as it does behind the mirror.
This kind of symmetry is called **reflection symmetry**.

The Town Hall has one line on which you can stand a mirror and see reflection symmetry. This is called a **line of symmetry**.

This green cross, seen on first aid kits, has *four* lines of symmetry.
Two of them are diagonal, one is horizontal and one is vertical.
Try them out with a mirror.

 How many lines of symmetry does a rectangle have?

You can use squared or dotted paper to complete symmetrical shapes.

Here is a shape with two lines of symmetry.

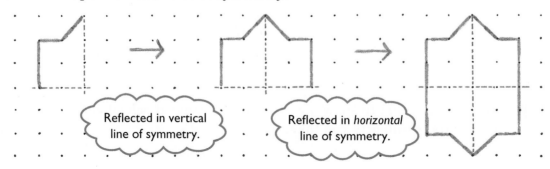

Reflected in vertical line of symmetry.

Reflected in *horizontal* line of symmetry.

Exercise

1 Which of these road signs have reflection symmetry?

(a) (b) (c) (d) (e) (f)

2 Copy or trace each of these shapes and draw their lines of symmetry. Write down how many lines of symmetry each shape has.

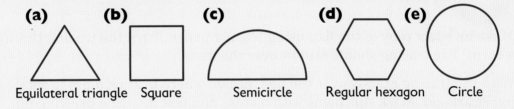

(a)   (b)   (c)   (d)   (e)

Equilateral triangle   Square   Semicircle   Regular hexagon   Circle

3 Copy these shapes on to squared paper. For each one, copy the line of symmetry and use it to draw the rest of each symmetrical shape.

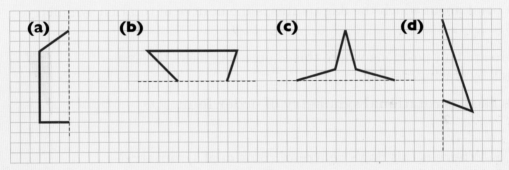

(a)   (b)   (c)   (d)

4 Copy and complete these shapes which have two lines of symmetry.

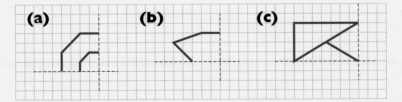

(a)   (b)   (c)

5 Copy and complete these shapes.
The dashed lines are lines of symmetry.

(a) 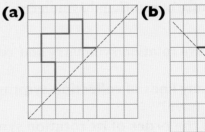 (b)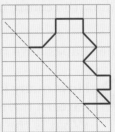

Rotation symmetry

Here is a drawing of Avonford Town Council's flag.

Task

Make an exact copy of the flag using tracing paper. Turn the tracing through 180° (half a turn). The tracing should still fit over the flag.

With the tracing exactly over the flag, decide where to stick a pin to rotate the tracing paper around. Mark this point with a cross and test it with a drawing pin.

There are two positions the flag can be in where it looks exactly the same.
We say that the flag has **rotational symmetry of order two**.
The point about which the flag rotates is the **centre** of rotation symmetry.

There are four positions where this square flag looks the same.
Check by tracing the flag.

This flag has **rotational symmetry of order four**.

? **Where is this flag's centre of rotational symmetry?**
How could you find it and mark the centre?
Why *is* this point the centre?

Task

Design a flag which has rotational symmetry. Decide the order of rotational symmetry *before* you start.

Use squared paper if you wish. Check the symmetry with tracing paper.

Show the centre of rotational symmetry.

Some shapes have rotation symmetry *and* reflection symmetry.

? **How many lines of reflection symmetry does this pattern have?**
What is the order of its rotation symmetry?

Exercise

1 Write down the order of rotational symmetry of these patterns.
Use tracing paper to help if you wish.

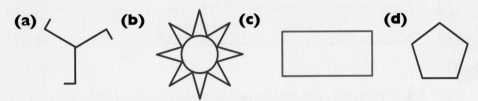

(a)   **(b)**   **(c)**   **(d)**

2 Trace each of these shapes. For each one

(i) write down how many lines of symmetry it has and draw them
(ii) write down the order of rotation symmetry and mark the centre
with a cross.
Explain how you decided the position of the centre.

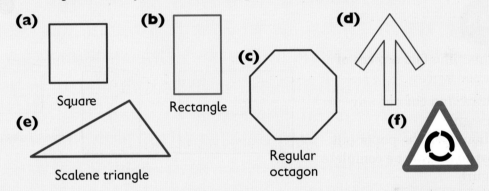

(a)   Square   **(b)**   Rectangle   **(c)** Regular octagon   **(d)**

(e) Scalene triangle   **(f)**

3 Complete these shapes so that they have both reflection and rotation
symmetry. Mark the centre of rotation symmetry with a cross.

For each one write down
how many lines of
reflection symmetry it has,
and the order of rotational
symmetry.

(a) 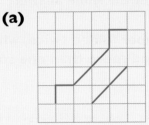   **(b)**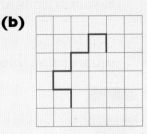

Activity Design a car wheel which has rotation symmetry.
Before you start decide what the order of rotation symmetry will be.
Use a pair of compasses and a protractor to help you.
When you have finished use tracing paper to check the symmetry.

Investigation Find out what a kaleidoscope is.
Draw a pattern you might see in one, and describe its symmetry.

Paper folding

Try this – it was a popular Victorian pastime.

1 Draw the silhouette (outline) of a friend's face on a folded piece of paper.

2 Cut this out and open it to give a double silhouette.

3 You can mount this against paper of a different colour.

? Describe the symmetry of your double silhouette. Where is its line of symmetry?

Task

1 This time fold a piece of paper twice:

2 Draw and cut out any design.
Then open the paper out flat to reveal the complete figure.

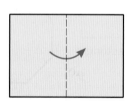 

3 How many lines of symmetry does your figure have?

4 What order of rotational symmetry does it have?
Do your friends all get the same answer?

? Using a piece of paper folded twice, what shape could you cut out to produce a square? Can you find more than one solution?

Task

1 This time give the paper a third fold.

2 Again, draw any design and cut it out.
Then open the paper out flat to reveal the complete figure.

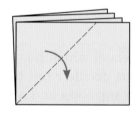 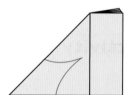

3 Give a full description of the symmetries of your figure.

? Using a piece of paper folded three times, what designs would you cut to make
(a) a four-pointed star **(b)** an eight-pointed star?

Exercise

1   **(a)** Make one fold in a piece of paper. With two straight cuts make a
shape which, when unfolded, is a letter **V**.

(b) Repeat **(a)**, but this time make a letter **T**.

2   **(a)** Fold a piece of paper twice. With two straight cuts make a shape
which, when unfolded, is a letter **H**, with all parts of the letter
having the same thickness.

3   A piece of paper is folded three times.
The corner is then cut off, as shown here,
and the paper is unfolded.
What shape does this produce?
How many lines of symmetry are there?

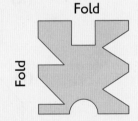

equal lengths

Starting with another piece of paper folded
three times, describe carefully how to produce
the same shape in a different way.

4   Peter folds a square piece of paper twice.
He then cuts out some shapes so that it
looks like the diagram on the right.

(a) Which of the diagrams below show what the
paper will look like when Peter opens it out again?

Fold

Fold

A   **B**   **C**   **D**

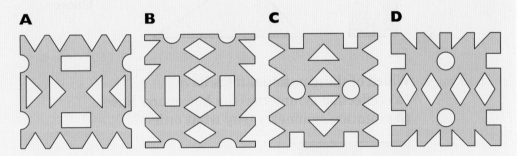

(b) Could any of the other diagrams A, B, C or D be produced by
cutting the same shapes but with the folds along different sides?
If so, give the details.

Finishing off

Now that you have finished this chapter you should be able to:

- recognise reflection symmetry and draw lines of symmetry
- reflect part of a shape in a line of symmetry to complete it
- recognise rotation symmetry and say what its order is.

Review exercise

1. For each of these shapes write down whether they have reflection symmetry or not. Copy each one that does and add to it the lines of symmetry.

(a)   **(b)**   **(c)**   **(d)**   **(e)**

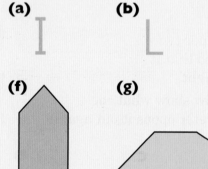

(f)   **(g)**   **(h)**   **(i)**

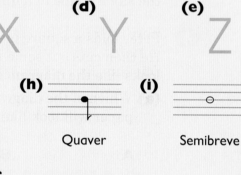

Quaver   Semibreve

2. Which of these national flags have
   (a) reflection symmetry (say how many lines)
   (b) rotation symmetry (say what order)?

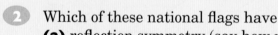

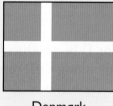   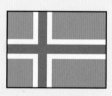

Denmark   Jamaica   Japan   Norway

Bangladesh   Trinidad and Tobago   Botswana

3 Here is a photograph of Vaux-le-Vicomte, a chateaux outside Paris in France. Can you spot three things about it which are *not* symmetrical? Write them down.

4 Here are six square sheets of paper, each one folded twice. Cuts are made in them so that when the paper is unfolded each sheet contains holes. Some of the holes are circles, some are squares and some take other shapes.

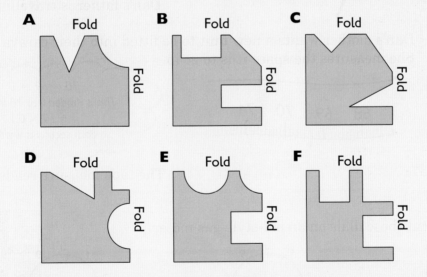

Which sheet of paper (if any) has three of its holes as follows:

(a) three squares   **(b)** three circles

(c) two squares and a circle   **(d)** two circles and a square?

Investigation   Is it possible to draw figures which have

(a) one line of symmetry but no rotational symmetry

(b) more than one line of symmetry but no rotational symmetry

(c) rotational symmetry but no line of symmetry?

Clio owners

R - reg Fiesta
5 door, power steering,
red, under 14 000 miles

K - reg
2 door,
white,

Dan's father sees this advert in the newspaper.
He goes to look at the car and Dan checks the car's mileage.

The gauge says

The white numbers are the whole number of miles and the red digit gives the tenths of a mile.

It could be written as **13 785.6** miles.

Example 1   Dan's father takes the car for a test drive.
Dan looks at the speedometer.

> $40 - 30 = 10$
> This is divided into 5 intervals
> $10 \div 5 = 2$
> so each section is worth 2.

Dan's father is travelling at 34 mph.

Example 2   Dan's mother wants a new unit to be fitted into their caravan.
She measures the space it is to go in.

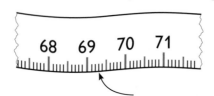

> $70 - 69 = 1$
> This is divided into 10 intervals
> $1 \div 10 = 0.1$
> so each section is worth 0.1.

The tape measure reads 69.3 cm.

Task

Look carefully at these dials on an old-style gas meter.

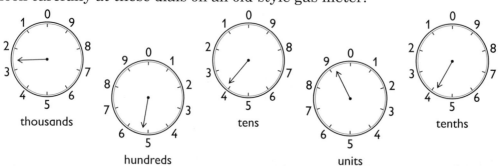

thousands   hundreds   tens   units   tenths

? **What do you notice? Behind the meter face are meshing gear wheels which turn the pointers. How does this explain the strange numbering of the dials?**

? **What meter reading is shown? On a copy of these dials show a reading of 3807.6.**

Exercise

1 Write the numbers shown on these mileage gauges as decimals:
(a) 7619   (b) 41293   (c) 63217   (d) 11193
(e) 362148   (f) 712350   (g) 42895   (h) 732152

2 The dials show speeds in m.p.h. Read the speeds below:

(a) 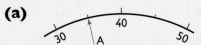   (b)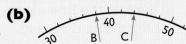

(c) 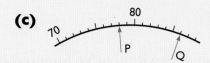   (d)

3 The tapes below are given in cms. What measurements are shown?

(a) 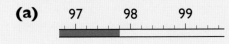   (b)

(c)    (d)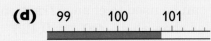

4 These thermometers show temperature in °Fahrenheit.
What temperature do they show?

(a) 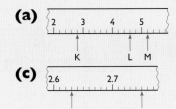   (b)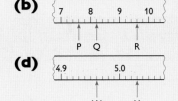

(e) Normal body temperature is 98.4°.
     Which of the thermometers shows normal body temperature?

5 Read the following scales:

(a)   (b)

(c) 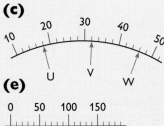   (d)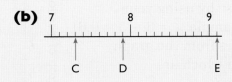

(e)

(f)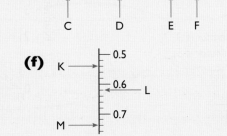

Decimal notation

In 1585 Simon Stevin of Bruges in Belgium published *De Thiende* ('The Tenth' – he wrote in Flemish).

This was the first clear explanation of the decimal system.

I want to teach everyone how to perform, with an unheard of ease, all computations necessary between men by integers without fractions.

The decimal point system is a way of writing numbers with tenths, hundredths, thousandths, etc. This table shows you how.

Fraction	H hundreds	T tens	U units	$\frac{1}{10}$ tenths	$\frac{1}{100}$ hundredths	$\frac{1}{1000}$ thousandths	Decimal
$\frac{3}{10}$			.	3			0.3
$\frac{7}{100}$			.		7		0.07
$6 + \frac{5}{10} + \frac{1}{100}$			6 .	5	1		6.51
$527\frac{39}{1000}$	5	2	7 .		3	9	527.039

Task

This graph can be used to change fractions to decimals.
The examples show that **(a)** $\frac{1}{8} = 0.125$ **(b)** $\frac{2}{6} = 0.33$ **(c)** $\frac{3}{5} = 0.6$ **(d)** $\frac{6}{7} = 0.86$.

Use the graph to change these fractions to decimals:

(e) $\frac{3}{4}$ **(f)** $\frac{7}{8}$ **(g)** $\frac{2}{7}$ **(h)** $\frac{5}{6}$.

Check all these by using your calculator (example: $\frac{3}{5} = 3 \div 5 = 0.6$).
Which answers from the graph are exact, and which are approximations?

For $\frac{3}{5}$ the numerator is 3 and the denominator is 5.

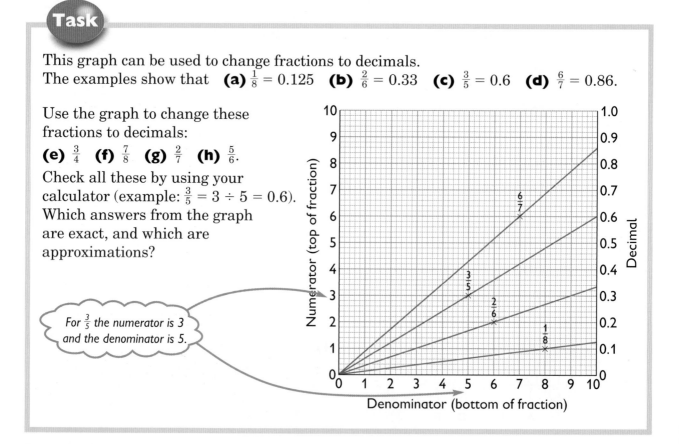

Exercise

1 What is the value of the red circled digit?

Example 61④3.71   Answer: 4 tens or 40
        8.3⑨4   Answer: $\frac{9}{100}$

(a) 1⑥.32   **(b)** 4.⑦8   **(c)** 19.7④   **(d)** 11.30⑧
(e) 3.⑥1   **(f)** 62.0⑨4   **(g)** ⑧.63   **(h)** 5.001⑨

2 Write these numbers as decimals:

(a) $\frac{5}{100}$ **(b)** $\frac{43}{100}$ **(c)** $\frac{17}{1000}$ **(d)** $\frac{156}{1000}$
(e) $\frac{37}{10\,000}$ **(f)** $7 + \frac{3}{10} + \frac{2}{100}$ **(g)** $6\frac{7}{100}$ **(h)** $2\frac{13}{10\,000}$

3 Change these fractions to decimals without using a calculator.
(Use the graph opposite, or do the division.)

(a) $\frac{2}{5}$ **(b)** $\frac{3}{8}$ **(c)** $\frac{1}{4}$ **(d)** $\frac{5}{8}$ **(e)** $\frac{2}{3}$

4 Use a calculator to change these to decimals.

(a) $\frac{7}{16}$ **(b)** $\frac{31}{40}$ **(c)** $\frac{13}{25}$ **(d)** $\frac{1}{7}$
(e) $\frac{5}{12}$ **(f)** $3\frac{4}{7}$ **(g)** $5\frac{7}{8}$ **(h)** $12\frac{5}{6}$

5 Arrange these numbers in order of size, smallest first.

(a) 0.87, 0.871, 0.78, 0.718

(b) 0.4, 0.44, 0.404, 0.044

(c) 0.059, 0.065, 0.0096, 0.0906, 0.5006

Investigation

Here is an extract from Stevin's *De Thiende*.
It explains how to add three numbers.
In the enlarged section he shows how he
writes $27\frac{847}{1000}$ as a decimal.

You can follow this without knowing any Flemish.
How would Stevin have written

(a) 37.675
(b) 88.52963?

THIENDE.   13
HET ANDER DEEL
DER THIENDE VANDE
WERCKINCHE.

I. VOORSTEL VANDE
VERGADERINGHE.

*Wefende ghegeven Thiendetalen te ver-
gaderen: hare Somme te vinden.*

'GHEGHEVEN. Het fijn drie oirdens van
Thiendetalen, welcker eerfte 27 ⓪ 8 ① 4 ②
7③ , de tweede, 37 ⓪ 6 ① 7 ② 5 ③ , de derde,
875 ⓪ 7 ① 8 ② 2 ③, TBEGHEERDE. Wy
moeten haer Somme vinden. WERCKING.
Men fal de ghegheven ghe-   ⓪ ① ② ③
talen in oirden ftellen als   2 7 8 4 7
hier neven, die vergaderen-   3 7 6 7 5
de naer de ghemeene manie   8 7 5 7 8 2
re der vergaderinghe van   ───────
heelegetalen aldus: 9 4 1 3 0 4
Comt in Somme (door het 1. probleme onfer
Franfcher Arith.) 9 4 1 ; 0 4 dat fijn (t'welck de
teeckenen boven de ghetalen ftaende, anwijfen)
9 4 1 ③ ; ① 0 ② 4 ③. Ick feghe de felve te wefen
de ware begheerde Somme. BEWYS. De ghegeven 27 ⓪ 8 ① 4 2 7 3, doen (door de 3e. hepa-
ling) 27$\frac{8}{10}$, $\frac{4}{100}$, $\frac{7}{1000}$, maecke t'famen 27$\frac{847}{1000}$.
Ende door de felve reden fullen de 37 ⓪ 6 ① 7 ②
5 ③. weetdich fijn 37$\frac{675}{1000}$; Ende de 875 ② 7 ①
8 ②

BEWYS. De ghege-
ven 27 ⓪ 8 ① 4 ② 7 ③, doen (door de 3e. hepa-
ling) 27$\frac{8}{10}$, $\frac{4}{100}$, $\frac{7}{1000}$, maecke t'famen 27$\frac{8+7}{1000}$.

Addition and subtraction of decimals

BACK TO SCHOOL
Geometry set	£3.70
Fountain pen	£6.50
Calculator	£5.25

Special Offer

Joseph decides he needs all of these items before he goes back to school. How much does it cost altogether?

Joseph pays with two £10 notes. How much change does he receive?

$$
\begin{array}{r}
£20.00 \\
-£15.45 \\
\hline
£\ \ 4.55
\end{array}
$$

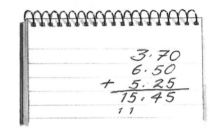

$$
\begin{array}{r}
3.70 \\
6.50 \\
+\ \ 5.25 \\
\hline
15.45 \\
{\scriptstyle 1\ 1}
\end{array}
$$

Task

Instead of paying with £10 notes, Joseph pays with money from his money-box. The coins he has are shown in the table.

Value of coin	1p	2p	5p	10p	20p	50p	£1
Number of coins	6	8	3	9	16	6	10

What is the smallest number of coins that Joseph can use to pay £15.45?
What is the largest number of coins that Joseph can use to pay £15.45?

As Simon Stevin said, addition and subtraction with decimals is just as easy as it is with whole numbers.

?   The number 484.064 contains three 4s. What does each of them mean?

?   Look at Joseph's addition and subtraction at the top of this page. Why does he put all the decimal points in a line?

Example 1   Work out 7.53 + 420 + 0.086.

$$
\begin{array}{r}
7.53 \\
420.0 \\
+\ \ 0.086 \\
\hline
427.616
\end{array}
$$

You can write 420 as 420.0 to help you.

Example 2   Subtract 8.306 from 46.1.

$$
\begin{array}{r}
46.100 \\
-\ 8.306 \\
\hline
37.794
\end{array}
$$

   ?   Why has 46.1 been written as 46.100?

Exercise

1 Work out the cost of the items for each of these people.

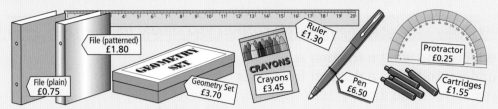

File (patterned) £1.80

File (plain) £0.75

GEOMETRY SET

Geometry Set £3.70

Ruler £1.30

CRAYONS

Crayons £3.45

Pen £6.50

Protractor £0.25

Cartridges £1.55

(a) Emily needs a pen, cartridges, crayons and a protractor.
(b) Simon needs a geometry set, a plain file and a pen.
(c) Anna wants cartridges, a protractor, a ruler and crayons.

2 **(a)** Amanda buys some emery boards, cotton wool, nail scissors, and nail polish.
    (i) How much is this altogether?
    (ii) How much change will she get from a ten-pound note?

  (b) Lionel buys some hair gel, deodorant and soap.
    (i) How much is this altogether?
    (ii) How much change will he get from a ten-pound note?

emery boards	99p
cotton wool	£1.45
nail scissors	£2.49
nail polish	£4.50
hair gel	£2.19
deodorant	£2.29
soap bar	£2.35

3 Think of a quick way to check the total on this bill.
Use this to find the total cost of these items.

(a)

Tee-shirt	£17.99
Shorts	£19.99
Sunglasses	£27.99

(b)

Trainers	£54.99
Sportsbag	£35.99
Sweatshirt	£39.99

SOCCER WORLD
HIGH ST. AVONFORD

SOCCER BOOTS	£39.99
SHORTS	£14.99
TRACKSUIT	£59.99
TOTAL	**£114.97**

THANK YOU FOR
YOUR CUSTOM

4 Work out.
(a) 23.75 + 647.8 + 2.954
(b) 93 − 76.348
(c) 38.06 + 0.412 − 18.571
(d) 1.0032 + 0.043 − 0.3

5 Terry was asked to subtract 3.04 from 9.63 but he subtracted 3.4 by mistake.
By how much was his answer wrong?
Was it too large or too small?

Finishing off

Now that you have completed this chapter you should be able to:

- understand what a fraction is
- understand what a decimal fraction is
- read scales and dials
- add decimals and decimal money
- subtract decimals and decimal money.

Review exercise

1 What are the shaded parts as fractions?

(a)   **(b)**   **(c)**   **(d)**   **(e)**

(f) Write the fractions above as decimals.

2 Write the numbers in the table as decimal numbers:

H	T	U	$\frac{1}{10}$	$\frac{1}{100}$	$\frac{1}{1000}$
		4	6		
	1	5		3	
					9
3		1	2		7
				5	9

3 Read the letters from the following scales.

(a)

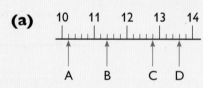

(b)

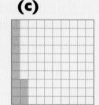

(c)

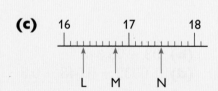

(d)

4 Put <, > or = between the two numbers to make a true statement.
($<$ means 'is less than', $>$ means 'is greater than', so $2 < 5$ and $9 > 7$)

(a) 5.3   5.03   **(b)** 7.49   7.490

(c) 0.0008   0.002   **(d)** 0.0066   0.0606

5 Carlo's mother buys these groceries:
(a) What is the total cost?
(b) How much change does she get from £5?

bread   53p
milk   57p
bacon   £1·43
eggs   £1·39

6 (a) Find the total cost of all of these items:

Winnie the Pooh book	£9.99	Slimline diary	£1.99
Return to Fantasia video	£12.99	Card	£1.40
Wrapping paper	95p		

(b) How much change would you get from £30?

7 David has £23.98 in his money box.
Find the amount he has left after each shopping trip.

(a) Flowers for Granny's birthday – £6.95
(b) Ticket and programme for Goliaths v Spartans – £8.50
(c) Easter eggs and card – £3.98

8 Carlo's father goes shopping with £200 of vouchers which he has been given for his birthday. He goes to the fishing shop and buys the following:

Carbon fishing rod	£84.99
Thigh waders	£59.99
Fixed spool reel	£34.99

(a) (i) How much is this altogether?
(ii) How much money has he still to spend?

He decides to buy a bite alarm for £36.99.

(b) How much money will he need to pay in addition to the vouchers?

Activity The number in each rectangle is the total of the numbers in the circles it is joined to. Copy the diagram and complete all the entries.

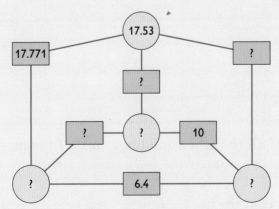

Phil draws a map of his town on a grid showing the important places.

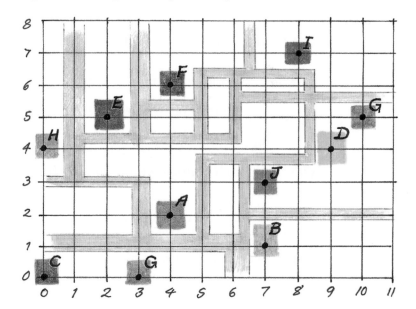

KEY

A	Library
B	Shop
C	Phil's house
D	Sports centre
E	Swimming pool
F	Windmill
G	School
H	Cinema
I	Church
J	Post Office

Each building is marked at a point.
You can use the gridlines to help you write down the exact position of a building.

The library is at position (4, 2).

Go up 2 squares.

Go along 4 from Phil's house.

We say that the library has **co-ordinates (4, 2)**.

The first number, **4**, gives the distance along.

The second number, **2**, gives the distance up.

? **What are the co-ordinates of the windmill?**
What are the co-ordinates of the school?

(Along, Up) is in alphabetical order.

Task

1 Look at Phil's map:

(a) What has co-ordinates (7, 1)?
(b) What has co-ordinates (9, 4)?

2 Write down the co-ordinates of all the other buildings on Phil's map.

! Phil says that the Post office is at (3, 7).
What has he done wrong? Why does Phil's mistake matter?

Exercise

Jane draws a map of her local boating lake.

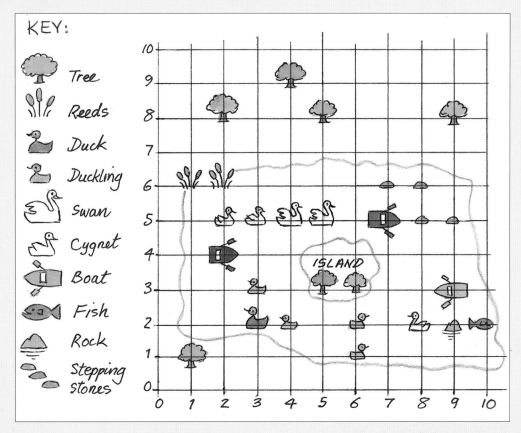

1 What is at the co-ordinates (9, 3)?

2 What is at the co-ordinates (10, 2)?

3 What is at the co-ordinates
(a) (8, 2) **(b)** (2, 8)?

4 What is at the co-ordinates
(a) (6, 2) **(b)** (2, 6)?

5 Write down the co-ordinates of all the trees.

6 Write down the co-ordinates of all the ducklings.

7 Write down the co-ordinates of:
(a) the red boat **(b)** the rock **(c)** the duck **(d)** the swans.

8 Write down the co-ordinates of all the stepping stones.

9 John says that there is a boat at (4, 2).
Explain why he is wrong.

Using co-ordinates in mathematics

In mathematics co-ordinates are plotted on a pair of axes like this:

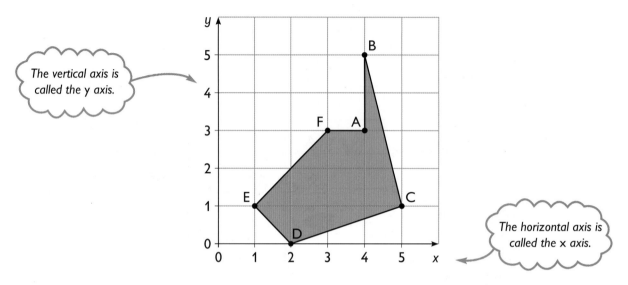

The vertical axis is called the y axis.

The horizontal axis is called the x axis.

The *x* co-ordinate is always given first.

The distance along from (0,0)

The point A is written (4, 3).
We say A has co-ordinates (4, 3).

Go along 4

Then up 3

? **What are the co-ordinates of points B and C?**
Would the point (3, 2) lie inside the shaded shape?
What about the point (2, 3)?

(x, y) is in alphabetical order

Any point can be plotted using co-ordinates.
The point (0, 0) has a special name. It is called the **origin**.

Task

1 Write down the co-ordinates of the points D, E and F.

2 (a) Draw a grid like the one above.
(b) Plot the points (2, 5), (5, 5), (5, 2) and (2, 2) and join them.
(c) What shape have you drawn?

3 (a) Draw another grid and make up your own shape.
(b) Give the co-ordinates of the corners to a friend so that they can draw
your shape.

? **Why is it important that the x co-ordinate is always given first?**

Exercise

1 Write down the co-ordinates of each of the points labelled A–L in these figures:

(a)

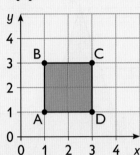

(b)

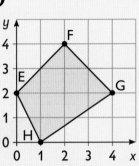

(c)

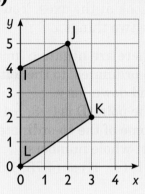

2 Draw axes, using the values of 0 to 14 for x and 0 to 6 for y.

(a) Plot these points and join them in order:
(0, 3), (4, 6), (9, 6), (13, 3), (9, 0), (4, 0) and back to (0, 3).
(b) Describe the shape you have drawn.
(c) Are all the sides the same length?
(d) Are all the angles the same size?

3 Follow these instructions.

> Draw an x axis from 0 to 10 and a y axis from 0 to 6.
> Plot the following points and join them up.
>
> (0, 3),   (4, 4),   (5, 5),   (5, 4),   (8, 3),   (9, 4),
> (9, 1),   (8, 2),   (5, 1),   (5, 0),   (4, 1),   (1, 2).
>
> Now put a dot at (2, 3).
> Draw a jagged line from (1, 2) to (2, 2).
> Draw straight lines from (3, 3) to (3, 2), from (4, 3) to (4, 2) and from (5, 3) to (5, 2).

What have you drawn?

Activity Draw your own picture and write a set of instructions giving the co-ordinates. Follow Question 3 as a guide.
Give your instructions to a friend to draw your picture from.

Using negative numbers, fractions and decimals

Look at this star.
Now look at the axes. You will notice two things.

- There are negative (minus) co-ordinates, to the left for x and down for y.
  The point D is $(-3, -4)$.
- Some of the co-ordinates are not whole numbers.
  B is $(4\frac{3}{4}, 1\frac{1}{2})$ or $(4.75, 1.5)$.

? **What are the co-ordinates of the other points, A, C and E?**

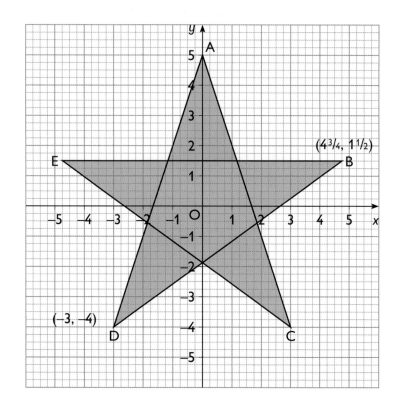

$(4^3/_4, 1^1/_2)$

$(-3, -4)$

Task

Here is a sketch of a star with 8 points. A is $(0, 5)$.

? **What is the length of OB? How many degrees is angle AOB?**

Draw this star accurately on graph paper.
What are the co-ordinates of the other points?

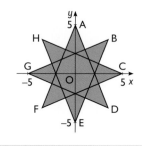

! Always look carefully at your graph paper to see how many small squares fit along each big one.

? **What are the co-ordinates of the labelled points on these two figures?**

(a)

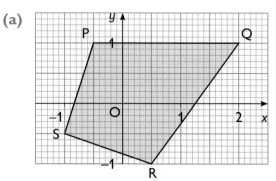

(b)

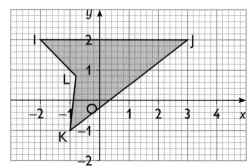

Exercise

1 Write down the co-ordinates of the labelled points on this bow-tie.

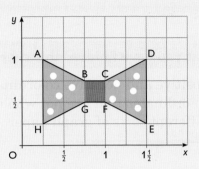

2 Draw axes, using the values of 0 to 5 for both x and y.
Plot these points and join them in order:

$(2, 4\frac{1}{2})$, $(4\frac{1}{2}, 4\frac{1}{2})$, $(2\frac{1}{2}, 1\frac{1}{2})$, $(0, \frac{1}{2})$ and back to $(2, 4\frac{1}{2})$.

Describe the shape you have drawn.

3 Draw axes, using the values of -1 to 6 for x and -4 to 4 for y.
Plot these points and join them in order:

$(-1, -1)$, $(2, 3)$, $(6, 0)$.

What fourth point would be needed to make a square?

4 Draw axes, using the values of -6 to 6 for both x and y.
(a) Plot these points and join them in order:

$(4, 6)$, $(6, 0)$, $(4, -6)$, $(-4, -6)$, $(-6, 0)$, $(-4, 6)$ and back to $(4, 6)$.

(b) Describe the shape you have drawn.
(c) Are all the sides the same length?
(d) Are all the angles exactly equal?

5 Write down the co-ordinates of the following points on this graph:
(a) A, B, C, D
(b) the point where the curve crosses the y axis
(c) the two points where the curve crosses the x axis
(d) the lowest point of the curve.

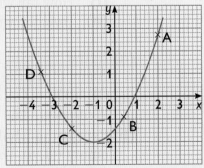

Investigation Find out how to draw a star with 9 points. Draw one for yourself. Now complete the instructions for a friend.
'Plot the following points and join them up in order:
....*'*

Finishing off

Now that you have finished this chapter you should be able to:

● use positive and negative co-ordinates
● use co-ordinates that are not whole numbers
● use different sorts of graph paper.

Review exercise

1 Here is a map showing seven towns and the roads between them. The distances along the axes are in kilometres.

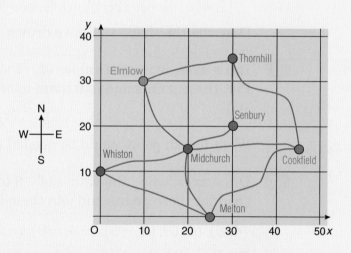

Elmlow is at the point (10, 30).
Melton is at (25, 0).

(a) What are the co-ordinates of **(i)** Whiston **(ii)** Midchurch?

(b) How far is it from **(i)** Thornhill to Senbury **(ii)** Midchurch to Cookfield?

(c) A new town is to be built at (45, 35).
   (i) How far will the new town be from Thornhill?
   (ii) How far will the new town be from Cookfield?

2 **(a)** In the diagram A is the point (4, 2).
      B and C are the points shown.
      OB = OC = OA and ∠AOB = ∠AOC = 90°.
      Write down the co-ordinates of B and C.

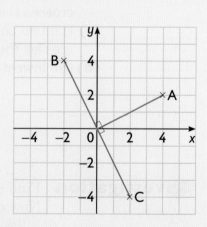

   (b) Repeat the whole of **(a)** when A is the point (−3, 5). Draw your own diagram.

   (c) Repeat **(a)** with a different point A of your choice.

   (d) What patterns do you notice in your answers?

3 Draw axes, using the values of −6 to 6 for x and −4 to 4 for y.
Plot these points and join them in order:
$(-4\frac{3}{4}, 0)$, $(-3\frac{1}{2}, 3\frac{1}{2})$, $(0, 0)$, $(3\frac{1}{2}, 3\frac{1}{2})$, $(4\frac{3}{4}, 0)$, $(3\frac{1}{2}, -3\frac{1}{2})$, $(0, 0)$.
What additional point is needed to make the shape you have
drawn symmetrical?

4 Greg and Debbie are playing a game called Treasure Hunt.
Their game is shown below.

Debbie 'buries' the
treasure at the
point (5, 7).
Greg has to guess
where Debbie has
hidden the treasure.
He guesses the
point (4, 4).
Debbie says that he is
a distance of 4 away.

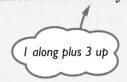
I along plus 3 up

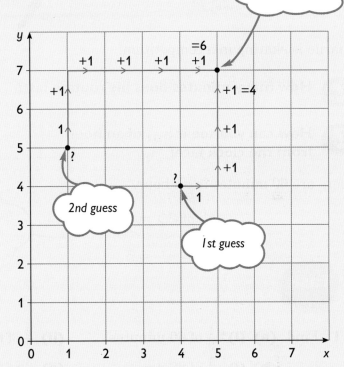
'Hidden' treasure

2nd guess

1st guess

The distance is the shortest distance away from the treasure travelling
only along the grid lines.

Greg then guesses (1, 5).
Why is this a sensible next guess?
He is now a distance of 6 away.
Greg will win when he works out where the treasure is.

Play the game with a partner.

Investigation Investigate what tactics you should use when playing
Treasure Hunt.
What is the least number of guesses which guarantees you find
the treasure?

Charlie's start time

Charlie's end time

Charlie is skating in a competition.

? **How many minutes does his routine last?**

? **How can you see it is $\frac{1}{12}$ of an hour from the clock face?**

That is $\frac{1}{12}$ of an hour

There are 60 minutes in an hour.

$$\frac{1}{12} \text{ of } 60 = \frac{1}{\cancel{12}_1} \times \cancel{60}^5$$
$$= 5$$

You can also write this as $\frac{60}{12}$ and then cancel

Task

1 Find **(a) (i)** $\frac{1}{3}$ of 60 minutes   **(ii)** $\frac{2}{3}$ of 60 minutes

      (b) (i) $\frac{1}{4}$ of 28 days   **(ii)** $\frac{3}{4}$ of 28 days

      (c) (i) $\frac{1}{7}$ of £56   **(ii)** $\frac{2}{7}$ of £56

2 How many degrees does the minute hand of a clock turn through in
  (a) 60 minutes   **(b)** 5 minutes   **(c)** 1 minute   **(d)** 23 minutes   **(e)** $2\frac{1}{2}$ hours?

Philip eats two pieces of cake at tea-time.

This means he has eaten a quarter of the cake.

So $\frac{2}{8} = \frac{1}{4}$.

? **Why are these fractions the same or *equivalent*?**

Dividing top and bottom by 2.

$$\frac{2}{8} = \frac{\cancel{2}^1}{\cancel{8}_4} = \frac{1}{4}$$

$$\frac{30}{60} = \frac{\cancel{30}^1}{\cancel{60}_2} = \frac{1}{2}$$

Dividing top and bottom by 30.

You can cancel as often as you like.

Cancelling by 2 and by 3.

$$\frac{12}{54} = \frac{\cancel{12}^6}{\cancel{54}_{27}} = \frac{\cancel{6}^2}{\cancel{27}_9} = \frac{2}{9}$$

OR

$$\frac{12}{54} = \frac{\cancel{12}^2}{\cancel{54}_9} = \frac{2}{9}$$

Cancelling by 6.

Exercise

1 By how much are these items reduced?

2 1 pound = 16 ounces. Work out

(a) $\frac{1}{2}$ of a pound (b) $\frac{1}{8}$ of a pound (c) $\frac{1}{16}$ of a pound

3 Find

(a) $\frac{2}{5}$ of 60 minutes (b) $\frac{3}{4}$ of 64 kg (c) $\frac{1}{4}$ of 100 cm (d) $\frac{1}{3}$ of 45 minutes

(e) $\frac{2}{3}$ of 18 kg (f) $\frac{5}{16}$ of 32 ounces (g) $\frac{3}{7}$ of 28 days (h) $\frac{4}{9}$ of 360°

(i) $\frac{4}{7}$ of \$42 (j) $\frac{6}{11}$ of £33 (k) $\frac{3}{10}$ of 1000 m (l) $\frac{4}{9}$ of 63 km

(m) $\frac{11}{25}$ of 100 kg (n) $\frac{3}{20}$ of £40 (o) $\frac{7}{12}$ of 132 g

4 Cancel to simplest terms.

(a) $\frac{5}{10}$ (b) $\frac{3}{12}$ (c) $\frac{2}{16}$ (d) $\frac{4}{20}$ (e) $\frac{6}{12}$

(f) $\frac{11}{44}$ (g) $\frac{9}{24}$ (h) $\frac{25}{30}$ (i) $\frac{24}{56}$ (j) $\frac{18}{66}$

(k) $\frac{27}{72}$ (l) $\frac{21}{49}$ (m) $\frac{21}{28}$ (n) $\frac{8}{48}$ (o) $\frac{18}{81}$

(p) $\frac{45}{60}$ (q) $\frac{24}{36}$ (r) $\frac{28}{35}$ (s) $\frac{54}{63}$ (t) $\frac{88}{96}$

5 Find the missing numbers.

(a) $\frac{9}{16} = \frac{9 \times \boxed{?}}{16 \times 3} = \frac{\boxed{?}}{48}$ (b) $\frac{7}{12} = \frac{7 \times \boxed{?}}{12 \times \boxed{?}} = \frac{\boxed{?}}{48}$

Which is larger, $\frac{9}{16}$ or $\frac{7}{12}$?

Activity Ask your teacher for the worksheet that goes with this activity.
Shade in every part of the worksheet which contains a fraction
equivalent to $\frac{7}{9}$.

Multiplying fractions

Sally's mother cuts a pizza into 2 halves.
She then cuts each half piece into 3 slices.

She has cut the whole pizza into 6 pieces,
so each slice is one-sixth, or $\frac{1}{6}$.

In fact she did $\frac{1}{3}$ of $\frac{1}{2} = \frac{1}{3} \times \frac{1}{2}$

> *Multiplying $1 \times 1 = 1$ at the top and $3 \times 2 = 6$ at the bottom.* $= \frac{1}{6}$.

The next day Sally's mother cuts a quiche into 3 equal pieces. She puts 2 of these pieces into Sally's lunch-box.

At school, Kevin has forgotten his lunch. Sally gives him one of her pieces of quiche. Kevin and Sally now each have one-third, or $\frac{1}{3}$, of quiche.

$$\frac{1}{2} \text{ of } \frac{2}{3} = \frac{1}{\cancel{2}} \times \frac{\cancel{2}^{1}}{3}$$

$$= \frac{1}{3}.$$

> *Multiplying $1 \times 1 = 1$ at the top and $1 \times 3 = 3$ at the bottom.*

Task

Draw your own fraction diagrams to find the following.

1 **(a)** $\frac{1}{2}$ of $\frac{1}{4}$ **(b)** $\frac{1}{2}$ of $\frac{1}{5}$ **(c)** $\frac{1}{3}$ of $\frac{1}{4}$ **(d)** $\frac{1}{4}$ of $\frac{1}{4}$ **(e)** $\frac{1}{4}$ of $\frac{1}{5}$

Now try these:

2 **(a)** $\frac{1}{2}$ of $\frac{4}{5}$ **(b)** $\frac{1}{3}$ of $\frac{3}{8}$ **(c)** $\frac{1}{3}$ of $\frac{6}{8}$ **(d)** $\frac{1}{4}$ of $\frac{6}{8}$ **(e)** $\frac{2}{5}$ of $\frac{5}{8}$

Check the results of your drawings by using the cancelling and multiplying method shown above.

Cancelling can be done with any number of fractions:

$$\frac{6}{7} \times \frac{14}{27} \times \frac{3}{4} = \frac{6 \times \cancel{14}^{2} \times 3}{\cancel{7}_{1} \times 27 \times 4} = \frac{6 \times 2 \times \cancel{3}^{1}}{\cancel{27}_{9} \times 4} = \frac{6 \times 2}{9 \times 4}$$

> *Cancel by 7 . . .*   *. . . and now by 3.*

> *Once the numbers are small you can just work it out.*

$$= \frac{12}{36} = \frac{1}{3}.$$

Exercise

1 (a) $\frac{1}{2} \times \frac{1}{5}$ (b) $\frac{1}{3} \times \frac{1}{7}$ (c) $\frac{1}{6} \times \frac{1}{4}$

    (d) $\frac{1}{3} \times \frac{2}{5}$ (e) $\frac{1}{4} \times \frac{3}{5}$ (f) $\frac{3}{7} \times \frac{5}{8}$

2 (a) $\frac{2}{5} \times \frac{1}{4}$ (b) $\frac{3}{8} \times \frac{4}{9}$ (c) $\frac{3}{10} \times \frac{5}{12}$

    (d) $\frac{7}{9} \times \frac{3}{14}$ (e) $\frac{5}{18} \times \frac{6}{25}$ (f) $\frac{8}{27} \times \frac{9}{32}$

3 (a) $\frac{5}{8} \times \frac{2}{3}$ (b) $\frac{3}{16} \times \frac{4}{5}$ (c) $\frac{7}{9} \times \frac{6}{14}$

    (d) $\frac{11}{12} \times \frac{2}{9}$ (e) $\frac{5}{14} \times \frac{7}{8}$ (f) $\frac{2}{39} \times \frac{13}{14}$

4 (a) $\frac{15}{8} \times \frac{8}{5}$ (b) $\frac{3}{2} \times \frac{4}{3}$ (c) $\frac{5}{2} \times \frac{2}{5}$

    (d) $\frac{13}{4} \times \frac{8}{13}$ (e) $\frac{14}{11} \times \frac{11}{7}$ (f) $\frac{15}{4} \times \frac{8}{3}$

5 (a) $\frac{2}{15} \times \frac{5}{12} \times \frac{8}{9}$ (b) $\frac{3}{8} \times \frac{5}{9} \times \frac{16}{25}$ (c) $\frac{7}{8} \times \frac{12}{21} \times \frac{16}{20}$

    (d) $\frac{15}{33} \times \frac{14}{25} \times \frac{11}{21}$ (e) $\frac{12}{45} \times \frac{15}{81} \times \frac{27}{2}$ (f) $\frac{54}{33} \times \frac{49}{56} \times \frac{11}{63}$

6 (a) $\frac{2}{5} \times 15$ (b) $\frac{5}{8} \times 40$ (c) $\frac{3}{7} \times 21$

    (d) $\frac{6}{7} \times 42$ (e) $\frac{5}{9} \times 45$ (f) $\frac{2}{13} \times 52$

Activity

Find this palindrome.

❖ ☆ ❖ ▲, ❖ ● ⊞ ❖ ▲, ❖ ❑ ❖ ▲ ❖ ⊞, ● ❖ ▲ ❖ ☆ ❖

1 First work out the answer to this question:

▲ $\frac{6}{11} \times \frac{33}{42}$

Now find the answer below and write the corresponding letter in place of every ▲ in the palindrome above.

2 Now try this one:

☆ $\frac{3}{10} \times \frac{5}{21}$

Find this answer and replace every ☆ with the corresponding letter from the answers below.

3 Continue with these:

● $\frac{1}{12} \times \frac{3}{4} \times 2$ ❖ $\frac{2}{5} \times \frac{10}{7} \times \frac{3}{9} \times \frac{14}{6}$

⊞ $\frac{5}{9} \times \frac{42}{48} \times \frac{45}{35}$ ❑ $\frac{5}{17} \times \frac{51}{42} \times \frac{28}{35}$

A $\frac{4}{9}$ C $\frac{2}{7}$ L $\frac{5}{8}$ M $\frac{1}{14}$ N $\frac{3}{7}$ P $\frac{1}{8}$

Adding and subtracting fractions

Jared eats $\frac{1}{4}$ of a cake. He then goes back for 'seconds' and eats another $\frac{1}{6}$ of the cake. How much of the cake has he eaten altogether?

> I ate $\frac{1}{4} + \frac{1}{6}$, but what is this as a single fraction? The denominators 4 and 6 are both factors of 12. So I can change each fraction to an equal fraction with denominator 12.

$$\frac{1}{4} = \frac{1 \times 3}{4 \times 3} = \frac{3}{12}, \qquad \frac{1}{6} = \frac{1 \times 2}{6 \times 2} = \frac{2}{12}$$

$$\frac{1}{4} + \frac{1}{6} = \frac{3}{12} + \frac{2}{12} = \frac{5}{12}$$

> I have eaten $\frac{5}{12}$ of the cake so $\frac{7}{12}$ is left.

> Add the numerators $3 + 2 = 5$.

 12 is called a **common denominator**. Why?

 You could use 24 or 36 or any multiple of 12 as the common denominator, but this would involve bigger numbers and cancelling.

For example $\frac{1}{4} + \frac{1}{6} = \frac{6}{24} + \frac{4}{24} = \frac{10}{24} = \frac{5}{12}$.

> cancel by 2

So it is better to use 12, which is the lowest common denominator.

Jacinta later eats $\frac{2}{5}$ of the cake. What fractions of the cake remains?

The fraction left is $\frac{7}{12} - \frac{2}{5}$. The lowest common denominator is $5 \times 12 = 60$.

You can now write $\frac{7}{12} - \frac{2}{5} = \frac{35}{60} - \frac{24}{60} = \frac{11}{60}$.

Task

For each of these pairs of fractions
(a) find the lowest common denominator
(b) add the two fractions
(c) subtract the second fraction from the first.

(i) $\frac{3}{4}$ and $\frac{2}{7}$ **(ii)** $\frac{5}{8}$ and $\frac{3}{10}$ **(iii)** $\frac{11}{15}$ and $\frac{5}{12}$

When you add $\frac{3}{4}$ and $\frac{1}{2}$, the answer is $\frac{5}{4}$.

$\frac{5}{4}$ is called a **top-heavy** or **improper** fraction.

You can write $\frac{5}{4}$ as $1\frac{1}{4}$. Now it is a **mixed number**.

Exercise

1 Work out the following.

(a) $\frac{3}{5} + \frac{1}{4}$ **(b)** $\frac{1}{3} + \frac{3}{10}$ **(c)** $\frac{5}{12} + \frac{2}{9}$ **(d)** $\frac{2}{5} + \frac{7}{16}$ **(e)** $\frac{13}{15} + \frac{19}{20}$

2 **(a)** Find the smallest number which has all of 4, 5 and 12 as factors.
Use this as the lowest common denominator to work out $\frac{3}{4} + \frac{2}{5} + \frac{7}{12}$.
(b) Work out $\frac{5}{6} + \frac{3}{8} + \frac{11}{12}$.

3 Work out the following.

(a) $\frac{2}{3} - \frac{1}{6}$ **(b)** $\frac{5}{8} - \frac{1}{5}$ **(c)** $\frac{13}{16} - \frac{7}{12}$ **(d)** $\frac{7}{8} + \frac{1}{4} - \frac{5}{7}$ **(e)** $\frac{7}{3} - \frac{5}{12} - \frac{3}{8}$

4 $\frac{3}{5}$ of a garden is lawn, and $\frac{2}{9}$ is used for growing vegetables.
What fraction is left for other uses?

5 A sponsored walk for charity is 15 miles long.
Checkpoint A is $6\frac{2}{3}$ miles from the start.
Checkpoint B is $4\frac{1}{4}$ miles from the finish.

(a) How far is B from the start?
(b) What is the distance between checkpoints?

6 In most harbours the tide rises from low water to high water in about 6 hours. This table gives the rise during each hour as a fraction of the total rise.

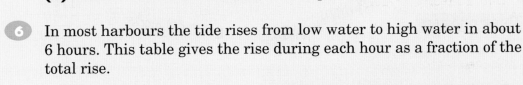

1st hour	2nd hour	3rd hour	4th hour	5th hour	6th hour
$\frac{1}{12}$	$\frac{1}{6}$	$\frac{1}{4}$	$\frac{1}{4}$	$\frac{1}{6}$	$\frac{1}{12}$

(a) Check that the sum of all these fractions is 1.
(b) What fraction of the total does the tide rise in
(i) the first 2 hours   **(ii)** the middle 4 hours?
(c) The depth at a certain place in Dover Harbour is 7 m at low water and the rise of the tide is 5 m. Find the depth.
(i) 2 hours after low water   **(ii)** 1 hour before high water.

Introduction to percentages

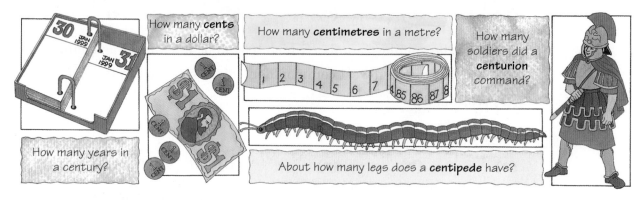

Percentage means *out of 100* and is written as %.   20% means $\frac{20}{100}$.

Task

Which percentage do you think belongs to each label?

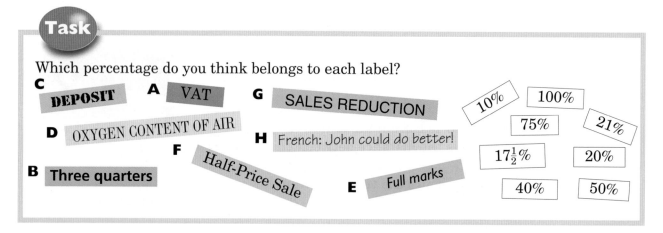

C **DEPOSIT**   A **VAT**   G **SALES REDUCTION**

D **OXYGEN CONTENT OF AIR**   H French: John could do better!

B **Three quarters**   F **Half-Price Sale**   E Full marks

10%   100%   75%   21% $17\frac{1}{2}\%$ 20%   40%   50%

Percentages can be written as fractions . . .

$$30\% = \frac{30}{100}$$

$$= \frac{\overset{3}{30}}{\underset{10}{100}} = \frac{3}{10}$$

$$65\% = \frac{65}{100}$$

$$= \frac{\overset{13}{65}}{\underset{20}{100}} = \frac{13}{20}$$

. . . and cancelled in the same way.

You can find a percentage of a quantity:

$$10\% \text{ of } £600 = \frac{10}{100} \times £600$$

$$= \frac{10}{\underset{1}{100}} \times £600^{\,6}$$

$$= £60$$

The whole amount is called **100%**.

Example   82% of apples in a box are good, ripe apples.
What percentage of the apples are not fit to eat?

(100 − 82)% = 18% of the apples are not fit to eat.

Exercise

1 Write these percentages as fractions.
   (a) 37%   **(b)** 53%   **(c)** 7%   **(d)** 11%

2 Write these percentages as fractions and cancel to their lowest terms.
   (a) 20%   **(b)** 24%   **(c)** 5%   **(d)** 64%

3 Find 10% of each of these amounts.
   (a) £30   **(b)** £500   **(c)** $450   **(d)** 240 m   **(e)** 64 litres

4 There is 30% off goods in a sale.
   Find the reduction for these items.
   (a) A computer game priced at £50
   (b) A computer priced at £1 000
   (c) A holiday priced at $800
   (d) A tent priced at £750

> *You may find it quicker to find 10% first and then multiply by 3.*

5 Find these percentages.
   (a) 25% of 840 m   **(b)** 75% of 20 km
   (c) 60% of 20 kg   **(d)** 30% of 80 kg
   (e) 5% of £300   **(f)** 2% of $450

6 **(a)** A jumper is made from a mixture of wool and viscose.
       It is 80% wool. What is the percentage of viscose?
   (b) 83% of the pupils in a school are present.
       What percentage are absent?

7 Write 50%, 25%, and 75% as fractions in their lowest terms.
   These results are useful to know off by heart.

8 Value Added Tax (VAT) of $17\frac{1}{2}\%$ is added to the price of many goods
   and services. Here is a quick way to work out VAT:

   Find 10% of the price, then half of this, then half of this again; the VAT is
   the sum of these three amounts.

   Example   Price £68

10% of this	= £ 6.80
half of this	= £ 3.40
half of this	= £ 1.70
VAT	= £11.90

> *You can do this in your head.*

   (a) Find the VAT when the price is **(i)** £52   **(ii)** £432   **(iii)** £12 800
   (b) Explain why this works.

Ratio and proportion

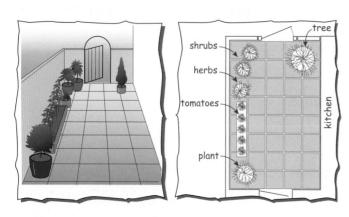

Andy and his father are making a patio.
They lay the slabs using mortar.
To mix the mortar they need 1 part cement to 4 parts sand.
This can be written as *the ratio* 1 : 4 (read as 1 to 4).

 They have a 50 kg bag of cement.
How much sand should be mixed with it?

Task

Air Wales has different sorts of aeroplanes. On all of them the ratio of 1st class to 2nd class seats is $1:9$.

1 One aeroplane has 20 1st class seats.
   (a) How many 2nd class seats does it have?
   (b) How many seats does it have overall?
   (c) What fraction of the seats are 1st class? 2nd class?

 $1 + 9 = 10$. **What has this got to do with the aeroplane?**

2 Another aeroplane has 400 seats.
   How many are 1st class? 2nd class?

3 Another airline has 3 classes of seats, in the ratio
$$First : Standard : Backpacker = 1 : 8 : 3$$
   How many of each are there on a 240-seater aeroplane?

Order matters with ratios.
Sand : cement = $4:1$.

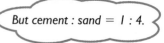 *But cement : sand = 1 : 4.*

 We will probably need 1250 kg of mortar altogether.

5 parts altogether (1 part + 4 parts) will be 1250 kg.
So 1 part is $\frac{1250}{5} = 250$ kg.
So 250 kg of cement are needed and $250 \times 4 = 1000$ kg of sand.

Ratios can be cancelled down like fractions:

Example 1 $2:8 = 1:4$

Cancelling by 2.

Example 2 $3:12:15 = 1:4:5$

Cancelling by 3.

Exercise

1 The ratio of cement : sand is 1 : 4.
How much sand is needed if:
(a) 200 kg of cement is used?
(b) 70 kg of cement is used?

2 The ratio of cement : sand is 1 : 4.
How much cement is needed if:
(a) 320 kg of sand is used?
(b) 240 kg of sand is used?

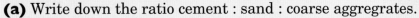

3 Andy's father makes a different mixture to use as a
base for a shed. It is 1 part cement, 2 parts sand,
and 3 parts coarse aggregates (tiny stones).
(a) Write down the ratio cement : sand : coarse aggregrates.
(b) 250 kg of cement is used.
(i) How much sand is needed?
(ii) How many kilograms of coarse aggregates are needed?

4 To fill the flower pots, Andy mixes a compost of 7 parts loam, 3 parts peat,
and 2 parts sand.
(a) Write down the ratio of loam : peat : sand.
(b) How much peat and how much sand is needed if 14 kg of loam is used?
(c) How much loam and how much sand is needed if $1\frac{1}{2}$ kg of peat is used?

5 Andy wants to make 60 kg of compost altogether.
(a) How many parts altogether?
(b) How many kilograms in one part?
(c) How much loam, peat and sand is needed?

> Compost mix is 7 parts loam, 3 parts peat and 2 parts sand.

6 Andy's mother makes 12 jars of strawberry jam and
8 jars of raspberry jam.
(a) (i) Write down the ratio of
strawberry jam : raspberry jam.
(ii) Simplify your ratio.
(b) What is the ratio of raspberry jam : strawberry jam?
(c) (i) What is the ratio of jars of raspberry jam : total number of jars
of jam?
(ii) Simplify your ratio.

7 Simplify these ratios:
(a) 6 : 8   **(b)** 8 : 6   **(c)** 8 : 4   **(d)** 40 : 45
(e) 16 : 24   **(f)** 6 : 3   **(g)** 7 : 28   **(h)** 11 : 33
(i) 12 : 15 : 21   **(j)** 25 : 20 : 40   **(k)** 9 : 12 : 15   **(l)** 63 : 28 : 56

Finishing off

Now that you have finished this chapter you should be able to:

- cancel a fraction
- find a fraction of a quantity
- change percentages to fractions
- find a percentage of a quantity
- multiply, add and subtract fractions
- understand ratios and proportion.

Review exercise

1 Cancel these fractions to their lowest terms.

(a) $\frac{6}{8}$
(b) $\frac{12}{15}$
(c) $\frac{25}{30}$
(d) $\frac{12}{16}$
(e) $\frac{21}{35}$

(f) $\frac{24}{32}$
(g) $\frac{12}{20}$
(h) $\frac{240}{360}$
(i) $\frac{72}{81}$
(j) $\frac{19}{38}$

2 Write these percentages as fractions.
(a) 11%
(b) 3%
(c) 79%
(d) 91%

3 Write these percentages as fractions, and cancel them to their lowest terms.
(a) 12%
(b) 4%
(c) 80%
(d) 92%
(e) 45%
(f) 18%
(g) 32%
(h) 75%

4 Work out the following.

(a) $\frac{1}{3}$ of £24
(b) $\frac{1}{4}$ of 1760 yards

(c) $\frac{5}{8}$ of 16 ounces
(d) $\frac{3}{4}$ of £16

5 A sale has 20% off the marked prices.
Work out how much each of these cost in the sale.

(a) Bag £35
(b) Shoes £40
(c) Jeans £45
20% OFF
(d) T-shirt £25
(e) CD £15
(f) Poster £5

6 Find
(a) 30% of £650
(b) 25% of $8
(c) 60% of 45 Euros
(d) 75% of 48 kg
(e) 5% of 40 metres
(f) 55% of 80 km

7 Work out (evaluate)

(a) $\frac{1}{4} \times \frac{1}{3}$
(b) $\frac{2}{7} \times \frac{1}{3}$
(c) $\frac{1}{2} \times \frac{8}{13}$
(d) $\frac{3}{4} \times \frac{1}{3}$
(e) $\frac{2}{5} \times \frac{4}{11}$
(f) $\frac{1}{7} \times \frac{14}{33}$

8 Simplify these

(a) $\frac{2}{3} \times \frac{9}{14} \times \frac{7}{8}$

(b) $\frac{2}{3} \times \frac{15}{16} \times \frac{4}{5}$

(c) $\frac{7}{8} \times \frac{3}{4} \times \frac{16}{49}$

(d) $\frac{12}{17} \times \frac{1}{5} \times \frac{5}{11}$

(e) $\frac{1}{4} \times \frac{2}{7} \times \frac{2}{9}$

(f) $\frac{2}{3} \times \frac{7}{10} \times \frac{5}{6}$

9 Work out (evaluate)

(a) $\frac{1}{4} + \frac{1}{3}$

(b) $\frac{2}{5} + \frac{4}{11}$

(c) $\frac{8}{13} - \frac{1}{2}$

(d) $\frac{7}{8} - \frac{9}{14}$

(e) $\frac{3}{4} + \frac{1}{6} - \frac{5}{8}$

(f) $\frac{3}{5} - \frac{8}{21} - \frac{1}{15}$

10 Simplify the following ratios:

(a) $16 : 20$

(b) $15 : 3$

(c) $48 : 36$

(d) $36 : 18 : 27$

(e) $33 : 55 : 66$

(f) $72 : 45 : 54$

11 A fertiliser is made of 2 parts hoof and horn meal, 2 parts lime and 1 part potash.

(a) How much lime and how much potash is needed if 3 kg hoof and horn meal is used?

(b) How much of each should be used if 20 kg of fertiliser is wanted altogether?

Activity

1 On a piece of graph paper, draw axes numbered from 0 to 12. Mark the points (0, 0), (1, 1), (2, 2), (3, 3), etc., up to (12, 12) and then use a ruler and a coloured pencil to join them together.

2 Now mark in pencil *all* the points with whole number co-ordinates AND the x-co-ordinate bigger than the y-co-ordinate. e.g. (2, 1), (3, 1), (3, 2), (4, 1), (4, 2), (4, 3), etc.

3 With your ruler join (12, 6) to (0, 0). There should be five other marked points on this line. What are they? Write these as fractions with the x-co-ordinate as the bottom line (*denominator*) and the y-co-ordinate as the top line (*numerator*). e.g. $\frac{6}{12}$, $\frac{3}{6}$.

The fractions you have written are all equal to each other.

4 Draw lines from (0, 0) through your chosen point to find which fractions are equivalent to

(a) $\frac{2}{3}$

(b) $\frac{4}{5}$

(c) $\frac{3}{4}$.

10 Number patterns

Factors

Terry is preparing for a party by putting glasses onto a shelf.
He arranges 18 glasses in a rectangle.

3 by 6

 Are there any other ways that Terry could arrange the glasses into rectangles? Is a 3 by 6 rectangle different from a 6 by 3 rectangle?

We say that 3 and 6 are **factors** of 18 because they divide exactly into 18.

 What are the other factors of 18?

Task

1 There are 24 children in a class. How many different ways can their desks be arranged in a rectangular shape?

2 How can 144 chairs be arranged for an assembly? Find all the possible rectangular arrangements. Which ones are the most practical?

Multiples

Terry has some trays which hold 6 glasses each.
He starts to stack the trays of glasses.

 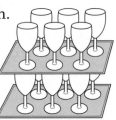 

 How many glasses are in each of the piles that Terry has made?

The numbers 6, 12, 18, 24, . . . are called **multiples** of 6.

They are the answers to the 6 times table:

$1 \times 6 = 6$
$2 \times 6 = 12$
$3 \times 6 = 18$
$4 \times 6 = 24$ and so on.

 What are the first 12 multiples of 2?

The multiples of 2 are called **even numbers**.
Numbers which are not multiples of 2 are called **odd numbers**.

 How can you decide that a number is odd?

Exercise

1 Write down all the multiplication sums that give an answer of 12.
What are the factors of 12? List them in order of size.

2 Write down in order of size all of the factors of the following.
(a) 8 **(b)** 6 **(c)** 7 **(d)** 16 **(e)** 20 **(f)** 15

3 Write down the numbers that are factors of both 24 and 36.
The largest of these is called the highest common factor (HCF).
What is the HCF of 24 and 36?

4 Write down the first 12 multiples of 4.
Which of these are also multiples of **(a)** 2 **(b)** 8 **(c)** 5?

5 Write down the first three multiples of the following.
(a) 3 **(b)** 7 **(c)** 13 **(d)** 10 **(e)** 5 **(f)** 11

6 Write down the first three multiples of both 24 and 36.
The smallest of these is called the lowest common multiple (LCM).
What is the LCM of 24 and 36?

7 Sean buys 36 plants.
(a) Show all the different ways he can arrange them into rectangular trays.
(b) Another day Sean buys 3 trays of 36 plants.
How many plants does he buy altogether?

8 James is stacking trays of 8 glasses. Sarah is stacking trays of 12 glasses.
When they have finished they find that they both have the same number of glasses in their piles. Say as much as you can about how many glasses they each have.

9 Chris is organising a barbecue.
The local shop sells rolls in packets of 6, and sausages in packets of 10.
Chris buys three packets of rolls and two packets of sausages.
(a) How much does he spend?
(b) How many hot dogs can he make?
(c) Chris does not want to have any rolls
or sausages left over.
How many packets of each does he buy?

Investigation You have an unlimited supply of 5p and 7p stamps, but no others.
Find what amounts of postage you *cannot* pay exactly.
Explain carefully how you can be sure that your answer is complete.

Squares

Jamie has several square patio slabs and he wants to arrange them to make a square patio. He has 16 slabs and he arranges them into a 4 by 4 square.

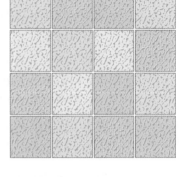

 Is there any other way of arranging 16 slabs into a square?

One of the slabs is cracked. Jamie now tries to arrange the remaining 15 slabs into a square.

 Can you arrange 15 patio slabs into a square?

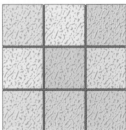

Jamie now uses some of the patio slabs to make smaller squares.

1 by 1

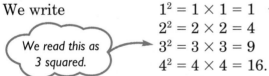

2 by 2

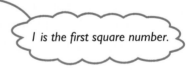

3 by 3

Task

1   How many slabs are used for each square above?
2   How many slabs would be used in the next 7 squares in Jamie's pattern?
3   What patterns can you spot in these numbers?

The numbers 1, 4, 9, and 16 are called **square numbers**.

Square numbers are the answers when a number is multiplied by itself.
We write

$$1^2 = 1 \times 1 = 1$$
$$2^2 = 2 \times 2 = 4$$
$$3^2 = 3 \times 3 = 9$$
$$4^2 = 4 \times 4 = 16.$$

We read this as 3 squared.

1 is the first square number.

 How can you find 97^2 using your calculator?

Square roots

A square which uses 25 patio slabs must have 5 slabs along each side.
5 is called the **square root** of 25.

$$5 \times 5 = 25$$

A quick way to write this is using the square root sign $\sqrt{}$.

$$\sqrt{25} = 5$$

 What size square should you use to arrange 49 patio slabs into a square?

 What is $\sqrt{49}$? What is $\sqrt{15}$?

Exercise

1 Write down the first ten square numbers.

2 Jenny wants to arrange oranges into different sizes of trays.
Which of the following numbers of oranges can she arrange into square trays?

(a) 9   **(b)** 27   **(c)** 16   **(d)** 64   **(e)** 58   **(f)** 100

Explain how you know in each case.

3

Number	Factors	Number of factors
9	1, 3, 9	3
27	1, 3, 9, 27	4

Continue this table for each of the numbers in Question 2.
When does a number have an odd number of factors?

4 Imad wants to break off squares of chocolate from a larger bar.
How many different sizes of square can he break off?

5 **(a)** How many small pieces of chocolate would there be in a square bar with 6 pieces along each side?

(b) How many small pieces of chocolate would there be in a square with 12 pieces along each side?

(c) Katy has a square bar with 64 pieces of chocolate. How many small pieces are there along each side of the square bar?

(d) What is the square root of 64?

6 Find

(a) $\sqrt{81}$ **(b)** $\sqrt{169}$ **(c)** $\sqrt{1}$ **(d)** $\sqrt{100}$ **(e)** $\sqrt{121}$

7 **(a)** Find

(i) $\sqrt{900}$ **(ii)** $\sqrt{1600}$ **(iii)** $\sqrt{2500}$ **(iv)** $\sqrt{3600}$

(b) What pattern do you notice?

(c) Now write down the value of

(i) 80^2 **(ii)** 90^2 **(iii)** 100^2 **(iv)** 700^2

8 Find

(a) (i) 0.1^2 **(ii)** 0.2^2 **(iii)** 0.3^2 **(iv)** 0.4^2

(b) What pattern do you notice? Continue this pattern up to 0.9^2.

Investigation   How many squares are formed by the lines on a chess board?
There are more than 64 squares!

Primes

Every whole number greater than 1 has at least two factors, the number itself and 1.
A number which has *exactly* two factors is called a **prime number**.
The smallest prime number is 2, and the next ones are 3, 5, 7 and 11.

 Why is 9 not a prime number? Why is I not a prime number?

 Are there any even prime numbers except for 2? Why?

Task

The Sieve of Eratosthenes. This is a method for finding prime numbers invented by the Greek mathematician Eratosthenes in about 230 BC.

1̸	②	③	4̸	5	6̸	7	8̸	9̸	1̸0̸
11	1̸2̸	13	1̸4̸	1̸5̸	1̸6̸	17	1̸8̸	19	2̸0̸
2̸1̸	2̸2̸	23	2̸4̸	25	2̸6̸	2̸7̸	2̸8̸	29	3̸0̸

This is part of Emily's sieve. What does she do next?

I Write the numbers 1 to 100 in a square. Cross off number 1.

2 Ring 2 and cross off all other multiples of 2 in red.

3 Ring the next uncrossed number: 3. Cross off all its other multiples in blue. (You need not cross out any number more than once.)

4 Ring the next number and cross off all its multiples in green. Carry on until all the numbers are either ringed or crossed off, using a different colour for each set of multiples.

 What is special about the ringed numbers?

 (a) How many numbers do you cross off as a result of ringing (i) 2 (ii) 5 (iii) 41?
(b) What is the largest ringed number that causes any other number to be crossed off?
(c) What is the answer to (b) for a sieve which goes up to 400?

The number 180 is not prime since it has factors other than 180 and 1.
For example $180 = 18 \times 10$.
These factors have factors themselves: $18 = 2 \times 9 = 2 \times 3 \times 3$ and $10 = 2 \times 5$.
So $180 = 2 \times 3 \times 3 \times 2 \times 5 = 2^2 \times 3^2 \times 5$.
We have written 180 as the *product of prime factors*.

Task

Write 180 as the product of two factors in a different way.
Write these factors as products of factors, continuing until you reach prime factors.
Now write your prime factors in ascending order.

Compare your prime factors with a friend's. What do you notice?

A number may have many sets of factors, but it has only one set of prime factors.

Exercise

1 13 and 31 are both prime numbers. List all the other 2-digit prime numbers that are still prime when their digits are reversed.

2 Draw a 2 – 61 grid like the one shown.

(a) On your grid put a ring around every number that is prime.

(b) Shade in all the multiples of 6. What do you notice about where all the prime numbers are? Why do you think this happens?

2	3	4	5	6	7
8	9	10	11	12	13
14	15	16	17	18	19
20	21	22	23	24	25
26	27	28	29	30	31
32	33	34	35	36	37
38	39	40	41	42	43
44	45	46	47	48	49
50	51	52	53	54	55
56	57	58	59	60	61

3 In 1742 Christian Goldbach claimed that every number greater than 2 is the sum of two prime numbers.
For example, $60 = 7 + 53$ and $62 = 31 + 31$.
Check that this is true for all the even numbers from 90 to 100 inclusive.
(It is still not known whether Goldbach's claim is correct.)

4 Write each of these numbers as the product of prime factors.
(a) 280 **(b)** 726 **(c)** 143 **(d)** 936 **(e)** 39 900

5 What is the smallest number (except 0) which has all the numbers 1, 2, 3, 4, 5, 6, 7, 8, 9, 10 as factors?

6 Write 1 000 000 as the product of two factors neither of which has a zero digit.

Investigation An odd prime number is put into list A if it is the sum of two square numbers, and into list B if not.
Put all the odd primes up to 97 into these lists.
Look at the remainder when each prime number is divided by 4.
What do you notice?

A	B
$5 = 1^2 + 2^2$	3
$13 = 2^2 + 3^2$	7
⋮	11
	⋮

Cubes

A **centicube** is a 1 cm by 1 cm
by 1 cm cube.
You can fit centicubes together
to make cuboids.

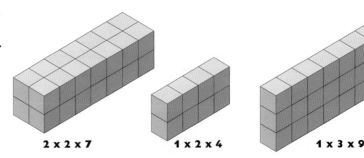

2 x 2 x 7   1 x 2 x 4   1 x 3 x 9

Task

How many centicubes are in each cuboid shown above?

? The first cuboid is pulled apart into 28 centicubes.

2 × 2 × 7 = 28

Can you use all these centicubes to make a cube?

You can use 28 centicubes to
make a 3 by 3 by 3 cube
with 1 centicube left over.

 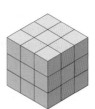

*A solid with all sides
the same length.*

? Is there a different way that you could make a cube without any centicubes
left over?

Task

1 **(a)** Can the $1 \times 2 \times 4$ or $1 \times 3 \times 9$
cuboids be turned into cubes?
(b) What size cube will they make?

2 How many centicubes are in the
cubes opposite?

  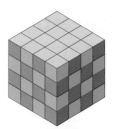

Numbers like 1, 8, 27, 64 ... are called **cube numbers**.

*$1^3 = 1 \times 1 \times 1 = 1$
$2^3 = 2 \times 2 \times 2 = 8$
$3^3 = 3 \times 3 \times 3 = 27$
$4^3 = 4 \times 4 \times 4 = 64$*

? Why do you think they are called cube numbers?

Example What size cube could you make from 27 centicubes?

*You can make a cube of side 3 from 27 centicubes.
3 is called the **cube root** of 27.*

3 × 3 × 3 = 27

Exercise

1 Which of these cuboids can be turned into cubes?

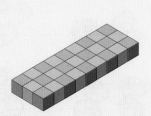

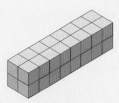

What is the biggest size of cube that can be made from each?
How many centicubes are left over?

2 Find the values of all the cubes from 1^3 to 12^3 inclusive.

3 Find the cube roots of
   (a) 8   **(b)** 64   **(c)** 343   **(d)** 1331   **(e)** 1 000 000.

4 Find the values of
   (a) $\left(\frac{1}{2}\right)^3$ **(b)** $\left(\frac{3}{4}\right)^3$ **(c)** 0.1^3 **(d)** 0.2^3 **(e)** 0.9^3.

5 Copy this table and continue it for three more rows.

   Look at the numbers in columns Ⓐ and Ⓑ.
   What do you notice?

Sums of numbers Ⓐ	Sums of cubes Ⓑ
$1 = 1$	$1^3 = 1$
$1 + 2 = 3$	$1^3 + 2^3 = 9$
$1 + 2 + 3 = 6$	$1^3 + 2^3 + 3^3 = 36$

Investigation

1 Steven has a box of 100 centicubes.
   He realises that he can't make one big cube but he can make several smaller cubes using all the centicubes.
   How many ways can *you* find of doing this?

2 Sarah has a box of 216 centicubes and she makes a large cube using all of these.
   What is the length of one of its sides?
   She can also use all of these to make three smaller cubes.
   How?

JMO Question

A crossnumber puzzle is like a crossword puzzle – except that the answers are numbers instead of words and each square contains one single digit. None of the answers start with the digit 0. How many solutions are there to this cross number?
(You must use logic, not guesswork.)

Across
1 square
3 square
4 square

Down
1 cube
2 square
3 cube times
   square

Powers of 2

A certain type of bacteria grows by splitting into 2 every hour.

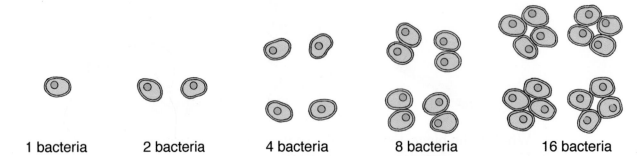

| 1 bacteria | 2 bacteria after 1 hour | 4 bacteria after 2 hours | 8 bacteria after 3 hours | 16 bacteria after 4 hours |

These are the numbers of bacteria present each hour:

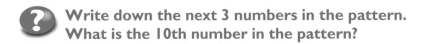

$$2, 4, 8, 16, 32, \ldots$$

This sequence of numbers has been obtained by doubling to get from one number to the next.

? **Write down the next 3 numbers in the pattern.**
What is the 10th number in the pattern?

The numbers are all **powers of 2**.

Task

David earns £5 a day for his newspaper round.

His employer wants to change the amount that he pays David.
He will pay 1p for the first day, 2p for the second, 4p for the third and will double his pay every day after that.

David thinks that he will be better off. His employer thinks that he will save money.

Who is right?

The mathematical way of writing the *powers of 2* is:

$$2^1 = 2$$
$$2^2 = 2 \times 2 = 4$$
$$2^3 = 2 \times 2 \times 2 = 8$$
$$2^4 = 2 \times 2 \times 2 \times 2 = 16$$

? **Work out 2^6 and 2^{10}.**

? **How many times would you have to double to get a number bigger than one million?**
What power of 2 is this?

Exercise

1 The diagram below shows how a knockout tournament is arranged to produce one winner when 8 people play.

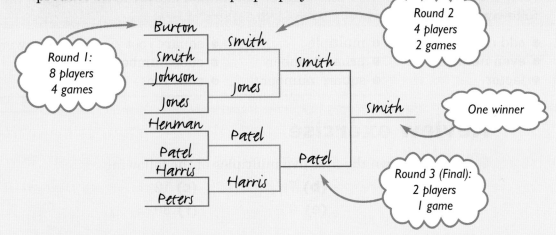

(a) How many games are played?

(b) Draw a diagram to show how to organise a tournament for 16 players. How many rounds are needed?

(c) How many rounds are needed if the number of players is
  (i) 64   **(ii)** 256   **(iii)** 512   **(iv)** 20?

2 BINARY numbers can be written using just the digits 0 and 1 if the column headings are powers of 2.

(a) Continue the pattern 1, 2, 4, 8, 16, 32, ... to find the next three column headings.

You add up all the columns with '1' in.

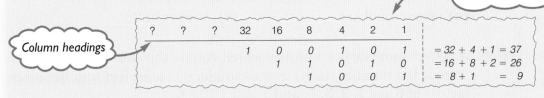

So 37 is represented by the binary number 100101.

(b) Change the following *binary* numbers to numbers from our usual counting system.
  (i) 110   **(ii)** 1011   **(iii)** 110101   **(iv)** 11011101

(c) Write the following as *binary* numbers
  (i) 5   **(ii)** 7   **(iii)** 12   **(iv)** 31

(d) Why are *binary* numbers used for computers?

3 A ream of paper (500 sheets) is 5 cm thick.
How thick is one sheet?
How many times would you need to fold a piece of paper until its thickness is more than your height? Could you do this?

Finishing off

Now that you have finished this chapter you should know the meanings of the following terms:

- odd number
- even number
- factor

- multiple
- prime number
- square number

- square root
- cube number
- cube root

- powers of two.

Review exercise

1 Write down the first five multiples of the following.
(a) 3
(b) 7
(c) 12
(d) 11
(e) 9
(f) 30

2 Write down all the factors of the following.
(a) 15
(b) 24
(c) 19
(d) 27
(e) 16
(f) 13
Which of the above numbers are prime?

3

Which of these numbers are
(a) multiples of both 3 and 7
(b) odd
(c) squares
(d) cubes
(e) prime numbers
(f) powers of 2?

4 A *perfect* number is a number which equals the sum of all its factors (except the number itself). For example, 6 is a perfect number since the factors of 6 are 1, 2, 3, 6, and 1 + 2 + 3 = 6.
(a) Find a perfect number between 20 and 30.
(b) Check that 496 is a perfect number.

5 (a) List all the factors of 220. Check that the sum of these (except 220) is 284.
(b) Now check that the sum of the factors of 284 (except 284) is 220. Two such numbers are called *amicable* (friendly) numbers.
(c) 1210 is one of the next pair of amicable numbers, discovered by a 16 year old Italian boy, Nicolò Paganini, in 1866. Find the other number of this amicable pair, and check that Nicolò was right.

6 **(a)** Write 4056 as the product of prime factors.

(b) Find the smallest number by which you can multiply 4056 so that the answer is a square number.
What is the square root of this answer?

(c) Find the smallest number by which you can multiply 4056 so that the answer is a cube number.
What is the cube root of this answer?

7 **(a)** Work out

(i) $2^2 - 1$ **(ii)** $2^3 - 1$ **(iii)** $2^5 - 1$

(iv) $2^7 - 1$ **(v)** $2^{11} - 1$.

(b) Show that **(i)**–**(iv)** are all prime, and find the prime factors of **(v)**.
(Numbers like these, where the power of 2 is prime, are called Mersenne numbers, after Marin Mersenne who wrote about them in 1644.)

Investigation 1   Joe is investigating triangular numbers.

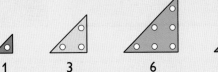

1   3   6   ?

(a) Why do you think these are called triangular numbers?

(b) What are the next three triangular numbers?
Draw their triangles.

(c) Joe puts two of the triangles together so that the dots make a square.
Which other triangular numbers can be used to make a square number?

6 + 10 = 16

(d) Which triangular numbers are also square numbers?

Investigation 2   Use the internet to find out what you can about the largest known prime number and the largest known perfect number.

Length

How tall are you?

What is the distance from York to London?

There are two types of units used when measuring length.

The **IMPERIAL SYSTEM** uses inches (in), feet (ft), yards (yd) and miles.

The **METRIC SYSTEM** uses millimetres (mm), centimetres (cm), metres (m) and kilometres (km).

Metric Measures	
1000 mm = 1 m	1000 m = 1 km
100 cm = 1 m *also* 10 mm = 1 cm	

Imperial Measures
12 in = 1 ft
3 ft = 1 yd   1760 yd = 1 mile

Task

What is the approximate length of the following items?

- The width of a thumb nail
- The height of a doorway
- A hand span
- The length of your longest stride

Use these measurements to help you estimate the length of 10 objects around your school.
Measure the lengths of the objects accurately.
How accurate are your estimates?

Measuring – to the nearest cm and the nearest mm

The ruler shows that the length of the line is a bit more than 5 cm.

The length of the line is 5 cm (to the nearest cm)

or   54 mm

or   5.4 cm.

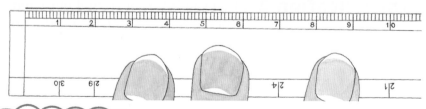

These measurements are accurate to the nearest mm.

 Is 54 mm the EXACT measurement of the line?

Exercise

1 Match each of the objects or distances in List A with an appropriate measure of length from List B.

There may be more than one suitable answer.

> **List A**
>
> The distance from London to Edinburgh
> The length of a swimming pool
> The width of a man's hand
> The height of a fully grown woman
> The width of a sewing needle
> The width of your maths book

> **List B**
>
> 4 inches
> 20 centimetres
> 1.6 metres
> 1 millimetre
> 440 miles
> 50 metres
> 8 inches
> 5 ft 4 in

2 How many centimetres are there in
(a) 3 m **(b)** 4.2 m **(c)** 500 m **(d)** 36 mm?

3 How many metres are there in
(a) 8 km **(b)** 32 km **(c)** 1.7 km **(d)** 320 cm
(e) 25 cm **(f)** 52 cm **(g)** 2.6 km **(h)** 64 mm?

4 How many millimetres are there in
(a) 5 cm **(b)** 23 cm **(c)** 2.6 cm **(d)** 0.35 cm?

5 Measure the following lines
(a) to the nearest cm **(b)** to the nearest mm.

6 The map shows the position of Jody's house, and Jody's friends' houses.

(a) Which of Jody's friends lives furthest away from her house?
(b) One day Jody decides to visit Jill, Mary, Ben and Oliver, in that order.
    How far must she walk?
(c) After visiting Oliver she returns home.
    Has she walked more or less than 1 mile?

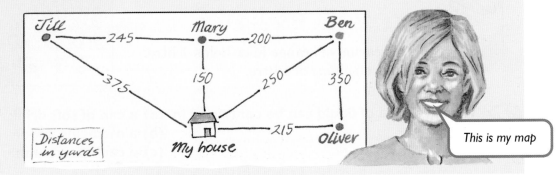

This is my map

Mass (or weight)

The *weight* of the cake is 3 pounds 2 ounces or 1.5 kilograms.
In science and maths this is called the *mass* of the cake.

Imperial
16 ounces (oz) = 1 pound (lb)
14 pounds = 1 stone
160 stone = 1 ton
also 2240 lb = 1 ton

Metric Measures
1000 milligrams (mg) = 1 g
1000 grams (g) = 1 kilogram (kg)
1000 kg = 1 tonne

 What is the mass of (a) a brick
 (b) an elephant
 (c) a grain of rice?

Find a selection of objects in your classroom. For example, pencil, ruler, rubber, exercise book, board rubber, wrist watch, ink cartridge, thick pen, computer disc, pencil case.

Without weighing them, compare the weights of these objects.

Make a list of the objects in order of their weight, from lightest up to heaviest.

Compare your list with a friend's. Do you agree?

Volume

This bucket holds 2 gallons.
It has a *volume* of 2 gallons.

We can also say it
has a *capacity* of
2 gallons

Imperial
8 pints = 1 gallon

This carton of orange juice holds 1 litre.
It has a *volume* of 1 litre.

Metric Measures
1000 millilitres (ml) = 1 litre
100 centilitres (cl) = 1 litre

 What volume of liquid can be contained in (a) a can of soft drink
 (b) a medicine spoon
 (c) a car's petrol tank?

Exercise

1 How many grams are there in **(a)** 2 kg   **(b)** 3.5 kg?

2 How many litres are there in **(a)** 5000 ml   **(b)** 330 ml?

3 The ingredients needed to make a fruit cake are listed in this recipe.
A beaten egg weighs 25 g or 1 oz.

Find the total weight of the ingredients
(a) in metric units
(b) in imperial units.

Fruit Cake		
Margarine	100 g	(4 oz)
Caster Sugar	100 g	(4 oz)
Self-raising Flour	225 g	(8 oz)
Currants	50 g	(2 oz)
Mixed peel	25 g	(1 oz)
2 eggs, beaten		

4 A bottle contains 250 ml of shampoo. How many times can you wash your hair if you use 25 ml each time?

5 A 2 litre bottle of lemonade is used to fill two 330 ml glasses, a 150 ml cup and 10 ml is spilt.
How much lemonade is left in the bottle?

6 The luggage allowance on an aircraft is 20 kg.
Louise wishes to pack the following items in her suitcase.
The suitcase has a mass of 2 kg.

Item(s)	Mass
Coat	500 g
Shoes	1500 g
Toiletries	400 g
Hairdryer	800 g
Clothes	5 kg
Books	2 kg
Travel documents/money	200 g

(a) What is total mass of her luggage?

(b) What is the total mass of souvenirs that she can buy without exceeding the luggage allowance on the return trip?

7 In the USA people usually give their weight in pounds. What is the weight in stones and pounds of someone weighing
(a) 110 pounds   **(b)** 135 pounds   **(c)** 167 pounds?

Activity

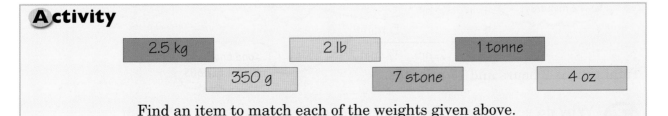

2.5 kg   2 lb   1 tonne
350 g   7 stone   4 oz

Find an item to match each of the weights given above.

Time

The clocks below all show
the same time.

This clock uses Roman numerals.

This is a 24-hour clock.

It is five minutes past four in the afternoon.

 Which of the clocks let you know that it is afternoon?

> ### Units of time
>
> 60 seconds = 1 minute   24 hours = 1 day
> 60 minutes = 1 hour   365 days = 1 year (except in a leap year)

Task

Work out the following.

1 What is your age in days?   **2** What is your age in minutes?
3 Are you older or younger than 350 000 000 seconds?

Timetables

This is part of the timetable for the Trans-Pennine Express:

This train leaves before midnight

This train does not stop at Manchester Piccadilly

York	2309	0048	0238	0348
Leeds	2338	0117	0307	0417
Huddersfield	2359	0140	0330	0440
Manchester Vic.	0034	0225	0417	0531
Manchester Picc.	–	0243	0433	0548
Manchester Airport	0115	0310	0500	0605

This is exactly 5 o'clock in the morning.

 How long does the 0348 train from York take to reach Manchester Airport?

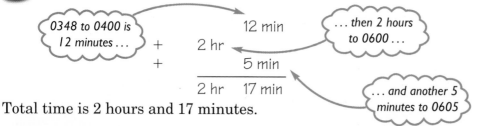

0348 to 0400 is 12 minutes ...

... then 2 hours to 0600 ...

... and another 5 minutes to 0605

```
      12 min
+   2 hr
+       5 min
  _____
    2 hr  17 min
```

Total time is 2 hours and 17 minutes.

 Why do you not get the correct answer if you work out 605 − 348?

Exercise

1. Write these times using the 24-hour clock.
   (a) 9.25 am
   (b) 12.15 pm
   (c) 12.15 am
   (d) twenty to three in the afternoon.

2. Write these times using am or pm.
   (a) 0728
   (b) 1305
   (c) 2311

3. (a) How many hours in 240 minutes?
   (b) How many seconds in 5 minutes?

4. Use the train timetable printed opposite to answer the following questions.
   (a) Where will the 2309 departure from York be at midnight?
   (b) Humza's flight departs from Manchester Airport at 0515 and he has to check in 30 minutes before that. Which train should he catch from York?
   (c) Humza's friend lives in Huddersfield. What time should he be at Huddersfield station if he is to catch the same train?
   (d) Which is the fastest train?

5. (a) How long do the Sports Highlights last?
   (b) Rosa wishes to record the X-Files and the Late Night Film.
   What is the start time for these programmes using the 24-hour clock?
   (c) Rosa has a 120 (2 hr) tape and a 180 (3 hr) tape. Which should Rosa use to record both the X-Files and the Late Night Film? Will there be any spare tape?

TV Guide	
9.00 pm	News and Weather
9.25 pm	The X-Files
10.10 pm	Sports Highlights
11.25 pm	Late Night Film
1.10 am	Close

6. The time required to cook a turkey is 20 minutes, plus 20 minutes for each pound weight.
   (a) How long will a 10 pound turkey take to cook?
   Peter wants to have the turkey ready for 1.00 pm.
   (b) When should he start cooking?

Investigation

The time for the earth to orbit the sun is not exactly 365 days. Every 4 years we have a leap year.

What does this tell you about the true length of a year?

Every 100 years is not a leap year but every 400 years is.
Was the year 2000 a leap year?

Use all this information to calculate the true length of a year.

Finishing off

Now that you have finished this chapter you should be able to:

- find length, mass, capacity and time
- use metric and imperial units
- estimate lengths
- change units

- use the 24-hour clock and read timetables
- measure to the nearest cm and mm.

Review exercise

1 How many seconds are there in a day?

2 For each of the objects in List A, select a suitable mass from List B.

List A	List B
An elephant	5 lb
A feather	1 ton
A new born baby	8 oz
A sack of potatoes	3 g
A bag of sweets	4.5 kg

3 Borrow a copy of the *Guiness Book of Records* from the library. How many of these records can you find, and what are they?
(a) The length of the world's longest river.
(b) The height of the tallest woman.
(c) The record for running 100 metres.
(d) The volume of blood in the human body.
(e) The weight of the heaviest man.`

Now list four more interesting records that you have discovered.

4 The timetable shows the times of the late buses to Tom's village each evening.

Railway station	1905	1925	1945	2005	2025
Theatre	1919	1939	1959	2019	2039
High Street	1922	1942	2002	2022	2042
Back Lane	1935	1955	2015	2035	2055
Village green	1945	2005	2025	2045	2105

(a) How much time is there between buses?
(b) How many buses is this each hour?
(c) Tom arrives at the railway station at 7.15 pm.
   (i) Which bus will he catch?
   (ii) How long will he have to wait?
(d) Tom wishes to see a show at the theatre. The performance does not finish until 8.30 pm. Should he book a taxi to get him home?

5 **(a)** How many ml are there in 2 litres?
   (b) How many feet are there in 6 yards?
   (c) How many ounces are there in 3 pounds?

6 A rectangular parcel is to be decorated
   with ribbon as shown. How much
   ribbon is needed?

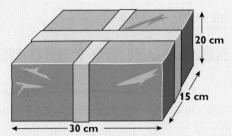

20 cm

15 cm

30 cm

7

FRIARS FISH AND CHIPS
OPENING TIMES

	Lunch	*Evenings*	
Monday	–	5.00 – 10.30	
Tuesday	11.30 – 1.30	6.00 – 11.00	
Wednesday	11.30 –1.30	6.00 – 11.00	
Thursday	–	4.30 – 6.30	8.00 – 11.00
Friday	11.30 – 1.30	4.30 – 11.00	
Saturday	11.30 – 1.30	6.00 – 11.00	

   (a) On which days is the fish and chip shop closed at lunch time?
   (b) Can you buy chips at 7.00 pm on a Thursday?
   (c) For how many hours a week is the shop open?
   (d) On which evening is the shop open for the longest time?

8 A lift has a weight restriction of 1000 kg.
   An average person has a mass of 65 kg.
   How many people can safely be carried in the lift?

Activity   Find 10 examples of *capacity* (or volume) written on packaging or
in catalogues.
Make a table like this and say whether the units are imperial or metric.

Item	Capacity	Units
Shampoo	200 ml	metric

Investigation   Find the meanings of these other measures:
scruple, ream, point, perch, peck, mach, knot, hundredweight, hand, gill,
farthing, ell, cubit, carat, barleycorn
Which of these measures are still used?

THE AVONFORD STAR

New Boating Pond in the Park

Avonford Council are to create a new boating pond in the civic park. Here are several possible shapes for the pond, proposed by the council architects.
All these shapes have the same area of water.

Task

1   Draw a shape *with straight sides* which you think would make a good boating pond.
    Write down a description of the shape.
    Your teacher may ask you to describe the shape to the rest of your class, so be precise!
    Write down why you think it would be a good boating pond.

2   Draw a shape which you think would be unsuitable for a boating pond.
    Write down a description of the shape.
    Write down your reasons for it being unsuitable.

Any shape made with straight sides is called a **polygon**.
There are many different types of polygon. To describe them we give them special names.

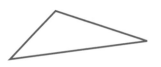

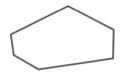

Triangle	*Quadrilateral*	*Pentagon*	*Hexagon*
3 straight sides, 3 angles	*4 straight sides*	*5 straight sides*	*6 straight sides*

If all the *sides* of a polygon are *the same length* and if all its *angles are the same* it is called a **regular polygon**.

Regular triangle   Regular quadrilateral   Regular pentagon   Regular hexagon

Exercise

In this chapter you are asked to describe some polygons. This vocabulary will help you.

A polygon has a number of **sides**.
A point where two sides meet is called a **vertex** (plural **vertices**).

In a quadrilateral a **diagonal** joins two opposite vertices.

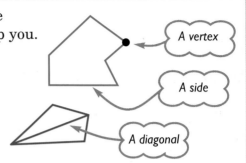

1   Write down a description of these shapes.
    Say whether they are regular or non-regular.

(a)   **(b)** 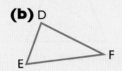   **(c)**   **(d)**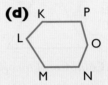

(e) 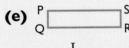   **(f)**    **(g)** 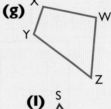   **(h)**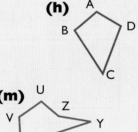

(i)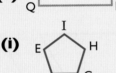

(j) 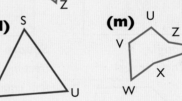   **(k)**   **(l)**   **(m)**

2   Which of the following shapes are
   (a) regular   **(b)** quadrilaterals
   (c) irregular (this means *not* regular)   **(d)** hexagons
   (e) squares (regular quadrilaterals)   **(f)** triangles
   (g) irregular pentagons   **(h)** regular hexagons.

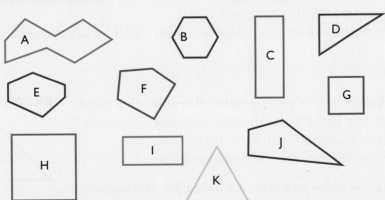

Classifying triangles and quadrilaterals

Task

Copy the three boating pond designs which are triangles on page 104.
Next to each one write down how it is different to the others.

Ten of the designs are quadrilaterals.
Sketch each one and write down how each quadrilateral is different from the others.

Types of triangle

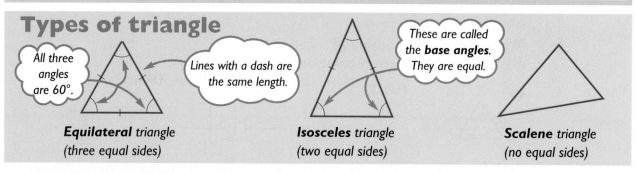

All three angles are 60°.

Lines with a dash are the same length.

These are called the **base angles**. They are equal.

Equilateral triangle
(three equal sides)

Isosceles triangle
(two equal sides)

Scalene triangle
(no equal sides)

Types of quadrilateral

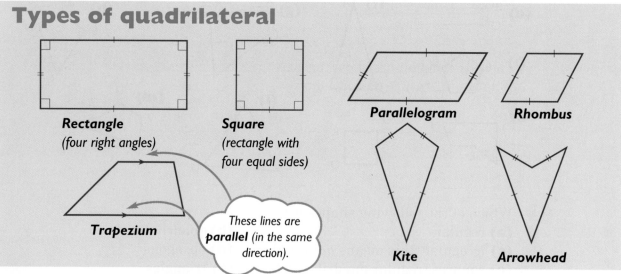

Rectangle
(four right angles)

Square
(rectangle with four equal sides)

Parallelogram

Rhombus

Trapezium

These lines are **parallel** (in the same direction).

Kite

Arrowhead

?

How many rectangles are there in the newspaper article on page 104?
Why is a parallelogram so called?
What is the difference between a kite and an arrowhead?

Task

Make a sketch copy of each quadrilateral on this page.
Make sure you include the dashes or arrows correctly.
Next to each quadrilateral write its name
and the *rules* it must obey to be that shape.

Compare your rules to a friend's. Are they the same?
Do they have to be?

Example

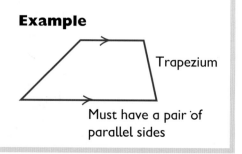

Trapezium

Must have a pair of parallel sides

Exercise

1 Which of these triangles are
(a) equilateral
(b) scalene
(c) isosceles?

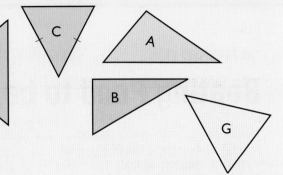

2 Which of these quadrilaterals are
(a) squares   **(b)** irregular   **(c)** rectangles
(d) regular   **(e)** kites   **(f)** parallelograms
(g) rhombuses   **(h)** trapeziums   **(i)** arrowheads?

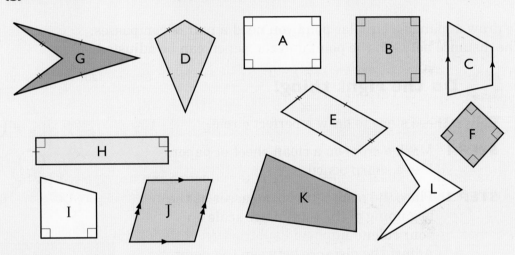

3 Describe the symmetries (if any) of the quadrilaterals in Question 2.

4 Describe each of these shapes as fully and as accurately as you can.

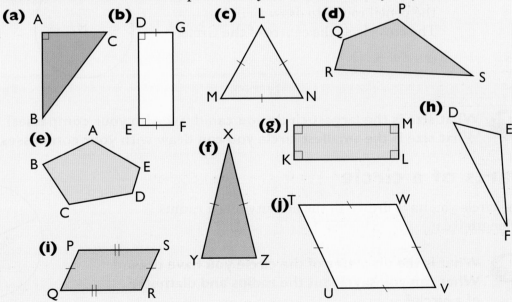

Circles

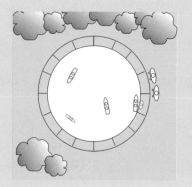

To draw a plan of a circular pond you need a pair of compasses. The distance between the point and the pencil can be adjusted.

 ## Do the right thing!

Follow these steps to draw a perfect circle.

STEP 1   Mark a cross on a clean sheet of paper. Use a sharp pencil.

STEP 2   Place the point of the compasses at the beginning of the centimetre scale on your ruler.
Adjust the distance between the point and the pencil to 6 cm.

STEP 3   Place the point on the cross and move the pencil round to draw a circle.
The cross is at the centre of the circle.

Hold here to draw circle.

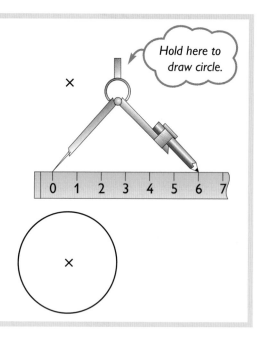

 What size is the largest circle you can draw with your compasses?
What size is the smallest circle you can draw with your compasses?

Parts of a circle

The circle you have drawn in the activity has a radius of length 6 cm.

 What is the diameter of the circle you have drawn?
What can you say about the radius and diameter of a circle?

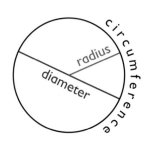

Exercise

1 Follow these steps to draw a six pointed star.

(a) Open your compasses to about 5 cm and draw a circle.

(b) *Without adjusting the compasses* use them to make marks around the circumference. Draw the first mark on the circumference as a starting point. To make the second mark put the point of the compasses on the first mark, draw a mark, and so on.

(c) Join the marks with straight lines as shown.

2 Use your compasses to draw this flower.

3 Use your compasses and a straight edge to draw a regular hexagon.

4 Use your compasses to draw these patterns. They can be any size.

 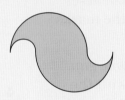 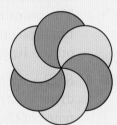

Activity In this diagram there is a circle with points marked on its circumference, this is called the base circle.
Ask your teacher for a copy of this.

(a) With centre at one of these marked points on the base circle, draw the circle which passes through P.

(b) Keep repeating **(a)**. In this diagram **(a)** has been done three times. You will see that your circles produce another curve.
This curve is called a *cardioid*. Why?

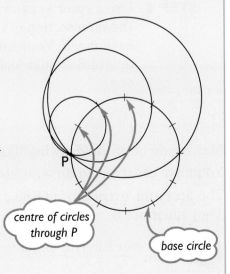

centre of circles through P

base circle

Constructing triangles

You need to use a pair of compasses to make an accurate drawing of a triangle.

 Do the right thing!

Follow these steps to draw an accurate equilateral triangle.

STEP 1 About half way down a clean sheet of paper draw a line across the page. Make a mark on the line near one end.

STEP 2 Put the point of the compasses on the mark and open them out to make a mark near the other end.

STEP 3 *Without adjusting the gap between the point and the pencil* draw part of a circle above the line.
The point of the compasses must be on one of the marks on the line.

STEP 4 *Still keeping the same gap*, draw another arc with the point of the compasses on the other mark.
The two arcs must cross.

STEP 5 Use a ruler to draw lines from the intersection of the arcs to each mark. Your finished diagram should look like this one.

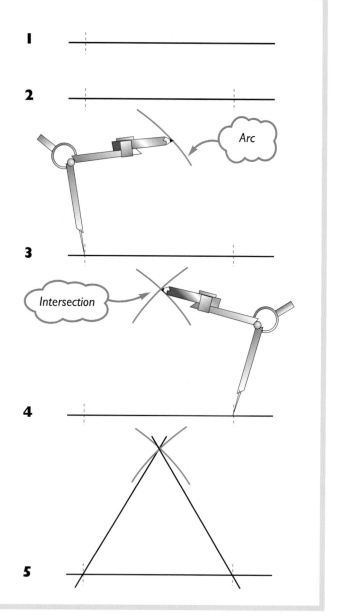

Making an accurate drawing like the one above is called a **construction**.

You have constructed an equilateral triangle.

The arcs and 'extra bits' of line are an important part of a construction. They must not be rubbed out!

 Without measuring, how do we *know* that all the sides are the same length?

 Measure the angles of your triangle. What do you find?

Exercise

1 Construct equilateral triangles with the following side lengths.
(a) 8 cm **(b)** 5.2 cm **(c)** 11 cm **(d)** 2.6 cm

2 **(a)** Follow these steps to draw a triangle which is **isosceles** but not equilateral.

> **STEP 1** Draw a line and make two marks on it 7 cm apart.
>
> $\longleftarrow$ 7 cm $\longrightarrow$
>
> **STEP 2** Adjust the compasses to 9 cm to draw two intersecting arcs.
>
> **STEP 3** Complete the isosceles triangle. It has one side of 7 cm and two sides of 9 cm.
>
> These are called the **base angles**.

(b) Measure the base angles. What do you find?

3 Follow the method above to construct isosceles triangles with sides of these lengths:
(a) 6 cm, 8 cm and 8 cm **(b)** 10 cm, 6 cm and 6 cm.

4 To construct a **scalene** triangle the compasses have to be different for each arc. Construct the triangles which have the following lengths:
(a) 8 cm, 7 cm and 5 cm **(b)** 9 cm, 5.5 cm and 6 cm

5 Construct a triangle with sides of 3 cm, 4 cm and 5 cm.
Measure and write down the angles and the perimeter.
A gardener sometimes uses a 12 ft length of string, with knots 3 ft and 7 ft from one end. What is this used for?

6 Try constructing triangles with the following sides
(a) 11.2 cm, 6.7 cm, 4.5 cm **(b)** 12.3 cm, 5.8 cm, 4.9 cm.
Comment on what happens.

7 A surveyor measures a field and records these lengths.
Using 1 cm to represent 10 m, draw an accurate plan of the field.
By measuring your plan find the length of the other diagonal across the field.

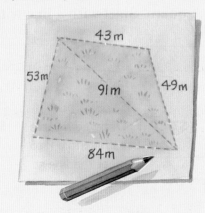

Constructions with angles

New 'Safe' Slide in the Park

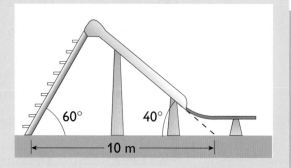

A new children's slide has been built in the civic park.

'The old one was too steep for new regulations', said Leisure Manager John Stubbs.

The steps must be at an angle of 60 degrees to the horizontal and the slide at 40 degrees.

'The old one was more fun', said Tom Wilson, aged 4.

The council's engineers need an accurate drawing of the new slide.
Follow these steps to construct one.

 ## Do the right thing!
Constructing triangles with angles

STEP 1 Draw a line across the page.
This represents the horizontal ground.
Make two marks 10 cm apart.

STEP 2 On one mark use a protractor to draw an angle of 60°.

STEP 3 On the other mark draw an angle of 40°. Label both angles.

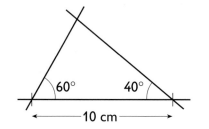

 The triangle you have constructed has been drawn to a scale of 1 cm to 1 m.
What is the height of the top of the slide above the ground?

 ## Do the right thing!
Constructing an angle of 90°

Follow these steps to construct a right angle without using a protractor or set square. Start with a line with a point P marked on it.

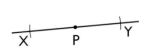

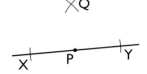

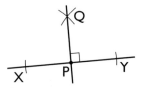

STEP 1 Draw equal arcs with centre P to meet the line at X and Y.

STEP 2 Increase your compass radius and draw two equal arcs with centres X and Y. These meet at Q.

STEP 3 Draw the line through P and Q. This is at right angles to the original line.

Exercise

1 Make accurate constructions of these triangles. For each one measure and write down the lengths of the other two sides.

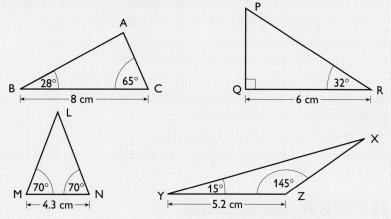

2 Using a ruler and compasses only, construct an accurate drawing of a rectangular postcard with sides of lengths 14 cm and 7 cm.

3 Here is a sketch of a triangle.

Make an accurate copy of it using the measurements shown. Measure and label the length of the unlabelled side.

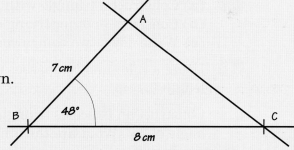

4 Construct a triangle with sides of length 5.8 cm and 7.2 cm with an angle of 63° between them.

5 Explain how to construct angles of
(a) 60° **(b)** 30° **(c)** 150°
without using a protractor.

Activity

1 On thin card make accurate drawings of these shapes. Each marked length is 4 cm. Cut these out to make 3 squares and 12 rhombuses.

2 Arrange these 15 shapes to fill (without overlap) the interior of a regular dodecagon (12 sided polygon) of side 4 cm. Can you do this in more than one way?

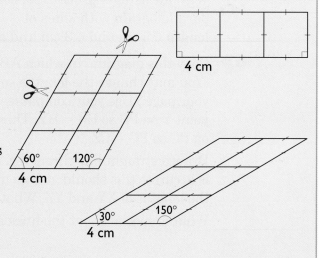

Finishing off

Now that you have finished this chapter you should:

- know what a polygon is, and when it is a regular polygon
- be able to recognise and construct rectangles and squares
- be able to recognise and construct equilateral, isosceles and scalene triangles
- be able to construct triangles with given angles and lengths
- be able to recognise and sketch quadrilaterals which are parallelograms, rhombuses, trapeziums, kites and arrowheads
- be able to recognise and sketch pentagons and hexagons
- be able to construct a circle, and know what a radius and diameter of a circle are.

Review exercise

1 Construct an equilateral triangle with sides of length 6.3 cm.

2 **(a)** Construct a triangle with lengths 3 cm, 4 cm and 5 cm.
(b) Construct another triangle with lengths 6 cm, 8 cm and 10 cm.
(c) Write down two things you notice about these triangles.

3 Using a ruler and compasses only, construct a square with sides of length 5.1 cm.

4 Construct an isosceles triangle with two sides of length 5.9 cm and *one* angle of 26°. What are the other two angles?

5 Julie wishes to measure the height of a tree. Using a **clinometer** she measures angle A to be 25°.
The ground is horizontal.
Construct a scale drawing to find the height of the tree.

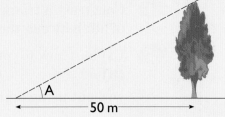

6 Without using a protractor, construct a parallelogram with sides of length 6.5 cm and 4.3 cm and an angle of 150°.

7 Copy this diagram, in which AB = BC and PA = AX. (You may change the lengths so that they fit well on your page.) Use your compasses to mark the point Y on PB so PB = BY. Then mark the point Z on PC so PC = CZ.

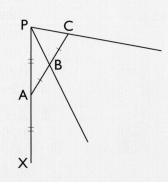

Draw a straight line through X and Y. If your work is accurate this should also go through Z. Compare the lengths of XY and YZ. What do you notice?

What is special about the lines ABC and XYZ?

8 Construct a regular dodecagon (12 sided polygon) using a straight edge and compasses only.

Activity

I Construct a polygon of your choice.
On a separate piece of paper write down a description of it, including angles and lengths.
Swap your *description* with a friend's.
Do not let your friend see your polygon.

2 Construct the shape described by your friend.

Has your friend produced an exact copy of *your* shape?
Use tracing paper to check.

If one shape will fit *exactly* over another shape we say that the two shapes are **congruent**.
Congruent shapes are the *same shape* and the *same size*.
Two shapes are congruent even if one has to be turned over to fit over the other.

Investigation Cairo Tiles

This tile pattern is common in the area around Cairo.
A Cairo tile is a pentagon with
• five equal sides
• two right angles
• one line of symmetry.

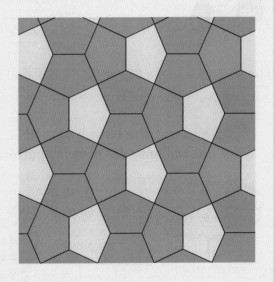

(a) Draw two different Cairo tiles.
(b) Each Cairo tile has three angles which are not 90°.
What is the sum of these three angles?
(c) Using one of your tiles as a template, draw and colour your own version of the pattern.
(d) Explain how you can be sure that every Cairo tile will tessellate.

JMO Question

The diagram shows an equilateral triangle inside a rhombus. The sides of the rhombus are equal in length to the sides of the triangle.

What is the value of *x*?

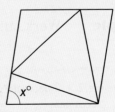

Jenny invites her two pen pals, Monique and Anna, to stay with her.

Monique arrives from Hong Kong, and Anna arrives from the USA.

My dear friend,
* I would so much like you to come and visit me this summer. It would be great fun showing you round my hometown. We could go*

Monique and Anna both buy a souvenir when they are out shopping.

At that time the exchange rate was £1 = 9.98 Hong Kong dollars
£1 = 1.57 US dollars

Souvenir £8·00 OF LONDON

9.98 HK dollars is about 10 HK dollars

They calculate the cost of the souvenir in their own currencies.

Monique works out:

10 × 8 = 80, so the answer is about 80 HK dollars.

Anna works out:

$$\begin{array}{r} 998 \\ \times\ \ 8 \\ \hline 7984 \\ \scriptstyle 7\ 6 \end{array}$$

Remember there are two decimal places.

$$\begin{array}{r} 157 \\ \times\ \ 8 \\ \hline 1256 \\ \scriptstyle 4\ 5 \end{array}$$

The souvenir costs £8, or 79.84 HK dollars, or 12.56 US dollars.

Task

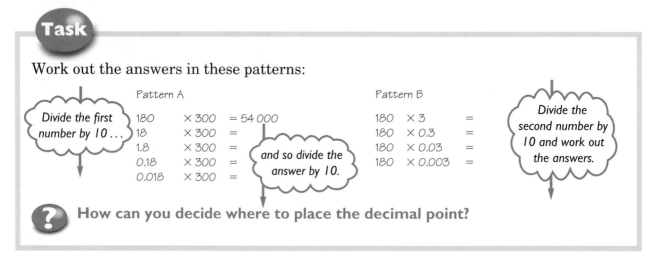

Work out the answers in these patterns:

Divide the first number by 10 ...

Pattern A

180	× 300	= 54 000
18	× 300	=
1.8	× 300	=
0.18	× 300	=
0.018	× 300	=

and so divide the answer by 10.

Pattern B

180	× 3	=
180	× 0.3	=
180	× 0.03	=
180	× 0.003	=

Divide the second number by 10 and work out the answers.

? How can you decide where to place the decimal point?

Example   Work out 12.99 × 1.57

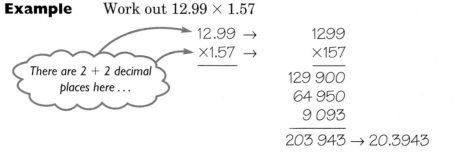

There are 2 + 2 decimal places here ...

$$\begin{array}{r} 12.99 \rightarrow \\ \times 1.57 \rightarrow \\ \hline \end{array} \quad \begin{array}{r} 1299 \\ \times 157 \\ \hline 129\ 900 \\ 64\ 950 \\ 9\ 093 \\ \hline 203\ 943 \rightarrow 20.3943 \end{array}$$

... so put 4 decimal places in your answer.

Exercise

1 Find the total cost of these items which Monique buys:
   (a) 3 CDs at £14.95 each
   (b) 5 books at £6.95 each
   (c) 2 lipsticks at £7.36 each

2 Change these amounts to Swiss francs by multiplying by 2.35
   (£1 = 2.35 Swiss francs).
   (a) £5   **(b)** £8   **(c)** £19

3 Change these amounts to US dollars by multiplying by 1.41 (£1 = $1.41).
   (a) £5   **(b)** £8   **(c)** £19

4 The numbers in these multiplications are correct, but there are no
   decimal points in the answers. Copy them and put the decimal point in
   the correct place.

   Example   Question   7.6 × 5.31 = 40 356
              Answer   7.6 × 5.31 = 40.356

   (a) 6.1 × 0.9 = 549   **(b)** 15.6 × 0.04 = 624
   (c) 0.79 × 0.03 = 237   **(d)** 1.4 × 2.68 = 3752
   (e) 0.816 × 13.7 = 111 792   **(f)** 0.98 × 3.71 = 36 358
   (g) 5.8 × 5 = 29   **(h)** 7.92 × 6 = 4752

5 Work out
   (a) 0.3 × 0.2   **(b)** 0.5 × 0.2   **(c)** 0.1 × 0.3
   (d) 0.6 × 0.8   **(e)** 0.01 × 0.4   **(f)** 0.06 × 0.3
   (g) 0.07 × 0.07   **(h)** 0.005 × 0.005

6 Work out (evaluate)
   (a) 8.3 × 0.6   **(b)** 0.69 × 7   **(c)** 15.3 × 0.8
   (d) 2.29 × 0.05   **(e)** 2.8 × 0.17   **(f)** 0.34 × 5.6
   (g) 18.7 × 0.61   **(h)** 0.12 × 0.12

7 **(a) (i)**   A rectangle is 3.7 cm long and 2.3 cm wide.
               What are these measurements in mm?
       (ii) Calculate the area of the rectangle in mm².
       (iii) How many mm² are there in 1 cm²?
               Use this to work out 3.7 × 2.3.

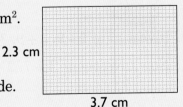
2.3 cm

3.7 cm

   (b) (i)   A rectangle is 5.24 m long and 6.35 m wide.
               What are these measurements in cm?
       (ii) Calculate the area of the rectangle in cm².
       (iii) How many cm² are there in 1 m²?
               Use this to work out 5.24 × 6.35.

Division of decimals by a whole number

On Saturday, Karen and three of her
friends go to the cinema.
The tickets total £19.

It is £4.75 each.

$$4\overline{)19} \rightarrow 4\overline{)19.00} \rightarrow 4\overline{)19.^30^20}$$
$$4.75$$

> Karen works it out and writes
> in two noughts for pence, and
> then divides.

 How can you work this out with ordinary numbers?

Task

Divide   **(a)** 11 by 4   **(b)** 17 by 4   **(c)** 17 by 8.

> You can add noughts in as many decimal places as you need.

The girls meet two more friends at
the cinema and buy some popcorn
for £4.40. Karen works out how
much this is each.

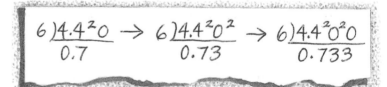

$$6\overline{)4.4^20} \rightarrow 6\overline{)4.4^20^2} \rightarrow 6\overline{)4.4^20^20}$$
$$0.7 \qquad 0.73 \qquad 0.733$$

Karen decides to call this amount
£0.73 each.

Jenny says that 0.73333 is a recurring decimal, and is written as 0.7$\dot{3}$.

Task

Investigate $1 \div 9$, $2 \div 9$, $3 \div 9$, and so on, up to $8 \div 9$.

Now investigate $1 \div 7$, $2 \div 7$, $3 \div 7$, and so on, up to $6 \div 7$.

When a group of digits recur, the dots are placed over the first and last recurring digits.

Example $\frac{1}{7}$ = 0.142857142857142 . . .
            = 0.$\dot{1}$4285$\dot{7}$.

$\frac{19}{55}$ = 0.3454545...
            = 0.3$\dot{4}\dot{5}$.

Exercise

1 Jenny needs a new toothbrush.
How much is this for each toothbrush?
Would it be cheaper to buy a single toothbrush
for 59 pence?

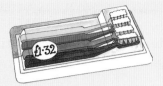

2

(a) How much is each packet of cereal?
(b) How much is each packet of crisps?

3 Divide these numbers by 4.
(a) 3.4   **(b)** 2.7   **(c)** 5.6   **(d)** 0.07   **(e)** 1.9   **(f)** 9

4 Divide these numbers by 8.
(a) 5.2   **(b)** 7.3   **(c)** 0.5   **(d)** 0.17   **(e)** 15.8   **(f)** 11

5 Divide these numbers by 6.
(a) 1.2   **(b)** 2.34   **(c)** 1   **(d)** 5   **(e)** 3.5   **(f)** 43.6

6 Write these numbers as decimals.
(a) $6 \div 10$ **(b)** $0.6 \div 10$ **(c)** $0.06 \div 10$
(d) $6 \div 100$ **(e)** $6 \div 1000$ **(f)** $0.06 \div 100$
Describe in words the effect of dividing a decimal by 10, 100 and 1000.

7 For each of these numbers **(i)** multiply it by 2   **(ii)** divide it by 5.
(a) 1.3   **(b)** 2.5   **(c)** 7   **(d)** 6.75   **(e)** 0.45   **(f)** 43.6
What do you notice about your answers? Now write down the result of
dividing each number by 50.

8 Divide 1 by 11, 2 by 11, 3 by 11, and so on up to 10 by 11.

Investigation

Work out $1 \div 13$, $2 \div 13$,
and so on, up to $12 \div 13$.

Comment on the patterns in
your answers.

Complete these number circles,
and explain how they work.

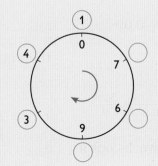

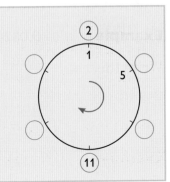

Division of decimals (short division)

Stephen has been collecting 5p coins and putting them into a bottle. He has exactly £7.

 How many coins does Stephen have?

5p = £0.05.
So the question is £7.00 ÷ £0.05.
Stephen changes both amounts to pence.

£7.00 = 7.00 × 100 pence = 700 pence
and
£0.05 = 0.05 × 100 pence = 5 pence

$$5\overline{)700} \qquad 5\overline{)7^{2}00}$$
$$140$$

Now the question is 700 pence ÷ 5 pence. He has 140 coins.

 Task

Work out these questions putting your answers into headed columns.

1

	TH	H	T	U	$\frac{1}{10}$	$\frac{1}{100}$	
(a)			2	0 . 0			×10
(b)				2 . 0	0		×10
(c)				0 . 2	0		×10
(d)				0 . 0	2		×10

2

	TH	H	T	U	$\frac{1}{10}$	$\frac{1}{100}$	
(a)			5	0			×100
(b)				5 . 0			×100
(c)				0 . 5			×100
(d)				0 . 0	5		×100

 What did you notice about these patterns?

3 What would the answers to these be?

(a) 0.4 × 10 **(b)** 0.04 × 100 **(c)** 0.004 × 1000
(d) 0.5 × 10 **(e)** 0.8 × 100 **(f)** 0.09 × 1000

This is used to divide a decimal by a decimal.

Example 0.0324 ÷ 0.09

Write this as $\dfrac{0.0324}{0.09}$ then multiply both numbers by 100.

$$\dfrac{0.0324 \times 100}{0.09 \times 100} = \dfrac{3.24}{9}$$

> You know how to divide by a whole number.

$9\overline{)3.24}$ works out as $9\overline{)3.2^{5}4}$ The answer is 0.36.
$$\qquad\qquad\qquad 0.36$$

Exercise

1 Find how many 2p pieces in
(a) £2   (b) £5   (c) £7   (d) £9.

2 Divide these numbers by 0.02.
(a) 2.00   (b) 5.00   (c) 7.00   (d) 9.00

3 Find how many half-hours in
(a) 3 hours   (b) 7 hours   (c) 15 hours   (d) 18 hours.

4 Divide these numbers by 0.5.
(a) 3   (b) 7   (c) 15   (d) 18

5 How many textbooks 1.2 cm thick will fit onto a shelf 132 cm long?

6 How many magazines 0.6 cm thick will fit into a magazine rack 9.6 cm wide?

7 Work out
(a) $8.4 \div 0.4$ (b) $7.5 \div 0.5$ (c) $6.9 \div 0.3$
(d) $7.2 \div 0.3$ (e) $3.76 \div 0.8$ (f) $4.626 \div 0.9$

8 Work out
(a) $0.224 \div 0.07$ (b) $1.542 \div 0.06$ (c) $24.75 \div 0.05$
(d) $2.912 \div 0.08$ (e) $0.861 \div 0.07$ (f) $32.76 \div 0.09$

9 Alice wonders what happens to answers when you divide by a number less than 1.
She tried these. Do them yourself and see what she discovered.
(a) $4.2 \div 0.1$ (b) $4.2 \div 0.02$ (c) $4.2 \div 0.01$
(d) $4.2 \div 0.003$ (e) $4.2 \div 0.002$ (f) $4.2 \div 0.0004$
(g) $4.2 \div 0.0003$

10 Copy and complete these statements.
(a) Dividing by 0.1 is the same as multiplying by ....
(b) Multiplying by 1000 is the same as dividing by ....
(c) Dividing by ... is the same as multiplying by 0.01.

11 Work out
(a) $1.95 \div 0.006$ (b) $2.24 \div 0.004$ (c) $0.4496 \div 0.008$
(d) $42 \div 0.005$ (e) $4.1157 \div 0.009$ (f) $3.3152 \div 0.007$

12 Work out (evaluate)
(a) $22.72 \div 0.4$ (b) $51.6 \div 0.06$ (c) $0.65 \div 0.001$
(d) $11.2 \div 0.2$ (e) $2 \div 0.005$ (f) $7.2 \div 0.4$

Equivalent percentages, fractions and decimals

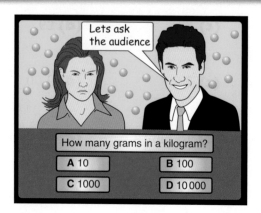

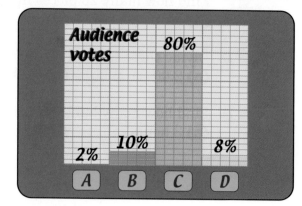

80% of the audience think there are 1000 grams in a kilogram.

$$80\% = \frac{80}{100}$$

$$= \frac{4}{5}$$

Remember % means 'out of 100'.

Cancelling by 20

10% thought there were only 100 g.

$$10\% = \frac{10}{100} = \frac{1}{10}$$

Four-fifths of the audience were right.

To change from fractions to percentages, multiply by 100.

$$\frac{4}{5} = \frac{4}{5} \times 100\%$$

$$= \frac{4}{\cancel{5}_1} \times \cancel{100}^{20}\%$$

$$= 80\%$$

$$\frac{3}{20} = \frac{3}{20} \times 100\%$$

$$= \frac{3}{\cancel{20}_1} \times \cancel{100}^{5}\%$$

$$= 15\%$$

Remember 100% is the same as $\frac{100}{100}$ths or one whole one.

Task

Aimée is doing practice tests for her life-saving theory exam on March 10th.

(a) Write Aimée's marks as percentages. Is she getting steadily better?

(b) The pass mark on the real exam is 70%.
How many marks is this out of **(i)** 20 **(ii)** 50 **(iii)** 25?

(c) Do you think Aimée will pass?

To convert a decimal into a percentage, you multiply by 100.

$$0.4 = 0.4 \times 100\% = 40\%$$
$$0.02 = 0.02 \times 100\% = 2\%$$

? **How do you convert a percentage into a decimal?**

Exercise

1 Change these percentages to fractions and cancel to their lowest terms:

(a)

25% of the audience liked Frosties

(b)

50% of the audience went to bed before 11 pm

(c)

75% of the audience thought Henry VIII had six wives

2 Here are performance figures for 3 train companies.
(a) Find the percentage of trains on time for each company.
(b) Place the companies in order, starting with the best.

Company	Trains run	On time
Gt. Southern	200	164
Rural	50	37
Best West	80	60

3 Change these percentages to fractions in their lowest terms.
(a) 10% further sales reduction
(b) 30% of the ballet students passed with grade A
(c) 70% of holiday-makers travel abroad

4 Change these percentages to decimals.

Example 1 $26\% = \frac{26}{100} = 0.26$ **Example 2** $7\% = \frac{7}{100} = 0.07$

(a) 10%   **(b)** 30%   **(c)** 45%   **(d)** 83%
(e) 6%   **(f)** 9%   **(g)** 11%   **(h)** $12\frac{1}{2}\%$

5 Change these decimals to percentages.
(a) 0.42   **(b)** 0.38   **(c)** 0.95   **(d)** 0.04
(e) 0.17   **(f)** 0.8   **(g)** 0.03   **(h)** 0.2

6 Change these fractions to percentages.

(a) $\frac{1}{5}$ **(b)** $\frac{1}{25}$ **(c)** $\frac{11}{20}$ **(d)** $\frac{3}{20}$ **(e)** $\frac{16}{25}$ **(f)** $\frac{7}{10}$

Write them in order, smallest first.

7 Change the following to decimals by dividing.

Reminder: $\frac{3}{8} \rightarrow 8\overline{)3.000}$ $8\overline{)3.^{3}0^{6}0^{4}0}$
$\phantom{8\overline{)}}0.375$

(a) $\frac{3}{4}$ **(b)** $\frac{7}{8}$ **(c)** $\frac{5}{6}$ **(d)** $\frac{1}{4}$ **(e)** $\frac{1}{6}$ **(f)** $\frac{5}{8}$

Write them in order, smallest first.

8

But what about changing decimals to fractions?

Remember the column headings T, U, $\frac{1}{10}$ ths, $\frac{1}{100}$ ths.

Example 1 $0.6 = \frac{6}{10}$
$ = \frac{3}{5}$

Example 2 $0.22 = \frac{22}{100}$
$ = \frac{11}{50}$

Change the following decimals to fractions.
(a) 0.7   **(b)** 0.4   **(c)** 0.5   **(d)** 0.24   **(e)** 0.85   **(f)** 0.84
(g) 0.12   **(h)** 0.04   **(i)** 0.05   **(j)** 0.72   **(k)** 0.88   **(l)** 0.02

Finishing off

Now that you have finished this chapter you should be able to:

- multiply a decimal by an integer (whole number)
- multiply a decimal by a decimal
- divide a decimal by a whole number
- divide a decimal by a decimal
- understand the equivalence of percentages, fractions and decimals.

Review exercise

1 Sally buys three hair-slides. How much is this altogether?

2 Monique buys two perfume sprays. How much is this altogether?

3 Robin buys six tickets for Stand A at Old Trafford. How much does he pay altogether?

4 Work out
  (a) 6.4×1.1 **(b)** 7.32×0.84 **(c)** 4.18×0.23
  (d) 8.99×0.15 **(e)** 6.214×0.027 **(f)** 30.6×4.7

5 Work out
  (a) $7 \div 4$ **(b)** $0.6 \div 5$ **(c)** $1.7 \div 2$
  (d) $3.9 \div 6$ **(e)** $26.7 \div 3$ **(f)** $14.7 \div 9$

6 Calculate
  (a) $4.1 \div 0.2$ **(b)** $0.36 \div 0.6$ **(c)** $0.61 \div 0.05$
  (d) $17.2 \div 0.08$ **(e)** $7.2 \div 0.01$ **(f)** $0.54 \div 0.09$

7 A pack of 24 coloured pencils costs £2.88.
  (a) How much is each pencil?

  Another pack of 18 pencils costs £1.98.
  (b) Which set has the cheapest pencils in it?

8 Is it possible to fit 26 magazines each 0.7 cm thick into a magazine rack 18 cm wide? Show how you would work this out

9 Put the decimal point in the correct place in these answers.
(a) $6.4 \times 2.7 = 1728$
(b) $9.83 \times 0.014 = 13\,762$
(c) $5.26 \times 41.7 = 219\,342$
(d) $0.025 \times 0.68 = 1700$
(e) $21.13 \times 48.7 = 1\,029\,031$
(f) $0.004 \times 0.28 = 112$
(g) $0.9 \times 2.6 = 234$
(h) $0.01 \times 35.6 = 356$
(i) $0.2 \times 16 = 32$
(j) $0.47 \times 0.03 = 141$

10 Change these fractions to decimals by dividing.

Example $\quad \frac{3}{8} = \frac{3.000}{8} \rightarrow 8\,)\overline{3.000}$

(a) $\frac{3}{8}$ **(b)** $\frac{3}{5}$ **(c)** $\frac{2}{5}$ **(d)** $\frac{5}{8}$
(e) $\frac{7}{8}$ **(f)** $\frac{1}{6}$ **(g)** $\frac{5}{6}$ **(h)** $\frac{7}{12}$

11 Change these to percentages.
(a) $\frac{11}{25}$ **(b)** $\frac{2}{5}$ **(c)** $\frac{3}{8}$ **(d)** $\frac{9}{20}$
(e) 0.11 **(f)** 0.07 **(g)** 0.6 **(h)** 0.75
Write them in order, smallest first.

12 Change these to fractions in their lowest terms.
(a) 0.6 **(b)** 0.15 **(c)** 0.28 **(d)** 0.02

13 Change these to decimals.
(a) $\frac{9}{10}$ **(b)** $\frac{3}{25}$ **(c)** $\frac{17}{20}$ **(d)** $\frac{5}{9}$

14 Change these to fractions in their lowest terms.
(a) 17% **(b)** 6% **(c)** 30% **(d)** $12\frac{1}{2}\%$

15 One day Robert had tests in four subjects.
These were his results.
Comment on Robert's overall performance.
Which are his best and worst subjects in
these tests?

Maths   72%
English $\frac{11}{15}$
Geography $\frac{17}{25}$
French $\frac{29}{40}$

Activity   **Speed test**

Work these out in your head and write down the answer as quickly as possible.
Either race with a friend, or record your time and compare times later.

(a) 0.3×0.2 **(b)** 41.8×100 **(c)** 0.01×0.6 **(d)** $16.73 \div 10$
(e) 0.009×100 **(f)** 0.3×0.07 **(g)** 0.003×1000 **(h)** $13 \div 100$
(i) 0.02×0.5 **(j)** $1.3 \div 1000$ **(k)** 0.04×10 **(l)** 0.8×0.9
(m) 0.007×1000 **(n)** 0.006×0.03 **(o)** $0.4 \div 10\,000$

Do you think there should be a penalty for mistakes?

Huyen is making a call from a phone box.
Phone calls cost 8p per minute plus a 6p connection charge.
The cost of her call is calculated using a number machine like this:

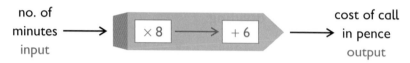 

Huyen is on the phone for 5 minutes.

The number of minutes that Huyen is on the phone for is called the **input**.

? **What is the cost of Huyen's call?**

The cost of the call is called the **output**.

Task

What would the *outputs* be for these inputs using the number machine above?

(a) 10 minutes   **(b)** 7 minutes   **(c)** 2.5 minutes

Think of some other examples of when you pay for what you use.

Huyen makes another phone call.
The output is 78 pence.

? **For how long was Huyen on the phone?**
How can you check that you are right?

Huyen reverses the number machine to find out what the input was.

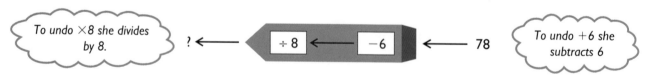

She finds out that the input was 9 minutes.

Task

Huyen's machine is used in reverse. What inputs give these outputs?

(a) 22 minutes   **(b)** 38 minutes   **(c)** 1 hour 26 minutes

? **Does swapping the parts of the original machine make any difference**
    (a) to the outputs
    (b) to the reverse machine?

Exercise

1 Different phone companies charge different amounts.
Work out the cost of the following telephone calls:

(a)

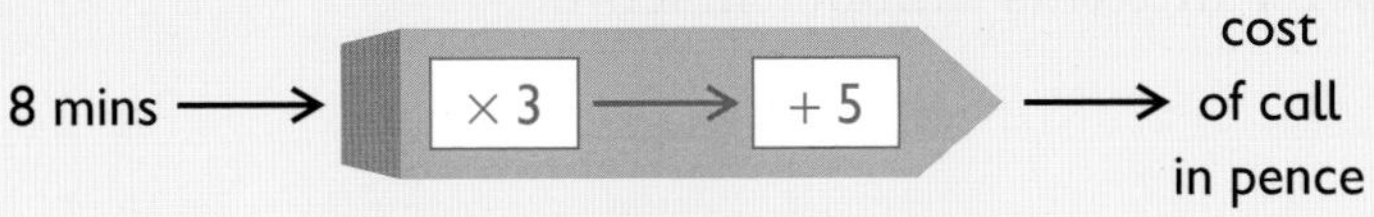

8 mins ⟶ | × 3 | ⟶ | + 5 | ⟶ cost of call in pence

(b)

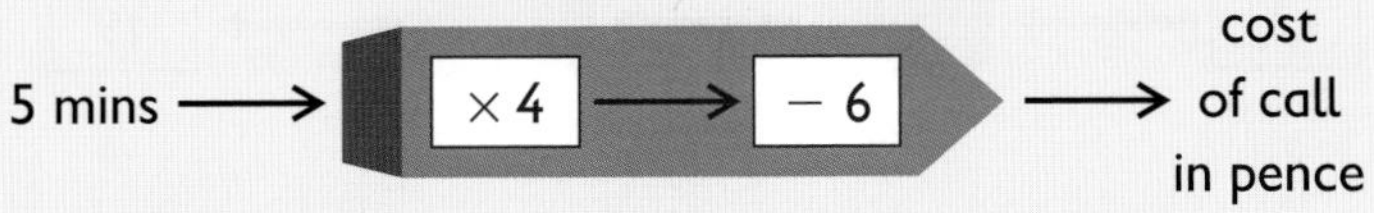

5 mins ⟶ | × 4 | ⟶ | − 6 | ⟶ cost of call in pence

2 A mobile phone company charges 5p per minute plus a connection charge of 10p for off-peak calls.

(a) Copy and complete the number machine to show this information.

time in mins ⟶ | ☐ | ⟶ | ☐ | ⟶ cost of call in pence

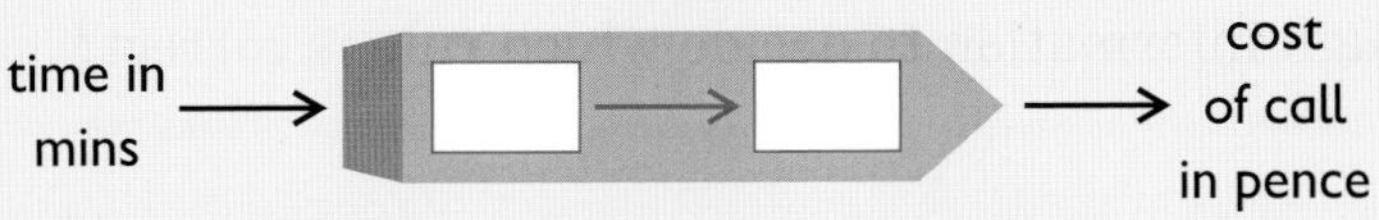

The same company charges 8p per minute plus a connection charge of 10p for peak time calls.

(b) Draw a number machine to show this information.

(c) How much would a 12 minute call cost
    (i) off-peak   **(ii)** at peak rate?

(d) Jason makes three phone calls costing the following:
    (a) 55p off peak   **(b)** 82p peak rate   **(c)** £1.30 peak rate.

How long was each call?

3 Find how long each of the following calls are by reversing the number machine. Check all of your answers.

(a) time in minutes ⟶ | × 5 | ⟶ 20p   **(b)** time in minutes ⟶ | × 5 | ⟶ 25p

(c) time in minutes ⟶ | × 4 | ⟶ | − 3 | ⟶ 45p   **(d)** time in minutes ⟶ | × 6 | ⟶ | − 8 | ⟶ £1.12

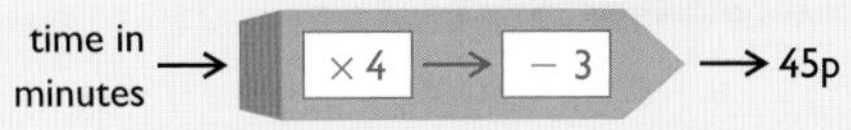

4 A phone company offers a choice between two charging systems:

(a) Pay 15p connection charge then add 5p per minute.

(b) Add 3 minutes to the call time, then pay 5p per minute.

Write each of these as a number machine.
Which system would you use? Why?

Finding the rule

Brian feeds the number 7 into this number machine.

The output is 19.

> Write down as many different rules as you can that the number machine could be using.
>
> Have you got enough information to decide which rule is correct?

Brian thinks that the number machine is adding 12 to his input.
He checks this by using the number 4 as his input.

 What answer is Brian expecting?

The number machine gives an output of 10.

Brian checks other inputs to find out what output he will get.
He makes a table of his results:

> *Brian chooses his inputs logically, so that he can spot the rule more easily.*

 What will the output be when the input is 5?
What will the output be when the input is 10?
What rule do you think the number machine is using?

Brian now draws the number machine with its rule:

 What is the input when the output is 34?
Check that you are right.

Exercise

1 Work out the rules for the following *adding and subtracting*
number machines.

(a) 7 ⟶ ▢ ⟶ 10 **(b)** 12 ⟶ ▢ ⟶ 8

(c) 8 ⟶ ▢ ⟶ 1 **(d)** 3 ⟶ ▢ ⟶ 13

Write down your rule in words.

2 Work out the rules for the following *multiplying and dividing*
number machines.

(a) 24 ⟶ ▢ ⟶ 6 **(b)** 7 ⟶ ▢ ⟶ 21

(c) 16 ⟶ ▢ ⟶ 2 **(d)** 3 ⟶ ▢ ⟶ 1

3 Tom has two number
machines.

(1) 3 ⟶ ▢ ⟶ ▢ ⟶ 4

(a) Write down three
possible rules for each
number machine.

(2) 6 ⟶ ▢ ⟶ ▢ ⟶ 17

Tom collects some inputs and outputs for each number machine. Here are
his results:

1.

Input	Output
1	0
2	2
3	4
4	6
5	8

2.

Input	Output
1	2
2	5
3	8
4	11
5	14

(b) What would the outputs be for each number machine if the input was
(i) 12 **(ii)** 20 **(iii)** 100?

(c) What is the rule for each number machine?

Investigation

Find 5 different rules. Compare your rules with a friend's.
Find 10 different rules between you.

4 ⟶ - - - - - - - - ⟶ 7

Writing down the rule

Nesrene wants to hire a boat at her local boating lake.

She wants to find the cost of hiring a rowing boat for one hour.

The boating company uses the following number machine to work out the cost of hiring rowing boats.

input
number of hours ➡️ [ ] ➡️ output
cost in £
2   7

 What rules could this machine be using?

She tries several different inputs and writes down her results:

Number of hours	Cost in £
1	4
2	7
3	10
4	?
5	?

 What rule is the number machine using?

Nesrene draws the number machine.

$$input \to \boxed{\times 3} \to \boxed{+1} \to output$$

She writes down a rule in words:

$$Cost = 3 \times number\ of\ hours + 1$$

Nesrene realises that it would be easier to write:

$$C = 3 \times h + 1$$

 What do C and h mean?

Task

Make up your own rule for a number machine and write it down. Get a friend to work out your rule by trying several different inputs.

How many inputs and outputs does your friend need to try before working out your rule?

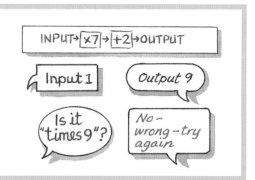

 Why does Nesrene think it is better to write the rule using letters? How can you check that the rule is correct?

Exercise

1 John wants to work out how his electricity bill is calculated.
He has used 6 units of electricity and is charged 13p.

(a) Write down four rules that the Electricity Board could be using.

John collects some more data to help him find the rule:

Number of units	Cost in pence
1	3
2	5
3	7
6	13

(b) What is the cost when the number of units used is
  (i) 4   **(ii)** 5   **(iii)** 10   **(iv)** 2.5?

(c) How many units are used when the cost is
  (i) 15   **(ii)** 23   **(iii)** 19   **(iv)** 29?

(d) Write down the rule that the Electricity Board is using.
Use U to represent the number of units and C to
represent the cost.

2 **(a)** You can find the sum of the interior angles
of a polygon by dividing it into triangles by
lines through one vertex.
Copy and complete this table.

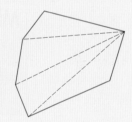

6 sides, 4 triangles

Number of sides	3	4	5	6	7	8
Number of triangles	1	2	3	4		
Angle sum	180°	$2 \times 180°$ $= 360°$	$3 \times 180°$ $= 540°$			

(b) Rewrite the information in the table in the form of number machines:

  (i) number of sides ⟶ ☐ ⟶ number of triangles

  (ii) number of sides ⟶ ☐ ⟶ ☐ ⟶ angle sum

(c) Now write down these two rules using letters.
Represent the number of sides by n, the number of triangles by t,
and the angle sum by s.

Finishing off

Now that you have finished this chapter you should be able to:

- know what number machines are
- find the output of a number machine
- find the input of number machine
- work out the rule for a number machine
- write down the rule using letters.

Review exercise

1 Work out the outputs for these number machines:

(a) $3 \rightarrow \boxed{\times 3} \rightarrow \boxed{-7} \rightarrow \boxed{?}$ (b) $8 \rightarrow \boxed{\div 2} \rightarrow \boxed{-1} \rightarrow \boxed{?}$

(c) $2 \rightarrow \boxed{\times 10} \rightarrow \boxed{+30} \rightarrow \boxed{?}$ (d) $12 \rightarrow \boxed{\div 3} \rightarrow \boxed{-4} \rightarrow \boxed{?}$

2 Two mobile phone companies are advertising their phones:

MICRO MOBILES
calls only
4p per minute
plus
20p connection

LO-CALLS
calls only
6p per minute
plus
10p connection

(a) Draw a number machine to show how to work out the cost of a call for each company.
(b) Omar wants to use his mobile phone for calls of more than ten minutes.
Which company should he use? Why?
(c) Tim wants to use his mobile phone for calls of no longer than 5 minutes.
Which company should he use? Why?
(d) Serina spends 64p on a call. Work out how long her call would be with each company.

3 Work out the inputs for the following number machines:

(a) $\boxed{?} \rightarrow \boxed{\times 2} \rightarrow \boxed{+1} \rightarrow 5$ (b) $\boxed{?} \rightarrow \boxed{+4} \rightarrow \boxed{-6} \rightarrow 10$

(c) $\boxed{?} \rightarrow \boxed{\times 3} \rightarrow \boxed{-2} \rightarrow 13$ (d) $\boxed{?} \rightarrow \boxed{-5} \rightarrow \boxed{\times 3} \rightarrow 15$

4 Michelle wants to find out what the rule is for this number machine. She tries using 4 as her input and gets an output of 21.

$$\boxed{4} \longrightarrow \boxed{} \longrightarrow \boxed{} \longrightarrow \boxed{21}$$

(a) Write down four different rules that the number machine could be using.

Michelle now tries some different inputs.
She makes a table of her results:

input	output
2	11
3	16
4	21
5	

(b) What would the output be if the input was:
  (i) 1 **(ii)** 5 **(iii)** 7 **(iv)** 20?

(c) What rule do you think the number machine is using? Draw the number machine.

(d) What would the inputs be if the number machine gave the following outputs?
  (i) 41 **(ii)** 51 **(iii)** 76 **(iv)** 126

5 **(a)** What are the
  (i) 7th
  (ii) 43rd
  even and odd numbers?

(b) Write down a rule for finding the nth even number and a rule for finding the nth odd number.
Use E for the even number and O for the odd number.

Position in list	Even number	Odd number
1st	2	1
2nd	4	3
3rd	6	5
4th	8	7

Investigation

(a) Find out how to change a temperature in degrees Celsius to the same temperature in degrees Fahrenheit. Describe this process
  (i) using a number machine
  (ii) using the letters C (for Celsius) and F (for Fahrenheit).

(b) Repeat **(a)** for converting Fahrenheit to Celsius.

How do you change a temperature from degrees Celsius to degrees Fahrenheit?

It's easy Gran! You multiply by 9, divide by 5 and then add 32.

15 Scale

This photograph is taken from a catalogue. The real height of the toy is 30 cm. Measure the height in the photograph.

The size of the photograph is $\frac{1}{10}$th of the size in real life.
The real toy is 10 times as big as the photograph.
This is a *scale of $\frac{1}{10}$th* when written as a *fraction*.
As a *ratio*, this is a scale of **1 : 10**.
Measure the width of Tigger's nose in the photograph.

 How wide is Tigger's nose in real life?

The two photographs have been taken from catalogues. Below each photograph a real measurement is given. Find the scale of each photograph.

800 mm length

3400 mm length

Using a scale

A toy car is made on a scale of $\frac{1}{50}$th. It is 6 cm long.

The real car will be 6 × 50 cm = 300 cm or 3 m long.

The real car is 1.7 m wide. That is 170 cm wide.

The model car will be 170 ÷ 50 = 3.4 cm wide.

The ground beneath the real car is a rectangle 3 m long and 1.7 m wide.
Work out the area in cm². Work out the area of the rectangle beneath the model.
Find the ratio model area : real area, simplifying as much as you can.

 Explain why this ratio is not 1 : 50.

Exercise

1. A doll's house is to be built on a $\frac{1}{100}$th scale. Complete the following table, which lists the lengths of various items in the house.

Item	True length	Length on model
Settee (length)	2 m	
Bookcase (height)		1.8 cm
Hall (length)	13.5 m	
Living room (length)		4.2 cm
Living room (width)	5.8 m	
Toothbrush	20 cm	
Bottle (height)		3 mm

Find the areas of the living room floor (which is rectangular) in true length and in the model. Find the ratio of these areas, simplifying as much as you can. What do you notice?

2. As a promotion, a firm wishes to place small toys in their packets of breakfast cereal. The toys are to be a series of 'mini beasts' and will include the following:

   - ant (real length 4 mm)
   - a centipede (real length 12 mm)
   - a bee (real length 15 mm)
   - a ladybird (real length 6 mm)
   - a spider (real length 9 mm)

   The toys must all be smaller than 100 mm but for safety reasons they must be larger than 20 mm.

   (a) Choose a suitable scale for the toys.
   (b) Work out the length of each toy.
   (c) The toys can all be displayed by hanging them from the cut out of a flower printed on the back of the cereal packet.
   This flower has a diameter of 10 cm.
   What size is the real flower using the same scale?

3. A road is 7 m wide, with a further 2 m pavement on each side. A bridge over the road has vertical sides 3 m high, and its arch is part of a circle. The centre of the circle is at the midpoint M of the road.

   (a) Make a drawing of the bridge on a scale of $\frac{1}{100}$th.

   (b) What is the greatest height of the arch?

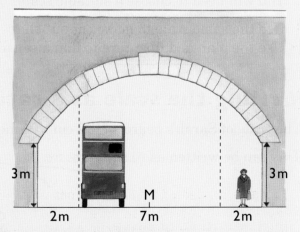

   (c) What height restriction should be placed on vehicles driving under the arch on the road (shown by the broken lines)?

Drawing plans

Sarah wishes to draw a plan of her bedroom. Her bedroom is 4 metres long.

The space available for her plan is only 10 cm long. She chooses a scale of *2 cm to 1 m*.

? **How wide is the plan of her bedroom? How much extra space is there?**
Why has Sarah chosen a scale that does not use all the available space?

Here is Sarah's plan:

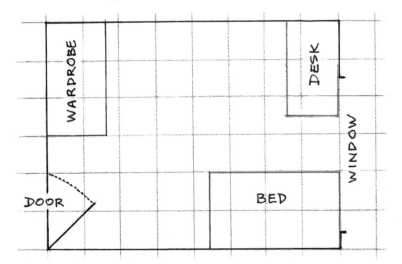

? **How wide is the bedroom?**

Sarah's bed is 1.8 metres long. On the plan this is 2 × 1.8 cm = 3.6 cm.

? **What is the actual area of Sarah's desk?**

? **Sarah has a rug that measures 1.5 m by 0.5 m.**
Is there enough room for this to go beside her bed?

Task

Draw an outline plan of your classroom on graph paper.
You will need to choose a suitable scale.

Use the same scale to make cut out shapes of the items of furniture in the room.
Use the plan and furniture to find a sensible way to rearrange your classroom.

Writing the scale as a ratio

The scale of Sarah's bedroom is 2 cm to 1 metre.

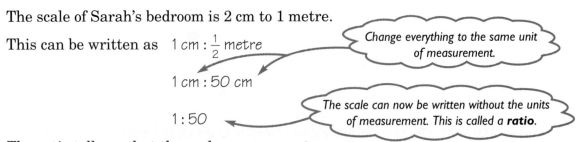

This can be written as $1 \text{ cm} : \frac{1}{2} \text{ metre}$

Change everything to the same unit of measurement.

$1 \text{ cm} : 50 \text{ cm}$

$1 : 50$

*The scale can now be written without the units of measurement. This is called a **ratio**.*

The ratio tells us that the real measurements are 50 times as big as the measurements on the plan.

Exercise

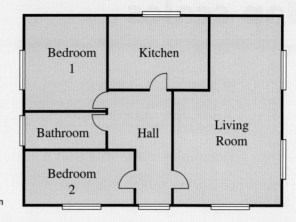

1 The plan is of a bungalow.
Find the real
measurements of
(a) bedroom 1
(b) the kitchen
(c) the living room.

Scale:
1cm to 2m

2 Complete this table for a scale of 2 cm to 1 metre.

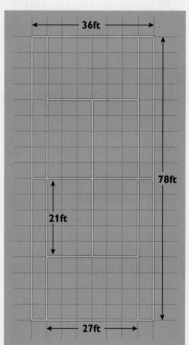

True length	Length on plan
10 m	
	3 cm
	1.6 cm
15 m	
25 cm	
	4 mm
165 cm	
328 cm	

3 The diagram shows a plan of a tennis court.
It is not drawn to scale.
Use the measurements on the diagram to
draw a scale drawing of a tennis court.

(a) What is the total length of the lines on
the court?
(b) What is the total length of the lines on your plan?

4 Use the plan of Sarah's bedroom on the opposite page to answer the
following questions.

(a) How wide is the window?
(b) Give the dimensions of the desk.
(c) Sarah has bought 2 sets of drawers. They are each 1 m wide.
Can she fit the drawers, her desk and her wardrobe along one wall of
her bedroom?

5 Write a scale of 2 cm to 1 m as a ratio.

Activity   Draw an outline plan of your bedroom.
Make cut outs for all the items of furniture in your room.
Use these to re-design the layout of your room.

Map scales

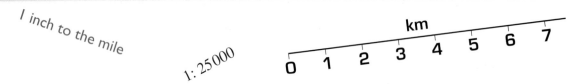

1 inch to the mile

1:25 000

km
0 1 2 3 4 5 6 7

These are all examples of the way that a scale might be given on a map or in an atlas.

The Ordnance Survey map has a scale of 1:50 000.

This means that any length on the map is 50 000 times as big in real life.

1 cm on the map is 50 000 cm in real life
50 000 cm = 500 m
500 m = 0.5 km

A scale of *1:50 000* is the same as *1 cm to 0.5 km*.

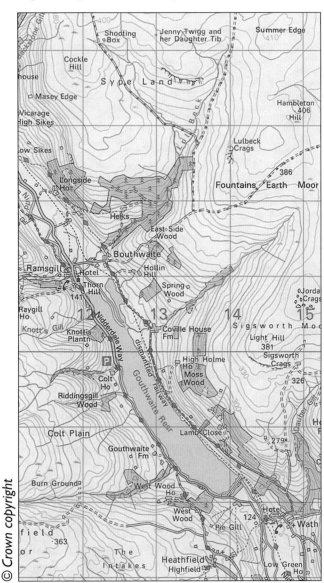

© Crown copyright

Task

Find Gouthwaite reservoir on the map and measure its length.
The length is about 6.5 cm.
That is a real length of
6.5 × 50 000 cm = 325 000 cm
325 000 cm = 3250 m
3250 m = 3.25 km
The length of the reservoir is 3.25 km.

You are going to walk round the reservoir starting from the village of Bouthwaite. Write a description of the route giving distances between points of interest.

 What is the total length of the walk?

Real distances to map distances

The hotel at Wath advertises that it is 'less than 1 km from the lake'.
1 km = 1000 m
1000 m = 100 000 cm
100 000 cm on the ground = 100 000 ÷ 50 000 cm = 2 cm on the map
The hotel should be less than 2 cm away from the lake.

 Is the advertising correct?

Exercise

1 Use the map on the opposite page to answer the following questions.

(a) How wide is the reservoir at its widest point?

(b) How far is it from Coville House Farm to Lamb Close?

(c) You set off from Longside House (written Ho) and walk along the lakeside path.
After walking 5 km you stop for lunch. Where will you be?

2 The map below shows some of the main features of Lambton Village. Use it to answer the following questions.

(a) Jo walks from Home Farm to school everyday.
How far is this?

(b) How far is it from the school to the playing field?

(c) There is a large oak tree in the middle of the village green.
It has a spread of 10 m. How wide is this when it is put on the map?

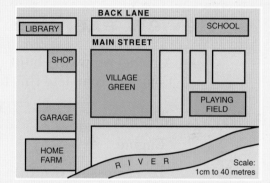

(d) Draw a line with measurements on it to show the scale of the map.

3 The scale on a map is 1:20 000.

(a) What are the real distances shown by distances of 2 cm, 12 cm and 3.8 cm on the map?

(b) What measurements on the map are needed to show real distances of 2 km, 25 km and 6.4 km?

4 From the scales shown below pick out any that are the same.

1 cm to 100 m

0   100   200   300   400   500 m

km
0   1   2   3

1 cm to 1 km

1: 100000

miles
4
2   3
0   1

1 in to 1 mile

5 A map has a scale of 1 cm to 10 km.

(a) Change 10 km to cm and write the scale as 1 cm to _____ cm.

(b) Now write your scale in the form 1:_____.

(c) Write the following scales in the form 1:_____.

(i) 1 cm to 5 km   (ii) 1 cm to 20 km   (iii) 2 cm to 1 km

Finishing off

Now that you have finished this chapter you should be able to:

- understand a scale when it is written as a fraction or as a ratio
- interpret scales on maps and plans
- convert lengths for a given scale
- use a plan to re-design a room.

Review exercise

1 A model railway is built using a scale of 1 : 200.
Copy and complete this table for the lengths of the objects shown.

Object	Real length	Model length
Engine	20 m	
Level crossing (width)		10 cm
Signals (height)		4 cm
Station (length)	100 m	
Tree (height)	5 m	
Suitcase (width)		5 mm
Station cat (length)	40 cm	

2 Write the following scales in the form 1 : ____.
   (a) 1 cm to 3 m   **(b)** 5 cm to 1 m   **(c)** 1 cm to 1 km   **(d)** 2 cm to 1 km
   (e) 1 cm to 5 km   **(f)** $\frac{1}{20}$th   **(g)** $\frac{1}{50}$th   **(h)** $\frac{2}{5}$ths

3 Write the following scales in the form 1 cm to ____ km.
   (a) 1 : 25 000   **(b)** 1 : 50 000   **(c)** 1 : 100 000

4 Write these scales in the form of 1 cm to ____ m or ____ to 1 m.
   (a) 1 : 500   **(b)** 1 : 25   **(c)** 1 : 50

5 A map has a scale of '1 mile to the inch'. What is the true distance
   represented by measurements on the map of
   (a) 2 inches   **(b)** 3.5 inches   **(c)** $4\frac{3}{4}$ inches?

6 A length of 2.75 m is represented on a scale drawing by a length of 11 cm.
   What is the scale of the drawing?

7 A fierce dog is fastened by a chain 4 m
long to a stake which is 3 m from a
straight path.

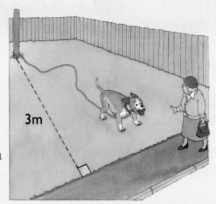

3m

Draw a scale drawing showing the path
and the region where the dog might be.
Choose your own scale, and state it
clearly.
By measuring your drawing find the length
of the section of path where the dog could
reach a person walking past. (Ignore the
width of the path and the size of the dog.)

8 The map shows part of the centre of York.
The Patel family arrive at York station.
They decide to start their visit by walking round the city walls from
North St. Postern Tower to Baile Hill.

How far is it from the front of the station to the start of their walk?
How far do they walk round the city walls?

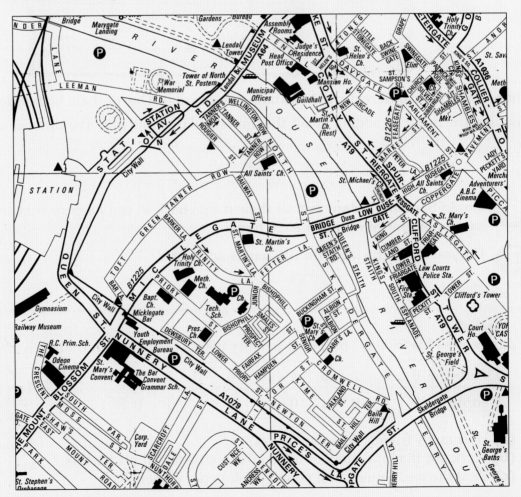

Scale   1 cm to 100 metres

16 **Averages**

The mean

 What does 'average contents' mean?
Are there 20 mints in every bag?

AVERAGE CONTENTS 20

Sam and Adam each buy a bag of Choco-mints.
They each count the number of mints in their bag.

Sam has 17 and Adam has 21.

Adam says he will give Sam some of his mints so that they
have the same number.

How many mints does Adam give Sam?
How many do they have each now?

Sam and Adam decide to find out if the average number of mints in each bag really is 20.
They count the number of mints in 16 bags.

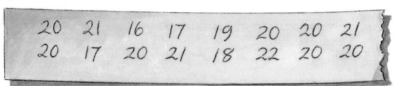

| 20 | 21 | 16 | 17 | 19 | 20 | 20 | 21 |
| 20 | 17 | 20 | 21 | 18 | 22 | 20 | 20 |

There are several different ways of finding an average. One of them is the **mean**.

You find the mean by adding up all the mints and dividing it by the number of bags.

Total number of mints = 312
Number of bags = 16
Mean number of mints = 312 ÷ 16 = 19.5.

Could Sam and Adam put all their mints back in the bags so that there are the same number of mints in each bag?

Do you think the label on the bag is accurate?

 Task

James asks his friends how many penalty points they have on their driving licences.

Points	0	1	2	3	4	5	6	7	8	9	10	11
People	9	0	0	4	0	0	3	0	1	0	1	2

If you get 12 or more points within three years, you are disqualified.

(a) How many friends does James ask?
(b) Work out the total number of penalty points for all his friends.
(c) Find the mean number of penalty points per person.

 Can you get $3\frac{1}{2}$ penalty points?

Exercise

1 Find the mean of each of these sets of numbers.
  (a) 4, 9, 11, 5, 6   **(b)** 1, 1, 2, 2, 2, 3, 3, 4
  (c) 5, 0, 3, 10, 12, 6, 5, 1, 13, 8

2 Alex and Paul are training for a 100 m race. They both keep a record of their times, in seconds, that they take to run 100 m.
  (a) Work out Alex's mean time.   **(b)** Work out Paul's mean time.
  (c) Who do you think is the faster runner?

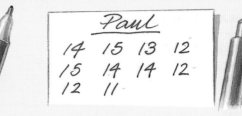

Alex
13 12 12 14
12 12 11 13
11 11 12 11

Paul
14 15 13 12
15 14 14 12
12 11

3 Matthew wants to compare the heights of boys and girls in his class. He measures the heights in centimetres. Here are his results.

Boys:	120	131	126	139	137	126	141
	132	129	135	136	128	131	137
Girls:	124	131	139	115	123	136	133
	131	140	113	118	135	123	134
	123	134					

Find the mean height of **(a)** the boys **(b)** the girls **(c)** the whole class.

4 Matthew's friend Jo has worked out the mean height of the boys and girls in *her* class. There are 13 boys and 11 girls in the class.
The mean height of the boys is 132.5 cm.
The mean height of the girls is 128.3 cm.
  (a) What is the total height of the boys in Jo's class?
  (b) What is the total height of the girls in Jo's class?
  (c) What is the total height of the whole class?
  (d) Work out the mean height of the whole class.

A new girl joins Jo's class. She is 129.5 cm tall.

  (e) What is the mean height of the girls now?
  (f) What is the mean height of the whole class now?

5 Seema goes ten pin bowling. At each turn she tries to knock the pins down, with these results:

Number of pins	0	1	2	3	4	5	6	7	8	9	10
Number of turns	5	0	2	2	1	4	6	5	3	2	0

  (a) How many turns does Seema have?
  (b) Work out the total number of pins Seema knocks down.
  (c) Work out Seema's mean score.

The median

Michelle is taking part in a skating competition.
There are 7 judges. Here are the scores each judge gives Michelle.

4.5   5.1   4.6   5.0   4.5   4.7   4.9

Michelle wants to find her middle score.

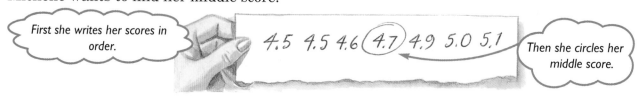

First she writes her scores in order.

4.5 4.5 4.6 (4.7) 4.9 5.0 5.1

Then she circles her middle score.

Michelle's middle score is 4.7.
There are 3 scores below 4.7 and 3 scores above 4.7.

Finding the middle value is another way of finding an average.
It is called the **median**.

 Find the mean of Michelle's scores.
Which average, *mean* or *median*, do you think Michelle will use when she tells her friends her average score?

To find the median, first write the data in order.
Then find the middle value.

Here are Sam and Adam's data about Choco-mints from the last page, written in order.

There are two middle values.

16, 17, 17, 18, 19, 20, 20, (20, 20) 20, 20, 20, 21, 21, 21, 22

The middle values are both 20, so the median number of sweets in a bag is 20.

 What would you use for the median if the two middle values had been 20 and 21?
What about if the two middle values were 20 and 22?
How can you tell whether there will be one middle value or two?

 Task

Look back to Matthew's data about boys' and girls' heights in Question 3 on the last page.

Compare the heights using the *median*.
Does this give you the same results?

Exercise

1 Write each list of data in order and find the median.
(a) 5, 10, 6, 8, 11, 5, 9, 1, 3, 4, 8
(b) 1, 7, 5, 4, 7, 6, 2, 4, 3, 0, 5, 6, 5, 3, 2, 8
(c) 17, 42, 11, 37, 84, 29, 56, 82, 36, 68, 49

2 This data shows the number of hours of television a group of children watched in a week.

7	10	4	9	15	12	8	6
13	12	8	10	18	9	11	7
12	11	3	6	13	12	10	

Find the median number of hours of television watched.

3 Amy does a survey to find out the shoe sizes of everybody in her class. Here are the results.

Shoe size	$2\frac{1}{2}$	3	$3\frac{1}{2}$	4	$4\frac{1}{2}$	5	$5\frac{1}{2}$	6	7
Number of people	3	6	4	4	3	4	2	1	1

(a) Find the median shoe size.
(b) Find the mean shoe size.

4 These are the ages of all the people going on a school skiing trip, including the teachers.

14	16	13	13
29	15	13	14
16	52	14	16
15	13	16	16
44	15	13	14
14	14	15	16
12	13		

(a) Find the mean age.
(b) Find the median age.
(c) Which average do you think describes the data better? Why?

5 Sanjay and Mark are comparing their scores on a computer game which they both have.

(a) Find the median score for each boy.

SANJAY'S SCORES
234 410 320 94 258 521 345 487
160 339 478 317

Mark's scores
156 32 79 289 541 443 689 220
374 498 168 753 226 413 114

(b) Find the mean score for each boy.
(c) Who do you think is better at the game?

The mode

7B are going to watch a video on the last day of
the school year.
Their teacher gives them a choice of four films.

He makes a tally chart to show the votes.

The most popular film is *Star Wars*.
This is called the **mode** of the data.

The mode is another kind of average. It is the most
common item in a set of data.

Titanic   III
Star Wars   ﾟﾟﾟﾟ ﾟﾟﾟﾟ III
Back to the Future   ﾟﾟﾟﾟ
Jurassic Park   ﾟﾟﾟﾟ II

?   **Why is the mode useful in this example?**
Why can't you use the mean or the median?
Think of some more situations when the mode is the best average to use.

When data are grouped, the group or
class with the most items is called
the **modal class**.

In a bar chart or frequency chart,
the modal class
has the highest bar.

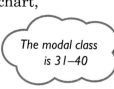

The modal class
is 31–40

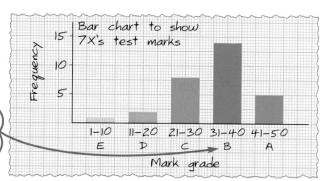

Task

Dawn and James go ten-pin bowling.
Here are their scores (the total number
of pins knocked down) in each turn.

Find the mean, median and mode of their scores.

Dawn:	4	0	2	5	10	3	4
	5	4	8				
James:	2	4	3	7	4	6	4
	4	5	6				

?   **Who do you think is the better bowler?**
Describe the differences between the two sets of data.

(You may find it helps to make a frequency table.)

The range

The mean, median and mode are all ways of finding an average, or typical value.

The **range** is the difference between the largest and smallest values of a set of data.

The range for Dawn's scores is 10 − 0 = 10.
The range for James's scores is 7 − 2 = 5.

The range is *not* an average. It tells you how spread out the data are.
Dawn's scores are more spread out than James's.
James is more consistent.

Exercise

1 David does a survey of the colours of cars passing his house.
Here are his results.

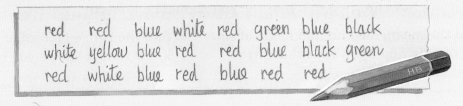

red   red   blue   white   red   green   blue   black
white   yellow   blue   red   red   blue   black   green
red   white   blue   red   blue   red   red

(a) Make a frequency table.   **(b)** What is the mode?
(c) Why can you not find the mean and median?
(d) When might these data be useful?

2 These are the temperatures, in degrees Celsius, in two seaside resorts
each day for two weeks in July.

Blackpool	21°	24°	20°	19°	17°	20°	20°
	22°	25°	26°	23°	20°	19°	15°
Brighton	24°	24°	23°	21°	18°	17°	21°
	22°	21°	23°	24°	22°	20°	19°

(a) Find the mode for each resort.   **(b)** Find the range for each resort.
(c) Which resort do you think had better weather? Why?

3 Nicole does a survey to find out how many days off school everyone in
her class has had over the last two weeks. Here are her results.

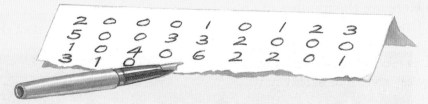

2 0 0 0 1 0 1 2 3
5 0 0 3 3 2 0 0 0
1 0 4 0 6 2 2 0 0
3 1 0

(a) Make a frequency table and draw a bar chart to illustrate these data.
(b) Find the mode, mean and median for these data.
(c) Which average do you think describes the data best? Why?

4 Mrs Green gives two Year 7 classes the same French vocabulary test. The
test is marked out of 20. Here are the results for the two classes.

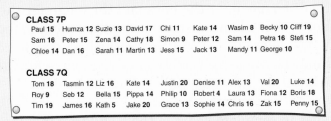

CLASS 7P
Paul 15   Humza 12 Suzie 13 David 17   Chi 11   Kate 14   Wasim 8   Becky 10 Cliff 19
Sam 16   Peter 15 Zena 14   Cathy 18   Simon 9   Peter 12   Sam 14   Petra 16 Stefi 15
Chloe 14 Dan 16   Sarah 11 Martin 13 Jess 15   Jack 13   Mandy 11 George 10

CLASS 7Q
Tom 18   Tasmin 12 Liz 16   Kate 14   Justin 20 Denise 11 Alex 13   Val 20   Luke 14
Roy 9   Seb 12   Bella 15 Pippa 14   Philip 10 Robert 4   Laura 13 Fiona 12 Boris 18
Tim 19   James 16 Kath 5   Jake 20   Grace 13   Sophie 14 Chris 16 Zak 15   Penny 15

(a) Find the mean for each class.   **(b)** Find the range for each class.
(c) Which class do you think has done better?
(d) Which classes' results are more spread out?

Finishing off

Review exercise

1 Samantha is captain of the school hockey team.
She keeps a record of the number of goals the team score in each match.
Here are Samantha's data.

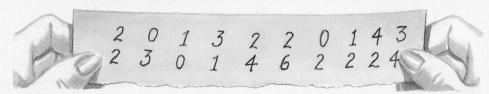

2 0 1 3 2 2 0 1 4 3
2 3 0 1 4 6 2 2 2 4

(a) Find the mode.   **(b)** Work out the mean number of goals scored.
(c) Work out the median number of goals scored.   **(d)** Find the range.

2 Mr Wilson wants to compare the attendance rates of boys and girls in his tutor group.
Here are the number of absences for one term.
One of the boys in the class has been in hospital for most of the term.

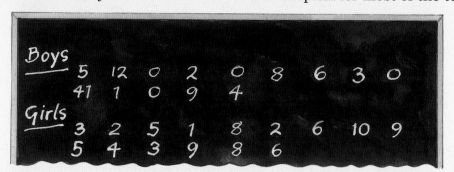

Boys
5 12 0 2 0 8 6 3 0
41 1 0 9 4

Girls
3 2 5 1 8 2 6 10 9
5 4 3 9 8 6

(a) Find the mean for the boys and the mean for the girls.
(b) Find the median for the boys and the median for the girls.
(c) Which average do you think is the best way to compare these data?
(d) Find the range for the boys and the range for the girls.
(e) What does the range tell you about the data?

3 The ages in complete years of the 5 children in a family have mean 14.2, median 15, mode 16 and range 5.
Find their ages.

4 Paul gets £3.50 pocket money per week.
He wants to persuade his parents to give him a rise, so he asks some of
his friends how much pocket money they get.

Here are the results.
(a) Find the median of the
    data.

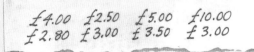

£4.00 £2.50 £5.00 £10.00
£2.80 £3.00 £3.50 £3.00

(b) Find the mean of the data.
(c) Which average should Paul use when he shows his survey to
    his parents?

The friend who gets £10 per week has to buy his own clothes out of his
pocket money.

(d) Find the mean of the data if the £10.00 is not included.
(e) Do you think Paul should get a rise? Explain your answer.

5 Boxes of drawing pins are labelled 'Average contents 50'.
A quality control inspector counts the number of drawing pins in 30 boxes.
Here are her results.

46	50	52	50	49	49	51	47
49	50	50	51	48	51	53	49
51	48	49	50	47	50	51	50
50	50	48	52	51	52

(a) Make a frequency table for this data and draw a bar chart.
(b) What is the mode?
(c) Find the mean number of drawing pins in a box.
(d) Find the median number of drawing pins in a box.
(e) Do you think the labelling is accurate?

6 A company which makes plant food is testing two new products.
Two batches of identical seeds are planted and each batch is treated with
one of the new plant foods. After three weeks the height of the seedlings,
in centimetres, is measured to the nearest millimetre.

```
Batch A
    1.5   2.3   2.1   1.8   2.8   1.4   1.8   2.0   1.7
    0.8   1.2   1.8   2.3   0.9   1.3   1.2   0.9   1.6
    2.2   1.7   1.2   1.3   1.5   2.3   2.6

Batch B
    1.8   2.4   1.9   1.8   2.9   3.1   1.6   0.2   1.3
    2.5   1.4   0.3   3.5   1.2   1.5   2.3   1.4   2.4
    3.6   1.4   0.6   0.5
```

(a) Find the mean, the median and the range for each batch of seeds.
(b) Which plant food do you think is more effective? Why?
(c) Make frequency tables for Batch A and Batch B, using the classes
    0–0.9, 1.0–1.9, 2.0–2.9, 3.0–3.9, and draw two bar charts.
    What is the modal class for each batch?

THE AVONFORD STAR

Thursday Sport Special

Avonford Girls Make Top of League

Following a stunning 4-3 victory over arch rivals Shellbury last night, Avonford Ladies Football Club went top of the table.

Here are the positions of the first four clubs today.

Team	P	W	D	L	Points
Avonford	8	6	2	0	20
Shellbury	8	6	1	1	19
Plystar	8	5	1	2	16
Swynton	8	5	0	3	15

Winning goal scorer, star Karen Eccles

? **Look at the table in the newspaper article.**
What do the letters P, W, D and L stand for?

Task

I Use the information in the newspaper article.
  (a) Work out how many points a team gets for a win.
  (b) How many for a draw?
  (c) What about if they lose?

Bannington scored 12 points in 8 matches. How many wins, losses and draws could they have had?

The next team in the table is Newchurch.
They have won 4 matches, drawn 2 and lost 4.

Kevin works out their points.

He uses a formula:

$$Points = 3 \times Number\ of\ wins + 1 \times Number\ of\ draws$$
$$Points = 3 \times 4 + 1 \times 2$$
$$Points = 12 + 2$$
$$Points = 14$$

An easier way to write the formula is

$$Points = 3 \times W + 1 \times D$$

W stands for the number of wins.

D stands for the number of draws.

Exercise

1 The cost of buying milk in a supermarket is given by the formula

Cost (in pence) = 50 × Number of litres

(a) Find the cost of buying
    (i) 1   **(ii)** 2   **(iii)** 3   **(iv)** 4   **(v)** 5
    litres of milk.
(b) How many litres of milk can you buy for £5?
(c) The supermarket increases the price of milk to 60 pence per litre.
    Write down the new formula for the cost.

2 A railway company works out its fares using this formula:

> Divide the length of the journey in kilometres by 10 and then add 5.
> The answer is the fare in £.

(a) Find the fares for journeys of
    (i) 50 km   **(ii)** 100 km   **(iii)** 200 km   **(iv)** 5 km.
(b) Ashley has £55. How far can she travel?
(c) Write the formula using L for the length of journey (in kilometres) and
    F for fare (in pounds).

3 Look back to the newspaper article on the opposite page.
Here are the bottom four teams in the league.

Team	P	W	D	L	Points
Six Stars	*	2	1	5	*
Torness	9	*	0	7	*
Parkby	8	1	2	*	*
Lower Pass	7	*	*	*	0

(a) Nine of the numbers are missing from the table.
    Copy it out and fill in the missing numbers.
(b) Work out the value of W + D + L for Six Stars.
    What information does the formula W + D + L give you?
(c) The *Avonford Star* article tells you that Avonford beat Shellbury 4–3
    last night.
    How many points did Avonford and Shellbury have before the match?

4 Jenny travels regularly on the motorway for her job.
She says

> *'I work out roughly how long a journey will take using this formula:*
> *Every 100 km takes 1 hour and every stop for a meal takes 1 hour.'*

How long does Jenny take on the following journeys?
(a) 400 km with 1 meal   **(b)** 600 km with 2 meals
(c) 150 km with no meals.

One journey takes Jenny $7\frac{1}{2}$ hours, including 2 meals.
(d) How many km is the journey?

Working with formulae

You can give a formula in words or
you can write it using letters.

A party of adults and children are going to
this aquarium.

The cost can be written

Avonford Aquarium

Entrance Fee:	Adults	£8.00
	Children	£5.00

Last entrance 4.50pm

- **In words**
  The cost in pounds is eight times the number
  of adults added to five times the number of
  children.

- **In letters** $P = 8 \times a + 5 \times c$

P is the cost in pounds.

a stands for the number of adults.

c stands for the number of children.

An expression has letters and usually some numbers too.

It is common to leave the $\times$ signs out when you use letters.
So the formula is $P = 8a + 5c$. $8a + 5c$ is called an **expression**.

Example   Find the value of $8a + 5c$ when $a = 3$ and $c = 6$.

Solution

$$8a + 5c$$
$$= 8 \times 3 + 5 \times 6$$
$$= 24 + 30$$
$$= 54$$

Notice that you have to put the $\times$ signs in to work this out.

When you write a formula in letters you are using **algebra**.
The letters stand for the numbers.
The numbers are not always the same.
In the example above, $a = 3$, $c = 6$ is a party of 3 adults and 6 children.

Task

1 Work out the value of $8a + 5c$ when:

   (a) $a = 7$ and $c = 5$ **(b)** $a = 9$ and $c = 8$
   (c) $a = 0$ and $c = 3$ **(d)** $a = 4$ and $c = 30$

2 The cost of a party is £40.

   Work out how many different combinations of adults and children could go to the
   aquarium for £40 using the prices given above.

      How do you work out $8 \times 3 + 5 \times 6$ on your calculator?

You must make sure you know how to get the right answer on your calculator.
The order for pressing the keys can be different for different calculators.

Exercise

1 Find the value of $p + q + r$ when
(a) $p = 2$, $q = 3$ and $r = 1$
(b) $p = 5$, $q = 3$ and $r = 2$
(c) $p = 99$, $q = 101$ and $r = 100$
(d) $p = 0$, $q = 0$ and $r = 0$
(e) $p = 5$, $q = 19$ and $r = 1$
(f) $p = 59$, $q = 99$ and $r = -99$

2 Find the value of $x + y - z$ when
(a) $x = 3$, $y = 4$ and $z = 5$
(b) $x = 10$, $y = 10$ and $z = 10$
(c) $x = 6$, $y = 12$ and $z = 0$
(d) $x = 8$, $y = 2$ and $z = 10$
(e) $x = 23$, $y = 17$ and $z = 30$
(f) $x = 0$, $y = 73$ and $z = 73$

3 Find the value of $8a + 5c$ when
(a) $a = 2$, $c = 5$
(b) $a = 1$, $c = 6$
(c) $a = 2$, $c = 2$
(d) $a = 5$, $c = 0$
(e) $a = 5$, $c = 8$
(f) $a = 8$, $c = 5$
(g) $a = 0$, $c = 0$
(h) $a = 10$, $c = 10$
(i) $a = 100$, $c = 100$
(j) $a = 5$, $c = -8$

4 Use the formula
$$C = 5b - 2$$
to find the value of C when
(a) $b = 2$ (b) $b = 8$
(c) $b = 12$ (d) $b = 20$
(e) The formula refers to the notice about paperback books.
(i) What does b stand for?
(ii) What does C stand for?
(f) Jane spends £43 on books. How many books does she buy?

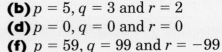

BOOKWORM

Paperback Books
£5.00 each

Discount of £2
for all customers

5 Use the formula
$$P = 2f + c$$
to find the value of P when
(a) $f = 4$, $c = 4$ (b) $f = 3$, $c = 2$
(c) $f = 5$, $c = 8$ (d) $f = 1$, $c = 0$
(e) The formula refers to the notice about fish and chips.
What do the letters f, c and P stand for?

— TODAYS SPECIAL —
FISH £2.00
CHIPS £1.00

Investigation   Four people try to work out the value of $2x + 4y$ when $x = 3$ and $y = 5$. Here are their answers.

Ali 68   Sam 70   Mel 50   Fran 26

Who is right?

What mistakes do you think the others made?

Finishing off

Now that you have finished this chapter you should be able to:

- understand what a formula is
- be able to write a formula
- be able to use a formula.

Review exercise

1 The price of cinema tickets is given by

$$P = 4A + 3C$$

The formula refers to the cinema advert.

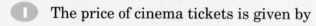

Avonford Cinema

Prices: ADULTS   £4.00
         CHILDREN £3.00

(a) What does A stand for?
What does C stand for?
What does P stand for?

(b) Find the cost of
  (i)   2 adults and 2 children   (ii) 2 children
  (iii) 5 adults and 3 children.

(c) How many children can go to the cinema for £12?

(d) How many adults can go to the cinema for £12?

The cinema has a special offer '£1 off all tickets!'

(e) Write a new formula for the price of the tickets.

(f) How many children can now go to the cinema for £12?
How many adults can now go to the cinema for £12?

2 Find the value of $2x + 3y$ when:
  (a) $x = 7, y = 2$ (b) $x = 1, y = 1$ (c) $x = 2, y = 3$
  (d) $x = 0, y = 10$ (e) $x = 5, y = 5$ (f) $x = 3, y = 2$
  (g) $x = 6, y = 2$ (h) $x = 1000, y = 1000$ (i) $x = 3, y = -2$

3 For a particular type of picture frame the formula is

$$\text{cost} = 40 \times \text{perimeter} + 50 \times \text{area}$$

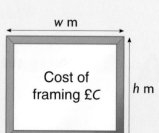

w m

Cost of framing £C

h m

(a) Write this formula using the letters C, w and h as shown in the diagram.

(b) Find the cost of framing a picture measuring
  (i)   2 m by 1.5 m   (ii) 60 cm by 30 cm.

4 A pet shop is selling hamsters for £3 and gerbils for £4.

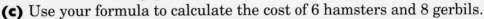

(a) Show how you would work out the cost of 2 hamsters and 4 gerbils.

(b) Write down a formula for the cost of h hamsters and g gerbils.

(c) Use your formula to calculate the cost of 6 hamsters and 8 gerbils.

(d) How many hamsters and gerbils can you buy for £24? How many different answers are there?

5 Paul is organising a trip to Alton Towers with his local club.

Minibuses large (16 people)   £25
small (10 people)   £15

(a) Show how you would work out the cost of 5 large minibuses and 3 small minibuses.

(b) Write down a formula for the cost of taking l large coaches and s small coaches.

(c) How much does it cost to hire 4 large and 3 small coaches?

(d) There are 50 members at the club. What is the cheapest way for them to travel to Alton Towers?

(e) Paul spends £95 on minibus hire. How many large and small minibuses did he hire?

Investigation   Karen is taking some members of her youth group to the zoo. Karen spends £17.00 on tickets for five people.

1 Karen uses the formula $P=5a+3s+2c$ to work out the total price. What do P, a, s and c stand for?

Francistown City Zoo

Entrance fees:
Adults   £5.00
Students (with I.D.)   £3.00
Children   £2.00
Enjoy your visit !

2 Find two different combinations of five people that Karen can take to the zoo for £17.

Chris is a keen golfer. On every golf course there is a target score for each hole.

Par 5 means the target for the hole is 5.
Chris scores 4.
He is one less than the target score.
He could write this as (-1).

The next hole is par 3. He scores 5.
He could write this as $(+2)$.

Competition:											Date:		
Tees Used	Par	SSS	✓									Start Time	Fi
White	72	71		PLAYER A	CHRIS								
Yellow	71	70		PLAYER B	STEVE								
Red	73	73		PLAYER C	PAUL								

Marker	Hole	White Yards	Par	Yellow Yards	Par	Stroke Index	A	B	C	Score	Points W+,L
−1	1	519	5	498	5	11	4	6	8		
+1	2	147	3	137	3	17	5	4	3		
+2	3	499	5	468	4	7	6	5	7		
+1	4	451	4	436	4	1	3	8	6		

Task

Write these scores as + or − numbers:

(a) par 5 / score 3 **(b)** par 5 / score 8 **(c)** par 5 / score 4 **(d)** par 2 / score 5 **(e)** par 4 / score 1 **(f)** par 4 / score 8

Plus (+) can be used in many circumstances, and minus (−) to mean the opposite.

? **Decide whether to call these numbers + or −:**

(a) A present of £10 / A bill for £6   **(b)** 30 steps backwards / 10 steps forwards   **(c)** A temperature of 20° above freezing / A temperature of 6° below freezing

Chris practises by playing consecutive holes. He scores as follows:

1 one below par then four above par
$(-1) + (+4) = (+3)$

2 two below par then three above par
$(-2) + (+3) = (+1)$

3 two above par then three below par
$(+2) + (-3) = (-1)$

4 one below par then two below par
$(-1) + (-2) = (-3)$

Numbers can be shown on a *number line*.

$$\leftarrow - \quad -7 \quad -6 \quad -5 \quad -4 \quad -3 \quad -2 \quad -1 \quad 0 \quad +1 \quad +2 \quad +3 \quad +4 \quad +5 \quad +6 \quad +7 \quad + \rightarrow$$

Numbers like $..., -3, -2, -1, 0, +1, +2, +3, ...$, are called **integers**.

Check the results above, starting at zero each time.

1
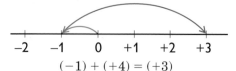
$(-1) + (+4) = (+3)$

2
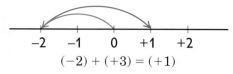
$(-2) + (+3) = (+1)$

3
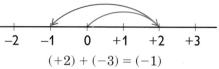
$(+2) + (-3) = (-1)$
this can also be written as
$2 - 3 = -1$

4
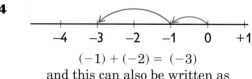
$(-1) + (-2) = (-3)$
and this can also be written as
$-1 - 2 = -3$

? **How do you enter a negative number into your calculator?**

Exercise

1 Choose a number to go with each statement.

A | The average winter temperature for Moscow | −36

B | The 'height' of the Dead Sea | +4406 feet

C | The goal difference for Division 1 champions | −2286 feet

D | Julius Caesar first arrived in Britain | −10°C

E | The goal difference for a relegated team | −55

F | The height of Ben Nevis | +42

2 Chris's aim is to score −2 after each pair of holes.
Which of these pairs give −2?
(a) $(-4) + (+2)$ **(b)** $(-1) + (-3)$ **(c)** $(+7) + (-2)$
(d) $(-1) + 0$ **(e)** $(-1) + (-1)$ **(f)** $(-2) + (+2)$

3 Copy the number line from the page opposite.
Mark the following numbers on it:
(a) -3 **(b)** $+1$ **(c)** -5 **(d)** -1 **(e)** $+2$

4 Work out the following:
(a) $(-4) + (+6)$ **(b)** $(-2) + (-3)$ **(c)** $(+1) + (-2)$
(d) $(+7) + (-5)$ **(e)** $(-3) + (+2)$ **(f)** $(-4) + (+4)$
(g) $(+17) + (-15)$ **(h)** $(-13) + (+12)$ **(i)** $(-14) + (+14)$

5 Work out the following:
(a) $-5 + 7$ **(b)** $-3 - 2$ **(c)** $8 - 11$
(d) $6 + 4$ **(e)** $6 - 9$ **(f)** $-3 + 5$
(g) $-2 + 3 + 1$ **(h)** $4 - 6 - 3$ **(i)** $-5 - 2 + 3 + 1$

Do these questions again using your calculator.
This checks that you can use your calculator with negative numbers.

Investigation This diagram (called a **nomogram**) can be used for addition.
For example, the broken line shows that $(-4) + (+6) = +2$.

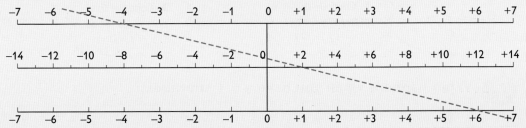

Use this nomogram to repeat as much as you can of Question 4.
(Use a ruler, but don't draw the lines.)
Which parts cannot be done this way? Why not?

Subtraction of negative numbers

F.A. Carling Premiership (up to and including 30 August 1998)

	Played	Won	Drawn	Lost	For	Against	Points
Liverpool	3	2	1	0	6	2	7
Aston Villa	3	2	1	0	4	1	7
Nottingham Forest	3	2	0	1	4	3	6
Charlton Athletic	3	1	2	0	5	0	5
Wimbledon	3	1	2	0	4	2	5
Middlesbrough	3	0	2	1	2	4	2
Newcastle United	3	0	2	1	2	5	2
Chelsea	2	0	1	1	2	3	1
Everton	3	0	1	2	0	3	1
Southampton	3	0	0	3	2	9	0

When two clubs have the same number of points, like Liverpool and Aston Villa above, their position in the table is decided by goal difference.

Goal difference = 'goals for' − 'goals against'

> So Liverpool are above Aston Villa.

Liverpool   goal difference = $6 - 2 = 4$
Aston Villa   goal difference = $4 - 1 = 3$.

Middlesbrough's goal difference = $2 - 4 = -2$
Newcastle have the same number of points as
Middlesbrough *but* Newcastle's goal difference = $2 - 5 = -3$.

> −2 is greater than −3, so Middlesbrough go above Newcastle.

Task

Look at these patterns.

$5 - 3 = 2$
$5 - 4 = 1$
$5 - 5 = 0$
$5 - 6 = -1$
$5 - 7 = -2$
$5 -$

> **1** Continue this pattern as far as $5 - 12 = -7$

Now look at this pattern in the opposite way.

$5 - 4 \quad = 1$
$5 - 3 \quad = 2$
$5 - 2 \quad = 3$
$5 - 1 \quad =$
$5 - 0 \quad =$
$5 - (-1) =$

> **2** Continue this pattern as far as $5 - (-5) =$

? **What happens when you have a − (−number)?**

Check that you have understood:

$4 - 2 = 2$ and $2 - 9 = -7$
but $5 - (-3) = 5 + 3 = 8$.

Exercise

1 Simplify
(a) $-(+2)$ (b) $-(-3)$ (c) $-(-6)$ (d) $-(+1)$
(e) $-(-1)$ (f) $-(-4)$ (g) $-(+7)$ (h) $-(+11)$

2 Put in order of size, smallest first.
(a) $-1, +2, -2, 0, +1, -3$
(b) $+1, -5, -1, +4, -2$
(c) $3, -5, -3, 1, -2$

3 Put in order of size, largest first.
(a) $-2, 2, 4, 0, -4$
(b) $4, -2, 1, -1, -3, -6$
(c) $10, 0, -2, 3, -6, 7, 17$

4 Work out these questions.
(a) $(-5) - (+2)$ (b) $(-1) - (+3)$ (c) $(+6) - (+2)$
(d) $(+7) - (+6)$ (e) $(+7) - (+8)$ (f) $(+5) - (-1)$
(g) $(+3) - (-2)$ (h) $(-6) - (-3)$ (i) $(-2) - (-2)$

5 Work out (evaluate)
(a) $6 - 2$ (b) $3 - 7$ (c) $1 - 5$
(d) $-4 - 9$ (e) $6 - (-1)$ (f) $3 - (-2)$
(g) $-4 - (-3)$ (h) $-1 - (-5)$ (i) $-6 - (-2)$

6 Work out (evaluate)
(a) $6 - 3$ (b) $6 - (-3)$ (c) $-6 + 2$
(d) $-4 - 4$ (e) $-1 - 7$ (f) $-2 - (-9)$
(g) $4 - (-1)$ (h) $3 - (-2)$ (i) $-8 - (-11)$

7 Find the value of
(a) $-2 - 3 + 1$ (b) $-6 - (-6) + 3$
(c) $-1 - 1 - 1$ (d) $-2 - 2 - 2 - 2$

Note **7(c)** is the same as   3 lots of (-1)
                                    $3 \times (-1) = -3$.

         7(d) is the same as   4 lots of (-2)
                                    $4 \times (-2) = -8$.

Investigation   Investigate how to use the nomogram on page 157 for subtraction.
Then write instructions for how to do it.
Use this to check your answers to Question 4.

Multiplying and dividing negative numbers

Avonford School has a tuck shop.
Pupils can either pay cash or write their name
and the amount owed in a book and pay later.

write down your money owed here

Joanne treats herself to a chocolate bar every
school day for a week.
She writes her name in the book.
At the end of the week she *owes*   5 lots of 30 pence.
$$5 \times (-30) = -150 \text{ pence.}$$

Simon buys two Munchie bars for 25 pence each. He *owes*   2 lots of 25 pence.
$$2 \times (-25) = -50 \text{ pence.}$$

Task

There is a pattern for multiplying + and − numbers.
Look at the 5 times table starting with $5 \times 3 = 15$
$$Or \ (+5) \times (+3) = (+15).$$

1   Copy and complete this table.

$$5 \times 3 \ = 15$$
$$5 \times 2 \ =$$
$$5 \times 1 \ =$$
$$5 \times 0 \ =$$
$$5 \times (-1) =$$
$$5 \times (-2) =$$

Subtract five

Red number going down by 1

$$\begin{array}{ccc} + & & + & & + \\ number & \times & number & = & number \end{array}$$

$$\begin{array}{ccc} + & & - & & - \\ number & \times & number & = & number \end{array}$$

2   Now do the same for the 4 times table and the 3 times table.

Use the last result of each of your tables to start the negative 2 times table
(i.e., the (-2) times table)
$$(-2) \times 5 = -10$$
$$(-2) \times 4 = -8$$
$$(-2) \times 3 = \qquad \text{and continue to } (-2) \times (-3)$$

 **What happens when you multiply a negative number by
a negative number?**

Multiplication questions can be changed into division questions using the same numbers.

Example 1 $6 \times 7 = 42$ so $42 \div 6 = 7$
and $42 \div 7 = 6.$

Example 2 $9 \times 8 = 72$ so $72 \div 9 = 8$
and $72 \div 8 = 9.$

   $(-3) \times (-7) = +21$ **What is** $(+21) \div (-3)$ **and** $(+21) \div (-7)$?
$(-4) \times (+5) = -20$ **What is** $(-20) \div (-4)$ **and** $(-20) \div (+5)$?

Exercise

1 Work out

(a) $(+2) \times (-5)$ (b) $(+3) \times (-7)$ (c) $(-6) \times (5)$

(d) $(-9) \times 4$ (e) $(-3) \times (-2)$ (f) $(-5) \times (-1)$

(g) $(-8) \times (-9)$ (h) $0 \times (-7)$ (i) 6×0

(j) $(-4) \times 3$ (k) $5 \times (-6)$ (l) $(-7) \times (-7)$

(m) $(-1)^2$ (n) $(-8) \times (-6)$ (o) $(+2) \times (+6)$

(p) $(+5) \times 7$ (q) $0 \times (-3)$ (r) $(-3) \times 4$

(s) $6 \times (-2)$ (t) $7 \times (-9)$ (u) $(-2) \times (-2)$

(v) $(-2)^3$ (w) $(-3)^2$ (x) $(-9) \times (-10)$

(y) $25 \times (-4)$ (z) $(-4)^2$

2 $(-4) \times (-6) = (+24)$ **3** $(-5) \times (+6) = (-30)$

Use this to work out

(a) $(+24) \div (-6)$

(b) $(+24) \div (-4)$

Use this to work out

(a) $(-30) \div (+6)$

(b) $(-30) \div (-5)$

4 Evaluate

(a) $(-8) \div 2$ (b) $(-10) \div 5$ (c) $(-6) \div (+3)$

(d) $8 \div (-4)$ (e) $16 \div (-8)$ (f) $(-24) \div (-3)$

(g) $(-30) \div (-6)$ (h) $(-42) \div (-6)$ (i) $42 \div (-3)$

(j) $48 \div 3$ (k) $(-26) \div (-13)$ (l) $(+20) \div (+5)$

(m) $36 \div 3$ (n) $(-36) \div 12$ (o) $(-28) \div (-7)$

(p) $(+10) \div (+10)$ (q) $(-26) \div 2$ (r) $(-12) \div (-12)$

(s) $52 \div (-4)$ (t) $63 \div (-9)$ (u) $(-72) \div (-9)$

(v) $100 \div (-4)$ (w) $(-100) \div 20$ (x) $(-60) \div (-5)$

(y) $(-1) \div (-1)$ (z) $14 \div (-2)$

5 Evaluate

(a) $(-3) \times (-2) \times (-1)$ (b) $(-2) \times (+5) \times (+4)$ (c) $(+72) \div (-8)$

(d) $(-2) \times (-2) \times (-2)$ (e) $(-2)^3$ (f) $(-3)^3$

(g) $(+32) \div (-8)$ (h) $(-48) \div (-12)$ (i) $(-48) \div 3$

(j) $(-98) \div (-7)$ (k) $(10) \times (-3) \times (-7)$ (l) $(-91) \div 7$

(m) $(+51) \div (-3)$ (n) $75 \div 5$ (o) $(-4)^2$

(p) $(-5)^2$

6 (a) An old clock gained 5 minutes each hour.

One day Christiaan noticed that the clock was correct at 12 noon.

How many minutes fast or slow was the clock at these times on that day?

(i) 4 p.m.   (ii) 8 p.m.   (iii) 9 a.m.   (iv) 5 a.m.

(b) Christiaan tried to mend the clock, but then it lost 6 minutes each hour. One day it was again correct at 12 noon. Find the new answers to (i)–(iv) of (a) for that day.

(c) Which of your answers in (a) shows that $5 \times (-3) = -15$?

What multiplications are shown by your answers in (b)?

Finishing off

Now that you have finished this chapter you should be able to:

- understand + (positive) and − (negative) numbers
- add + and − numbers
- subtract + and − numbers
- multiply + and − numbers
- divide + and − numbers.

Review exercise

1 Copy this number line.

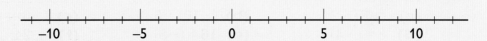

Mark these numbers on it
(a) −1   **(b)** −8   **(c)** 6   **(d)** +2   **(e)** −6   **(f)** 7

2 Put these numbers in order of size, starting with the smallest:
−1, 0, −6, +1, +5, −3.

3 Work out
(a) (+3) + (−4)   **(b)** (−3) + (+2)   **(c)** (−1) + (−2)
(d) (−5) + (+8)   **(e)** 0 + (−6)   **(f)** 7 + (−8)
(g) (−5) + (−3)   **(h)** 19 + (−12)   **(i)** 23 + (−27)
(j) (−33) + (−3)   **(k)** (−42) + (+18)   **(l)** 27 + (−19)

4 Work out (evaluate)
(a) 7 − 9   **(b)** −6 − 1   **(c)** 5 − 3
(d) −2 + 2   **(e)** −2 + 6   **(f)** −5 + 1
(g) −6 + 3   **(h)** 4 + (−2)   **(i)** 7 + (−1)
(j) −5 − 4   **(k)** −7 + 10   **(l)** −23 + 32

5 Work out
(a) (+6) − (−4)   **(b)** (−5) − (+3)   **(c)** (−4) − (+7)
(d) (+5) − (−2)   **(e)** (−9) − (−6)   **(f)** (−1) − (−8)
(g) (−7) − (−3)   **(h)** (−10) − (+5)   **(i)** (+7) − (+9)
(j) (+13) − (−20)   **(k)** (−17) − (+11)   **(l)** (−23) − (−45)

6 Evaluate

(a) $(-2) \times (+4)$ (b) $(5) \times (-3)$ (c) $(-6) \times (-7)$

(d) $(-4) \times (-9)$ (e) $(-2) \times (+3) \times (-5)$ (f) $(-6) \times 0$

(g) $(-1)^2$ (h) $(-3)^2$ (i) $(-2)^3$

(j) $(-5)^4$ (k) $(-2)^4$ (l) $(-2)^2 \times (-3)^5$

7 Evaluate

(a) $(-24) \div (+4)$ (b) $(-12) \div (-3)$ (c) $(-30) \div (-6)$

(d) $(+42) \div (-6)$ (e) $12 \div 3$ (f) $(-64) \div (-4)$

(g) $(-54) \div (+9)$ (h) $(+63) \div (-7)$ (i) $38 \div (-2)$

(j) $(-56) \div (-8)$ (k) $(-64) \div 8$ (l) $100 \div (-4)$

8 In a magic square you get the same answer when you add up the numbers in each of the rows, in each of the columns and in each diagonal.

Copy and complete this magic square.

-4			-5
		2	
	1	2	-4
4	-6		7

9 Copy and complete this *multiplying* magic square. The numbers in each row, column or diagonal have the same *product*.

2	-9	-12
		18

Activity   **Speed test**

How quickly can you do these correctly?

(a) $5 - 8$ (b) $-1 - 7$ (c) $6 - (-3)$

(d) $(-9) - (-1)$ (e) $(-2) + 5 + (-3)$ (f) $(-32) \div (-8)$

(g) $(-7) \times (-4)$ (h) $(-6) \times 5$ (i) $(-3) \times (-2) \times (-4)$

(j) $-20 \div 5$ (k) $56 \div (-8)$ (l) $(-7) \times 0$

(m) $(-4)^2$ (n) $(-3)^3$

19 Equations

James's teacher sets him a problem.

His teacher has two identical packages which she puts on some old-fashioned weighing scales.

She wants to know how much each package weighs.

James writes down:

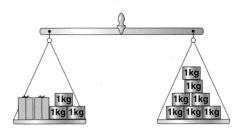

> *The weight of two packages + 3 kg = 7 kg*

James realises that it would be quicker to write:

> $2 \times p + 3 = 7$
> so $2p + 3 = 7$

This is called an **equation** – it only has one right answer.

? **What does 2p mean?**

James removes 3 kg from both sides of the scales.
The scales still balance.

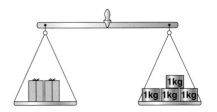

? **Why did James take 3 kg from both sides of the scales?**

James now writes:

> *Remove 3 kg from each side*
> $2p + 3 = 7$
> $2p = 4$

? **How can you work out how much one package weighs?**
How much is this?

Task

Invent your own problems with scales which balance.
Get a friend to solve them.

? **How can you check that your answers are right?**
Why is it important that the scales balance at each stage?

Exercise

Write down equations for each of the following sets of scales. Use the same method that James did to work out how much each package weighs.

Draw the scales at each stage in your working.

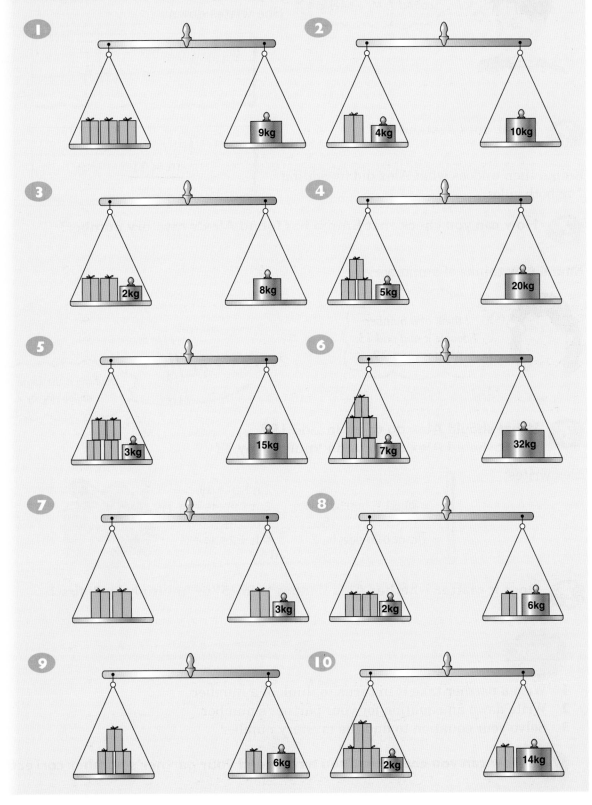

Solving equations

I think of a number and subtract 7. My answer is 4.

Alex thinks of a number.
Emma wants to find out Alex's number.
She writes down:

mystery number − 7 = 4
m − 7 = 4

? **What does *m* stand for?**

Emma then undoes what Alex did by adding
7 to both sides.

m − 7 + 7 = 4 + 7
m = 11

? **How can you check that Emma has found Alex's mystery number?**

Emma now thinks of a number:

I think of a number. I double it and add 15. My answer is 29.

Alex writes:

2 n + 15 = 29

Doubling is the same as multiplying by 2.

? **What should Alex do to undo 'add 15'?**
What should Alex do to undo 'multiply by 2'?

Alex writes:

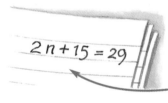

	2 n + 15 = 29
Subtract 15 from both sides	2 n + 15 − 15 = 29 − 15
So	2 n = 14
Divide both sides by 2	2 n ÷ 2 = 14 ÷ 2
So	n = 7

? **Does it matter whether Alex undoes 'add 15' or 'multiply by 2' first?**

Task

1 With a partner take it in turns to think of a number.
2 Write down an equation for your partner's number.
3 Solve your equation to find the mystery number.

? **How can you check that you have found your partner's number correctly?**

Exercise

In this exercise make sure you set out your work in the same way Alex and Emma did. Check in each case that you have found the correct answer.

1 Solve these equations by subtracting from both sides.
- **(a)** $m + 4 = 11$
- **(b)** $a + 11 = 15$
- **(c)** $6 + b = 8$
- **(d)** $x + 5 = 15$
- **(e)** $y + 7 = 17$
- **(f)** $z + 15 = 115$

2 Solve these equations by adding to both sides:
- **(a)** $p - 6 = 10$
- **(b)** $d - 7 = 13$
- **(c)** $a - 4 = 4$
- **(d)** $q - 5 = 15$
- **(e)** $s - 9 = 15$
- **(f)** $t - 25 = 975$

3 Solve these equations. (You will need to think carefully about whether to add or subtract in each case.)
- **(a)** $c - 7 = 10$
- **(b)** $5 + d = 7$
- **(c)** $g - 5 = 5$
- **(d)** $u + 5 = 19$
- **(e)** $h - 8 = 42$
- **(f)** $j + 125 = 1125$

4 Solve these equations.
- **(a)** $2a = 6$
- **(b)** $4b = 12$
- **(c)** $3m = 15$

5 Solve the following equations.
- **(a)** $3a + 4 = 10$
- **(b)** $5d + 3 = 18$
- **(c)** $2s - 6 = 4$
- **(d)** $2n - 4 = 8$
- **(e)** $6b + 5 = 17$
- **(f)** $4c - 5 = 11$
- **(g)** $2x + 5 = 45$
- **(h)** $3y - 8 = 28$
- **(i)** $9z + 35 = 125$

6 Jenny and Simon are both thinking of mystery numbers.

*I think of a number.
I multiply by 4.
I add 5.
My answer is 25.*

Jenny

*I think of a number.
I double it.
I subtract 6.
My answer is 10.*

Simon

- **(a)** Write down an equation for Jenny's mystery number.
- **(b)** Solve your equation.
- **(c)** Write down an equation for Simon's mystery number.
- **(d)** What number was Simon thinking of?

7 Suzanne thinks of a number. When she doubles it and subtracts 12 she gets the original number. Write down an equation for Suzanne's number and solve it.

8 Matt thinks of a number. When he multiplies it by 5 and adds 6 he gets the same as when he multiplies it by 6 and subtracts 5. Write down an equation for his number and solve it.

Solving problems with equations

The scoring in Rugby Union has varied over the last 50 years.

I remember a match when Llanelli scored 22 points from 5 tries, 2 conversions and 1 penalty. But I don't know when this was.

Rugby Union points system
Conversion: 2 points
Penalty: 3 points
Try: 3 points from 1950 to 1970
4 points from 1971 to 1991
5 points from 1992 onwards

Abbie uses an equation to help Dai's memory:

General plan

Suppose a try scored T points then.

So $5T + 2 \times 2 + 1 \times 3 = 22$
            $5T + 7 = 22$
               $5T = 15$
                 $T = 3$

1 Introduce a letter for what you want to find, with units.

2 Form an equation.

3 Solve the equation.

4 State what the solution means.

? **Explain how Abbie gets this equation.**

A try was worth 3 points, so the match was between 1950 and 1970.

Task

In a match in 1987 Bath's total score was 38 with 4 conversions and 2 penalties. How many tries did Bath score?

Example
The width of a rectangle is 4 cm less than its length, and the perimeter is 60 cm. Find the length.

Solution
Let the length be L cm.
The perimeter is $L + (L - 4) + L + (L - 4) = 4L - 8$ cm
           Therefore $4L - 8 = 60$
                $4L = 68$
                $L = 17$
The length of the rectangle is 17 cm.

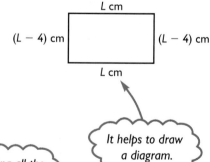

Collecting all the L's together.

It helps to draw a diagram.

L cm
$(L - 4)$ cm $(L - 4)$ cm
L cm

? **Explain how this solution fits the four stages of the general plan.**

Exercise

1. A china cup and saucer cost £12. The cup on its own costs £3 more than the saucer. Let £s be the cost of the saucer. Form an equation for s and solve it. Then find the cost of the cup.

2. Each obtuse angle of a parallelogram is 32° more than each acute angle. Let one obtuse angle be x°. Form an equation for x and solve it. Find all the angles of the parallelogram.

3. Each of the equal angles of an isosceles triangle is 24° greater than the third angle. Form a suitable equation and find all three angles.

4. April is 6 years older than her brother Daniel. In 16 years the sum of their ages will be 100 years. Suppose that April is x years old now.

   (a) Complete the table.

	April's age (years)	Daniel's age (years)
Now	x	$x - 6$
In 16 years		

   (b) Form an equation and solve it.
   (c) State their present ages.

5. Peter is now four times as old as his daughter Tara and in 5 years time their ages will total 50 years. Complete a table like the one in Question 4. Use it to find their ages now.

6. Isaak went fishing on Monday, Tuesday and Wednesday. He caught the same number of fish on Tuesday as he did on Wednesday and this was three more than he caught on Monday. His average was 7 fish per day. How many did he catch on Monday?

7. The houses on my side of the road were originally numbered with consecutive odd numbers. Blocks of flats have replaced most of the houses, but there are still five houses together at the end of the road.

   (a) Suppose that the number of the last house is N.
       Write down the numbers of the other four houses in terms of N.
   (b) The sum of the numbers of these five houses is 315.
       Form an equation for N, and solve it.
   (c) How many houses were there originally on this side of the road?

Activity   Make up two problems of your own that can be solved by using equations. Write out the solutions. Try them on a friend.

Finishing off

Now that you have finished this chapter you should be able to:

● understand what an equation is
● be able to write an equation
● be able to solve an equation
● be able to solve a problem by using an equation.

Review exercise

1 Find the weights of each of the lettered pieces in the following two mobiles.

(a)

(b)

2 Write down an equation for each of the following sets of scales. Solve your equations making sure that the scales balance at each stage.

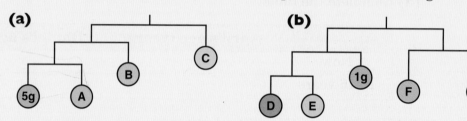

(a)

(b)

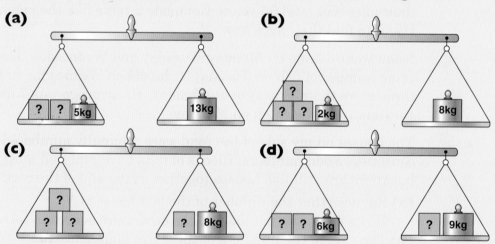

(c)

(d)

3 Solve the following equations.
(a) $5p = 20$ **(b)** $6 + f = 7$ **(c)** $8a = 32$
(d) $g - 2 = 8$ **(e)** $m - 11 = 21$ **(f)** $9h = 36$
(g) $12x = 72$ **(h)** $y - 8 = 22$ **(i)** $999z = 999$

4 Solve the following equations:
(a) $2a + 3 = 5$ **(b)** $4d + 1 = 9$ **(c)** $2 + 2c = 8$
(d) $6c + 2 = 20$ **(e)** $6m + 4 = 16$ **(f)** $3d + 2 = 5$
(g) $12x + 6 = 30$ **(h)** $5y - 18 = 22$ **(i)** $999z + 999 = 999$

5 Solve the following equations:

(a) $4b - 6 = 14$ (b) $4 + 6b = 10$ (c) $3f - 9 = 21$
(d) $4g - 1 = 7$ (e) $9b - 10 = 62$ (f) $7 + 3f = 37$
(g) $12x - 6 = 30$ (h) $15y - 8 = 22$ (i) $9z + 990 = 999$

6 Jenny thinks of a number.

> I multiply my number by 4 and add 6. My answer is 30.

(a) Write down an equation for Jenny's number.
(b) Solve your equation to work out Jenny's mystery number.

7 Kate buys 2 apples at 12p each and 4 bananas from her local shop.
She spends 84p altogether.

(a) Write down an equation for this information, using b as the cost of one banana.
(b) Solve your equation to find the cost of one banana.

8 One of the acute angles of a right-angled triangle is 38° greater than the other. Find both the acute angles.

9 Three prizes are given from a prize fund, with these conditions.

1 The first prize is twice the third prize.
2 The second prize is £5 more than the third prize.

(a) Find the values of the prizes when the total prize money is
(i) £65   (ii) £37.

(b) Then it is decided that:

3 The first prize is at least £5 more than the second prize.

Investigate the total prize money needed to meet all three conditions.

Investigation Leah and Ryan are making up equations for each other to solve.

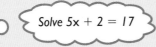

> Solve 5x + 2 = 17

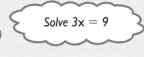

> Solve 3x = 9

What is the value of x in each case?
Write down five other equations which have a solution of $x = 3$.

Here is a piece of card before it is folded to make a fruit pastilles packet.

 Discuss the answers to the following questions with a partner.

- What will be the shape of the packet?
- What are all the different parts for?
- How many **faces** will the packet have?
- What shape will the faces be?
- Where the card is folded there will be an **edge** of the packet.
- How many folds have to be made?
- How many edges will the packet have?
- How many **vertices** (corners) will the packet have?

The card is a useful example of a **net**.

Here is an example of a mathematical net drawn on centimetre squared paper.
Copy it and add flaps for sticking.
Use the least number of flaps possible.

Before you make the solid shape answer these questions.

- How many flaps does your net have?
- How many folds will you need to make?

Compare your net with a friend's.
(Flaps are sometimes called tabs.)

 **Have you put your flaps in the same positions?
Can the arrangement of flaps be different?
Do you always need the same number of flaps for this net?**

The net above should make this **cuboid**.

Its **dimensions** are 3 cm long by 2 cm wide by 2 cm high.

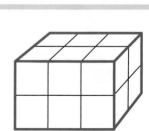

Exercise

1 Use centimetre squared paper to draw a net for a cuboid with these dimensions:

length 4 cm   width 2 cm   height 2 cm

Add flaps, cut out the net and construct the cuboid.

2 Use centimetre squared paper to draw a net and make a cuboid where all the faces are squares.

What name do we give to this special type of cuboid?

3 Use squared paper to construct a cuboid where none of the faces are squares.

4 Construct a cuboid where only two of the faces are squares. Can you construct a cuboid where exactly four of the faces are squares?

5 Which of these shapes are nets of cubes?

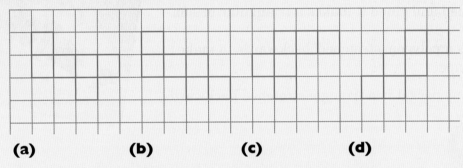

(a)   (b)   (c)   (d)

Draw four more arrangements of six squares, two which are nets of cubes and two which are not.

Activity 1 COMPETITION!

Each member of the class has the same sized piece of squared paper. Who can use it to construct the largest cuboid?

 What do we mean by largest?

Activity 2 Draw the net on the opposite page on plain paper.
You should use a ruler and a set square.

To test how well you have done it, cut it out and see if the cuboid looks right.

Are your perpendicular lines really at right angles?

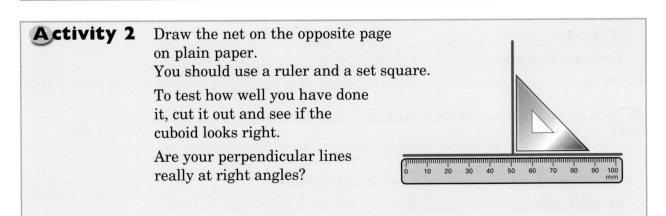

Prisms

Here is the card for a
Toblerone packet.

When folded and glued it makes a triangular prism.

A prism is a polygon 'stretched' backwards to make
a solid shape.

A Toblerone packet is a triangle stretched backwards.

triangular prism

 Task

 **A triangular prism has 5 faces.
What shapes are they?**

 **A triangular prism has 9 edges and 6 vertices.
Can you think of a solid shape which has 8 faces, 18 edges and 12 vertices?**

Copy and fill in this table.

Shape	Number of faces (F)	Number of vertices (V)	Number of edges (E)
Triangular prism	5	6	9
	8	12	18
Rectangular prism			
Pentagonal prism			

 Can you spot a relationship between the numbers for each shape?

Write down an **equation** connecting F, V and E.

The relationship you have found is called Euler's Rule.

Euler was a famous Swiss mathematician. He lived from 1707 to 1783.

Exercise

1 Use squared paper to construct a triangular prism.

2 Ask your teacher for nets to make these prisms:

Triangular prism   Cuboid
Hexagonal prism   L-shaped prism
Octagonal prism   Pentagonal prism

Cut out the nets and construct the prisms.
Copy and fill in the table as you make each prism.
Does each prism fit the relationship you found on the opposite page?

Shape	Number of faces (F)	Number of vertices (V)	Number of edges (E)

3 Glue together two prisms from Question 2 to make a new prism.
Does it fit the relationship?

4 Here are three **views** of a triangular prism.

      Plan   End elevation   Side elevation
  (from Above)   (from the sides)

Draw and label each view of the shapes in Questions 2 and 3.
You may find squared paper helpful for some of them.

Activity   Half the area has been cut away
from this net of a cube. The diagonal
lines go through the midpoints of
the edges.

Make your own copy of what remains,
cut it out and fold it to make a solid.
You will find that one face is missing.
What shape is this face? Draw the net
again with this face included. Add
flaps and construct the complete solid.
Show how to put two of these solids together
to make a complete cube.

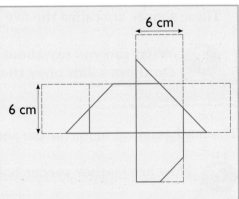

Further solid shapes

There are many other solid shapes besides prisms.

Here is a **tetrahedron** along with the net to make it.

Tetra means four, *hedron* means face.

On page 174 you should have discovered the relationship

$$F + V = E + 2$$

where F is the number of faces, V the number of vertices and E the number of edges.

Tetrahedron

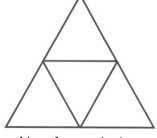

Net of a tetrahedron

 Does the tetrahedron obey this rule?

 Task

Ask your teacher for nets of the solids named in the table below. They are difficult to draw!

Cut out the nets and make the solid shapes.
Copy the table and fill it in as you make the shapes.

Shape	Faces (F)	Vertices (V)	Edges (E)
tetrahedron			
hexahedron (cube)			
octahedron			
dodecahedron			
icosahedron			

These shapes are called the five Platonic solids.

 What can you say about the faces of a Platonic solid? Do these solids obey the $F + V = E + 2$ rule?

Plato was a Greek philosopher who was born in the fifth century B.C.

The mathematical name for the shape of a soccer ball is a **sphere**.

 How are leather soccer balls like this one made?

Activity

1 Use squared paper to draw a net for a **square based pyramid**.
Construct the pyramid and check that it obeys $F + V = E + 2$.

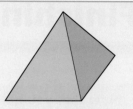

2 Draw a net and construct a model of a house like this one.
Does the model obey $F + V = E + 2$?

3 Draw a net and construct a model of a house with a different roof shape.

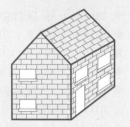

4 Use nets to make models of other objects.
Check that each one obeys Euler's Rule.

Investigation 1 Find the rule which links the least number of flaps needed on a net to the number of vertices of the solid.

Investigation 2 You will need your Platonic solids.

1 Mark the centre of each face of the cube.
Imagine these points as the vertices of a new solid.
What is this solid?

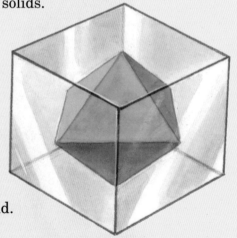

2 Mark the centre of each face of the octahedron.
Imagine these points as the vertices of a new solid.
What is this solid?

Becauses of this pairing the cube and octahedron are called **dual** solids.

3 Mark the centre of each face of the tetrahedron.
Imagine these points as the vertices of a new solid.
What is the dual of a tetrahedron?

4 Look carefully at the table on the opposite page.
What patterns do you see in the entries for dual solids?

Do these work for the dodecahedron and icosahedron too?

Finishing off

Now that you have finished this chapter you should:

- be able to recognise a cuboid
- know that a cuboid has six rectangular faces, twelve edges and eight vertices
- know that a cube is a special cuboid where all the faces are squares
- know that a prism is any flat shape 'stretched' backwards
- be able to recognise a triangular prism, a cylinder, a sphere, a square based pyramid and a cone, and their plans and elevations
- be able to construct solid shapes from nets.

Review exercise

1 Write down the **mathematical** names of these shapes.

(a)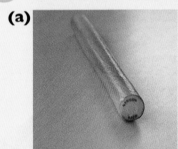

(b)

(c)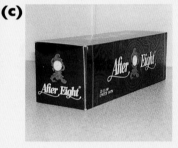

(d)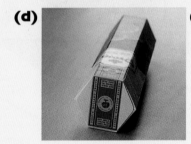

(e)

2 Match the names to the shapes:

cuboid　cylinder　hexagonal prism　irregular prism
equilateral triangle prism　isosceles triangle prism

(a)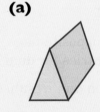

(b)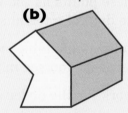

(c)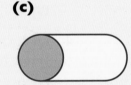

(d)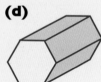

(e)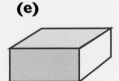

(f)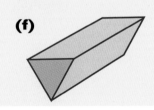

③ Using a pair of compasses, draw a net to make an equilateral triangle prism.

④ Here is the plan and elevation of a **cone**.

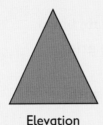

Plan	Elevation	Cone

Why is there only one elevation shown?
Draw and label the plan and two elevations of
(a) a cylinder   **(b)** a square based pyramid.

Activity 1   Make a die for playing board games, by first drawing a net on squared paper.
It can be as large as you like.
Draw the spots for the die *before* you fold the net. Make sure that the spots on opposite sides add up to seven.

Activity 2

1   Draw a large circle on stiff card.
By using angles of 72° at the centre of the circle, mark points A, B, C, D and E equally spaced round the circle. (Be careful to do this accurately.) Join these points to make a regular pentagon ABCDE.

2   Copy the rest of the diagram carefully.

3   You should now be able to see in your drawing the net for half a dodecagon. Cut this out (no flaps needed) and score (scratch) the fold lines (the edges of the central pentagon).

4   Make an exact second copy. Hold these two flat nets together, face to face, turned so that the vertices of each one line up with the gaps in the other one. Weave a small elastic band round these ten vertices, over the top net and under the lower net.

You can now 'pop up' your dodecagon into solid form, and then push it down flat for travelling.

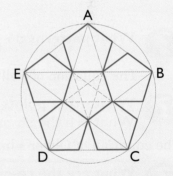

The equation of a line

Sally, Joe, and Oliver are playing co-ordinate bingo.

They each draw a line on their co-ordinate grid connecting 4 points.

They take turns to pick cards from a pack with co-ordinates on them.

The winner is the person whose line is completed with crosses first.

The co-ordinates of the points on Joe's line are: (1, 1)
(1, 2)
(1, 3)
(1, 4)

> The first co-ordinate is the x co-ordinate.

? **What is the x co-ordinate always equal to?**

Joe's points are on the line called $x = 1$.

> The second co-ordinate is the y co-ordinate.

? **What other points lie on the line x = 1?**

The co-ordinates of the points on Sally's line are: (1, 3)
(2, 2)
(3, 1)
(4, 0)

> This is called the **equation of the line**.

? **What patterns do you notice in these co-ordinates?**

The equation of Sally's line is $x + y = 4$.

? **What other points lie on the line x + y = 4?**
What are the co-ordinates of the points on Oliver's line?

The equation of Oliver's line is $y = x$.

? **What are the co-ordinates of some other points which lie on the line y = x?**

Task

Play your own game of co-ordinate bingo in a group. Use the same size grid as above.

Write down the co-ordinates of each line you use.
Find the equation of each line in your group.

? **Does every line have an equation?**
All the co-ordinates in co-ordinate bingo are whole numbers.
Does the equation of a line apply to other points as well, like $(1\frac{1}{2}, 1\frac{1}{2})$ and (2.4, 1.6)?

Exercise

1 Write down the co-ordinates of four points on each of the following lines. Comment on the patterns that you notice in the co-ordinates for each line. Find the equation of each line.

(a)

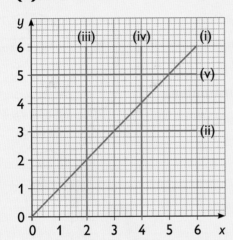

(b)

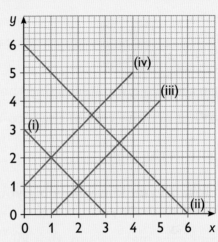

2 Write down the co-ordinates of four points which are on each of the following lines.

(a) $y = x$ **(b)** $x + y = 8$ **(c)** $y = x + 3$

(d) $y = x - 2$ **(e)** $y - x = 2$ **(f)** $x - y = 2$

Which two lines have the same points on them?

3 For each of the following sets of points;

    (i) plot them on graph paper

    (ii) draw a straight line through them

    (iii) write down the co-ordinates of 3 more points on the line

    (iv) find the equation of the line

    (a) $(-5, -5)$ **(b)** $(9, 6)$ **(c)** $(4, 3)$

         $(-4, -4)$ $(8, 5)$ $(3, 4)$

         $(-3, -3)$ $(7, 4)$ $(2, 5)$

         $(-2, -2)$ $(6, 3)$ $(1, 6)$

Activity   Make a poster showing the pattern formed by the following lines.

         (a) $x = 2$ **(b)** $x = 5$

         (c) $y = 2$ **(d)** $y = 5$

         (e) $y = x$ **(f)** $x + y = 7$

Find two more lines that will divide the four central triangles into eight.

?   How can you divide the eight triangles into sixteen?

Drawing lines

Follow these steps to draw the graph of $y = 3x$.

First of all make a table and choose some numbers for the x co-ordinates.

Multiply every x co-ordinate by 3.

x	−3	−2	−1	0	1	2	3
$y = 3x$			−3			6	

We chose the numbers −3, −2, −1, 0, 1, 2, 3 for x.

Then use the x co-ordinates to find the y co-ordinates.

 What are the rest of the y co-ordinates?

So, one of the points is (2, 6).

Look again at the table.

 How do you know how big you need to draw your axes?

Draw your axes making sure that all your points will fit on it.

Plot all the points that you have found.

Join up all your points with a straight line using a sharp pencil and a ruler.

⚠ Look at the scales on the x-axis and the y-axis. They are different.

However, you must have the same scale for $+x$ and $−x$, and the scale you use for $−y$ must be the same as for $+y$.

 What is the value of y when x = 2.5?
What is the value of x when y = 4?
How accurate are your answers?

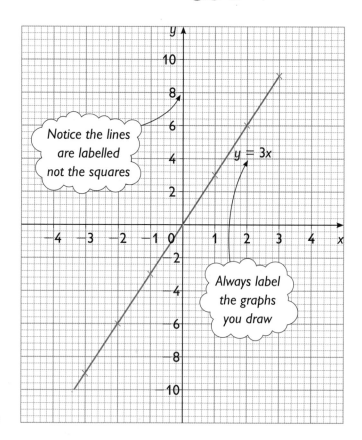

Notice the lines are labelled not the squares

$y = 3x$

Always label the graphs you draw

Task

Follow the steps above to draw the graphs of
$y = x$ $y = 2x$ and $y = 4x$ on the same axes.

Compare the three graphs. What do you notice?

 Which graph is the steepest?

Exercise

1 For each part of this question:

(i) copy and complete the table
(ii) write down the largest and smallest x and y co-ordinates
(iii) draw the graph

(a)

x	-4	-3	-2	-1	0	1	2	3	4
$y = x + 1$	-3			0				4	

(b)

x	-4	-3	-2	-1	0	1	2	3	4
$y = x + 5$		2		4			7		

(c)

x	-4	-3	-2	-1	0	1	2	3	4
$y = x - 2$	-6			-3			0		

(d)

x	-4	-3	-2	-1	0	1	2	3	4
$y = 5x$	-20			-5					20

2 Here is the graph of $y = 2x + 1$.

(a) What is the value of y when

(i) $x = 3$
(ii) $x = 0$
(iii) $x = 3.5$?

(b) What is the value of x when

(i) $y = 11$
(ii) $y = 6$
(iii) $y = 9$?

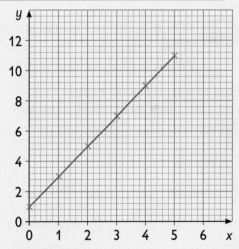

3 **(a)** Copy and complete this table for the graph $y = 2x - 3$.

x	-3	-2	-1	0	1	2	3
$2x$	-6					4	
-3	-3					-3	
$y = 2x - 3$	-9					1	

(b) Draw the graph.

Investigation Draw the graphs of **(a)** $y = 2x + 1$ **(b)** $y = 2x - 4$ on the same axes. What do you notice? Add the graph of $y = 2x + 2$ to your diagram without doing any further calculations.

Interpreting graphs

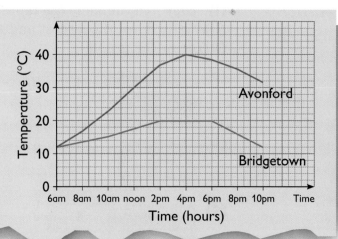

THE AVONFORD STAR

What A Scorcher!!

Temperatures in Avonford reach a record high!

Avonford has just got in to the record books with having the hottest day since records began. The temperature soared to a sizzling 40°C and only fell to 18°C last night.

Avonford compared with the coldest place yesterday in Britain, Bridgetown.

Look at the line graph in the newspaper article.
What is the temperature in both towns at 11 o'clock?
At which times is the temperature in Bridgetown 18°C?

? **When is the temperature difference the greatest between the two towns?**
What does each small square represent on each axes?
When is the temperature in both towns the same?

This is a conversion graph.
You can use it to convert between
Fahrenheit and Celsius temperatures.

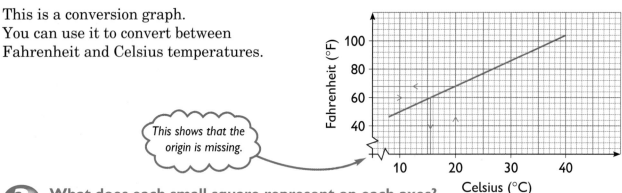

This shows that the origin is missing.

? **What does each small square represent on each axes?**
What is 20°C in Fahrenheit? What is 60°F in Celsius?

Task

Look again at the newspaper article above. Write down the temperature in each town for every hour. Use the conversion graph to convert the temperatures to Fahrenheit.

Make your own newspaper article and line graphs using the Fahrenheit temperatures.

Comment on the shape of your line graphs and the line graphs in the newspaper article.

? **Can you convert exactly between Celsius and Fahrenheit by using the conversion graph?**

Exercise

1 Look at the conversion chart on the page opposite.

    (a) Convert the following temperatures to celsius:
        (i) 100°F   **(ii)** 80°F   **(iii)** 50°F

    (b) Convert the following temperatures to Fahrenheit:
        (i) 15°C   **(ii)** 30°C   **(iii)** 35°C

2 This graph shows the temperatures of two hospital patients during one day.

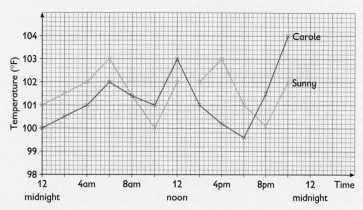

    (a) When do the two have the same temperature?
    (b) When is Carole's temperature the highest?
    (c) What are their temperatures at 12 noon?
    (d) Between what times is Sunny's temperature falling?

3 The graph shows the temperature of a cup of coffee at different times.

    (a) What is the temperature at time
        (i) 10 minutes   **(ii)** 20 minutes
        (iii) 30 minutes?

    (b) At what time is its temperature
        (i) 60°   **(ii)** 40°?

    (c) What is the temperature when it is made?

    (d) When is it cooling fastest?

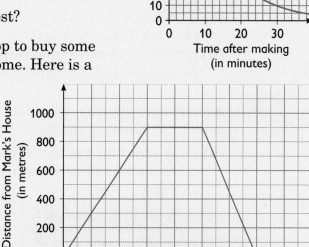

4 Mark walks to his local shop to buy some sweets and then returns home. Here is a distance-time graph for his journey.

    (a) Explain the shape of this graph.
    (b) How far is the shop from Mark's home?
    (c) How long does Mark spend in the shop?
    (d) How long does it take Mark to walk home?

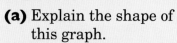

Finishing off

Now that you have finished this chapter you should be able to:

- interpret a line graph
- use a conversion graph
- find an equation of a line
- understand what an equation of a line is
- draw a graph.

Review exercise

1. Below is a conversion graph used to convert between miles and kilometres.

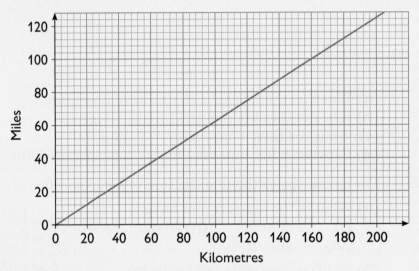

(a) Norwich is 100 kilometres from Cambridge .
How far is this in miles?

(b) Birmingham is 84 miles from Manchester.
How far is this in kilometres?

(c) Edinburgh is 170 kilometres from Newcastle.
How far is this in miles?

(d) London is 52 miles from Brighton.
How far is this in kilometres?

2. A telephone company called *In Touch* makes the following charges for calls:

(a) Copy and complete the following table showing the company's phone charges:

Stay 'In Touch'

| Calls only | 6p per minute |
| plus | 10p connection charge |

Length of call (in minutes)	1	2	3	4	5	6	7	8
Cost of call (in pence)	16			34				

(b) Draw a graph to show this information.

3 Complete the following tables for $y = x + 6$ and $y = 2x$.

(i)

x	-4	-3	-2	-1	0	1	2	3	4
$y = x + 6$		3		5			8		

(ii)

x	-4	-3	-2	-1	0	1	2	3	4
$y = 2x$	-8				0			6	

Draw the graphs of $y = 2x$ and $y = x + 6$ on the same axes.

4 This design is made from pieces of six different straight lines.

(a) Write down the co-ordinates of four points on each line.

(b) By looking for patterns in each set of co-ordinates find the equation of each of the lines.

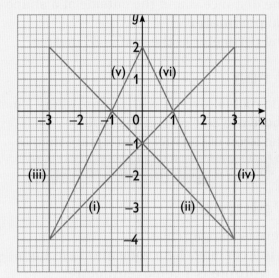

Investigation

(a) The graph shows how the average length of herring changes with age.

(i) What is the average length at $2\frac{1}{2}$ years?

(ii) About how old is a 15 cm herring?

(b) Draw a second graph to show this information about herrings.

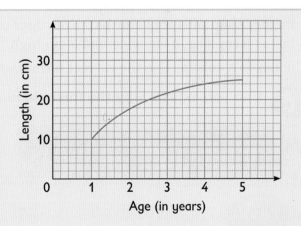

Age (in years)	1	2	3	4	5
Weight (in grams)	25	85	142	187	215

Use 2 cm to represent 1 year, and 1 cm to represent 20 grams.

(i) What is the average weight at $2\frac{1}{2}$ years?

(ii) About how long will it take for a 2 year old herring to double its weight?

(c) I buy a herring which weighs 200 grams and is 24 cm long. Is this fish plumper than average?

Perimeter

There is a guard rail right round the edge of this roof.

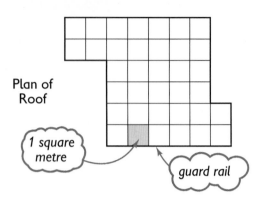

Plan of Roof

? **What is the total length of the guard rail?**

The distance round the outside of a shape is called the **perimeter**.
The perimeter of the roof is 28 metres.

1 square metre

guard rail

Area

The roof is covered with square slabs 1 metre wide and 1 metre long.
There are 36 slabs on the roof.
The **area** of the roof is 36 square metres.

| Area is an amount of flat space. |

 What is the formula for the area of a rectangle? How does it work?

Volume

Here is a sugar cube.
It is 1 cm long, 1 cm wide and 1 cm high.
Its **volume** is 1 cubic centimetre.

1 cm
1 cm
1 cm

| Volume is an amount of solid space. |

3 cm
4 cm
5 cm

A factory shop sells souvenir boxes of sugar cubes.
A box is 5 cm long, 4 cm wide and 3 cm high.

The box is a cuboid. Use the correct formula to calculate its volume.

 Can you explain why the formula for the volume of a cuboid works?

| Area of a rectangle = length × width. | Volume of a cuboid = length × width × height. |
| Area is measured in square units e.g. m². | Volume is measured in cubic units e.g. cm³. |

Task

Another cuboid souvenir box which holds 60 sugar cubes is 6 cm long, 5 cm wide and 2 cm high.

$$6 \, cm \times 5 \, cm \times 2 \, cm = 60 \, cm^3$$

1 Find other cuboids which could hold 60 sugar cubes. Write down the calculation of their volumes like the one above.
How many *different* cuboids are there which hold 60 sugar cubes?

2 Decide which would be the best and which would be the least practical souvenir box design. Write down your reasons.
Make a drawing of the best and the least practical designs.

Exercise

1 Find the perimeter and area of each of these shapes.
Each square represents 1 square cm.

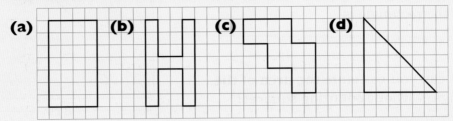

(a)   **(b)**   **(c)**   **(d)**

2 Calculate the perimeters and areas of these rectangles.
  (a) length = 7 m, width = 11 m   **(b)** length = 8 cm, width = 3.5 cm
  (c) length = 70 yards, width = 30 yards   **(d)** length = 6 inches,
                                                  width = $4\frac{1}{2}$ inches

3 Calculate the volumes of cuboids with these dimensions.
  (a) length 10 cm, width 3 cm, height 2 cm
  (b) length 4 inches, width 5 inches, height $2\frac{1}{2}$ inches
  (c) length 1 m, width 1 m, height 12 m
  (d) length 12 cm, width $2\frac{1}{2}$ cm, height 4 cm

4 Find the volume of this shape.
Each cube is a cubic cm.

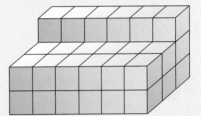

5 **(a)** Calculate the perimeter and area of
      (i) the end of the piano   **(ii)** the roof of the building.
  (b) Calculate the volumes of these objects.

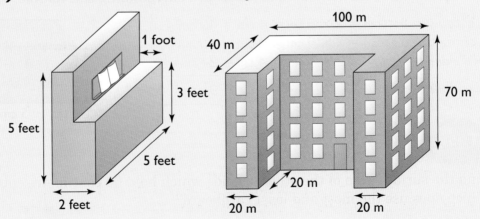

Investigation   Square slabs measuring 1 m by 1 m are arranged to form a
rectangle with perimeter 16 m.
What areas are possible?
Which rectangle with perimeter 16 m has the greatest area?

More areas

Here is a rectangle with a triangle drawn inside it.

The area of the rectangle is

$8\ cm \times 5\ cm = 40\ cm^2.$

How can you *calculate* the area of the triangle without counting squares?

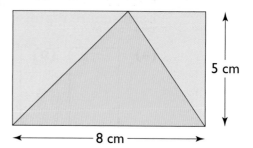

Task

Draw a rough copy of this shape. Write on it the measurements as shown. Calculate the area of the shape. Show on your diagram how you do this.

Compare your working with other people in your class.
Has everyone done it the same way?

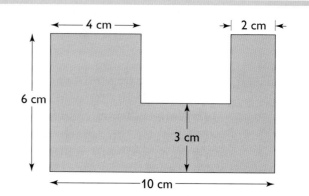

How many different ways are there of calculating the area of this shape?

Here is a cuboid souvenir box with the lid closed.
Its **surface area** is the total area of cardboard surrounding the volume.

Area of top plus bottom = $2 \times 5\ cm \times 4\ cm = 40\ cm^2$
Area of front plus back = $2 \times 5\ cm \times 3\ cm = 30\ cm^2$
Area of sides = $2 \times 3\ cm \times 4\ cm = 24\ cm^2$ +
_____
Total surface area $94\ cm^2$
_____

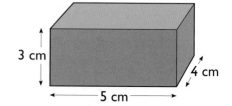

Task

Find the surface area of the other cuboids which hold 60 centimetre cubes.
Which ones use the most and least cardboard?

Can you think of a *formula* for the surface area of a cuboid?

Area of a triangle $= \frac{1}{2} \times$ base $\times$ height.

Some shapes can be split into rectangles to find their area.

Exercise

1 Calculate the areas of these triangles.

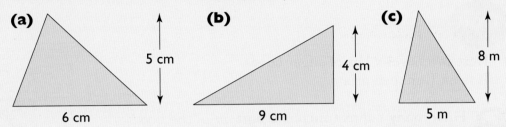

(a) 5 cm, 6 cm

(b) 4 cm, 9 cm

(c) 8 m, 5 m

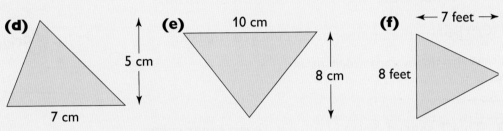

(d) 5 cm, 7 cm

(e) 10 cm, 8 cm

(f) 7 feet, 8 feet

2 Calculate the area of these shapes.

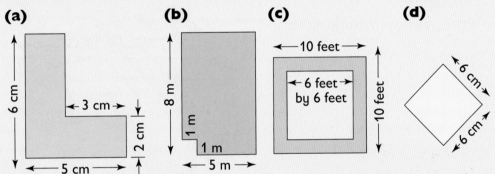

(a) 6 cm, 3 cm, 5 cm, 2 cm

(b) 8 m, 1 m, 1 m, 5 m

(c) 10 feet, 6 feet by 6 feet, 10 feet

(d) 6 cm, 6 cm

3 Liban is painting the end of his house.
Each tin of paint covers 25 m².
How much paint will he need to buy to
cover the wall?

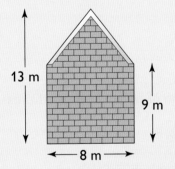

13 m, 9 m, 8 m

4 Estimate the area of this pond.
The squares are square metres.

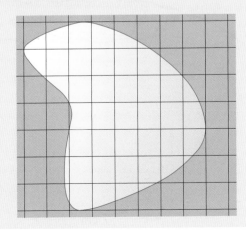

5 Estimate the area of the bottom
of this watch battery.
The squares
are square
millimetres.

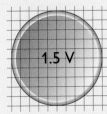

1.5 V

Volumes of prisms

Task

1 Here is a novelty box of sugar cubes.
It is an L shaped prism.

? **How many cubes touch the *bottom* of the box?**
What is the area of the bottom of the box?

Calculate the number of cm cubes in the box.

Write down your working out.

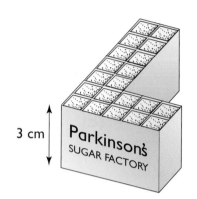

3 cm

2 This T shaped prism is filled with cm sugar cubes.
Calculate its volume.

Write down your working out.

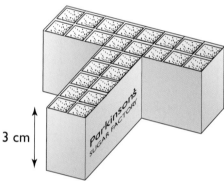

3 cm

Volume of prism = area of cross section × length

Example

Find the volume of this triangular prism.

Area of triangle = ½ × base × height

Area of cross section $= \frac{1}{2} \times 7 \text{ cm} \times 4 \text{ cm}$

$= \frac{1}{2} \times 28 \text{ cm}^2$
$= 14 \text{ cm}^2$

Volume of prism $= 14 \text{ cm}^2 \times 10 \text{ cm}$
$= 140 \text{ cm}^3$

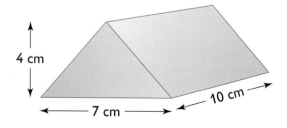

4 cm

7 cm

10 cm

Exercise

1 Calculate the volume of these prisms.

(a)

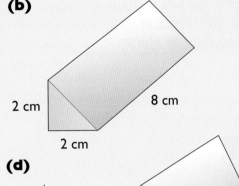

2 cm

8 cm

2 cm

2 cm

(b)

2 cm

8 cm

2 cm

2 cm

(c)

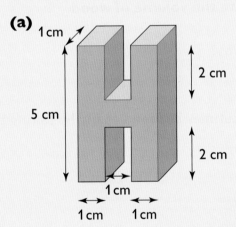

3 m

4 m

6 m

(d)

3 inches

4 inche

5 inches

2 Calculate the volume of these wooden letters.

(a)

1 cm

2 cm

5 cm

2 cm

1 cm

1 cm   1 cm

(b)

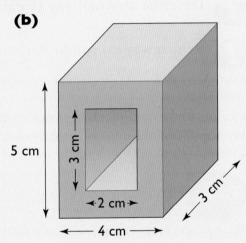

5 cm

3 cm

2 cm

3 cm

4 cm

3 What is the volume of this house?

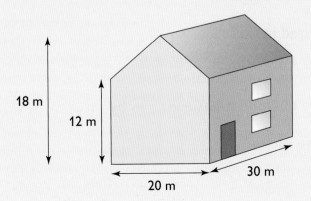

18 m

12 m

20 m

30 m

4 The area of the end of this tin is 150 cm². What is its volume?

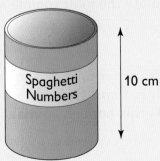

Spaghetti Numbers

10 cm

More volumes

This open-top box is made from five rectangular pieces of wood 1 cm thick, glued together as shown.

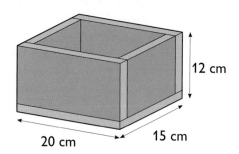

12 cm

20 cm   15 cm

Task

1 Write down the measurements of the pieces of wood.
    Calculate their volumes.

? **What is the total volume of wood used to make the box?**

2 Write down the measurements of the inside of the box.
    Calculate the capacity (inside volume) of the box.

? **Describe another way to calculate the volume of wood.**

? **Which way do you prefer, and why?**

The volume of a complicated shape can sometimes be found easily by taking the *difference* of the volumes of simple shapes.

Task

The box above is the largest of a nest of four open-top boxes, all made of wood 1 cm thick.
Each one fits snugly inside the next larger box, with all their open tops at the same level. Draw a plan of all the boxes fitting together.
How deep is the space in the middle?
Calculate the total volume of wood used in these four boxes.

? **A carpenter has a square piece of wood measuring $\frac{1}{2}$ m by $\frac{1}{2}$ m.
It is 1 cm thick.
Is this enough to make all these boxes?**

Exercise

1 Look at this Official British Red Cross
collection box.
Each red cross face, including the base,
is made of five red squares of side
length 3 cm.

  (a) Find the volume of the collection box.
  (b) Find the surface area of the box.
  (c) What fraction of the surface area
      is coloured red?

2 Mickey and Minnie have each cut a small
wedge from this wedge of cheese.
What volume of cheese is left?

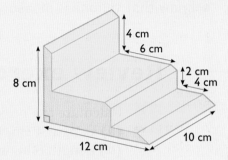

3 A cube has sides of length 8 cm.
Three square holes of side length 4 cm are
cut right through the cube, through the
centre of each face as shown.

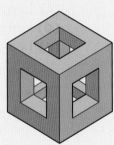

Imagine cutting the shape into three parts by
horizontal slices 2 cm and 6 cm up.
Sketch these three parts separately.
What is the volume of the solid and what
volume has been removed?

Investigation 1 Draw a net of the collection box above, showing red and
white squares.

Investigation 2 A 3 × 3 × 3 cube is made up of 27 small
cubes whose outside faces are coloured,
like this Rubik cube.

  (a) How many cubes have 3 coloured faces?
  (b) How many cubes have 2 coloured faces?
  (c) How many cubes have 1 coloured face?
  (d) How many cubes have 0 coloured face?
  (e) Find the sum of your answers
      for **(a)**–**(d)**. How does this check your
      accuracy?
  (f) Repeat these calculations for a 4 × 4 × 4 cube and a
      5 × 5 × 5 cube. Can you see any patterns in your results?

Finishing off

Now that you have finished this chapter you should:

- be able to calculate the perimeter of a flat shape
- be able to find the area of a flat shape
- be able to use the formulae to calculate the area of a rectangle and a triangle
- be able to use the formulae to calculate the volume of a cuboid and other prisms
- be able to use a formula to find the surface area of a cuboid
- know that area is measured in square units e.g. cm^2
- know that volume is measured in cubic units e.g. cm^3.

Review exercise

1 Calculate the perimeter and area of these rectangles.
(a) Length 4 cm, width 6 cm
(b) Length 8 m, width 3 m
(c) Length 6 inches, width $2\frac{1}{2}$ inches
(d) Length 4 yards, width $5\frac{1}{2}$ yards
(e) Length 1 mile, width 1 mile.

2 Estimate the area of this island. The squares are square miles.

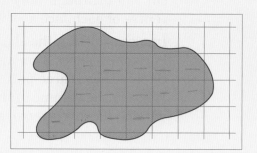

3 Calculate the volume of these solid shapes.
(a)   **(b)**

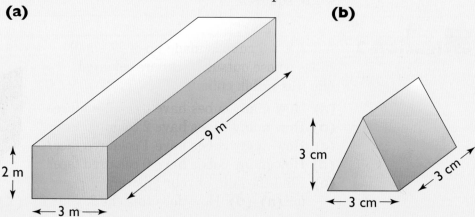

4 An ornamental concrete slab, used for building a garden wall, is a square prism 30 cm by 30 cm by 10 cm. It has four triangular holes and one square hole cut through symmetrically as shown. Find the volume of concrete in the slab.

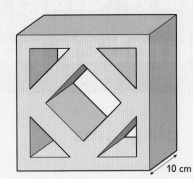

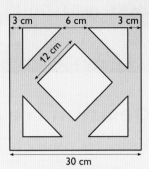

Investigation I

The volume of liquid or gas that a container will hold is often called its **capacity**.

The metric unit of capacity is the **litre**. 1 litre is equal to 1000 millilitres. Obtain a 1 litre carton in the shape of a cuboid. Measure its dimensions and calculate its volume in cubic centimetres. Litres and cubic centimetres are both metric units of volume. What is the relationship between them?

? The sizes of car engines are often given in litres or cubic centimetres (cc). Typical examples are 2.0 litres and 1800 cc. What are these values referring to?

Investigation 2

A fuel tank is to be made out of sheet aluminium in the shape of a closed cuboid.
Its capacity has to be 216 litres.
Design a suitable tank, giving its dimensions.
Sheet aluminium costs £24.50 per square metre.
What is the cheapest design you can come up with?

Activity

Find the volumes of the following objects:
- a cassette case
- a compact disc case
- a house brick
- this book
- one page of this book.

Use cm^3, m^3, mm^3 or whatever units you think are most suitable.

JMO Question

The diagram shows a large rectangle whose perimeter is 300 cm. It is divided up as shown into a number of identical rectangles, each of perimeter 58 cm. Each side of these rectangles is a whole number of centimetres. Show that there are exactly two possibilities for the number of smaller rectangles and find the size of the large rectangle in each case.

Decision tree diagrams

Michael is visiting his local aquarium.

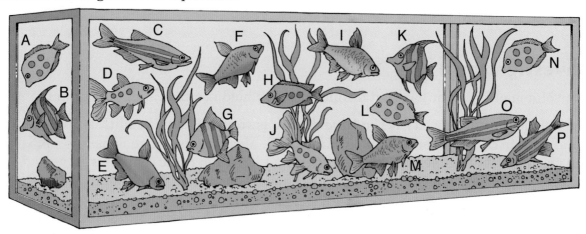

? How many different types of fish are there in the tank?
How many ways can you sort these fish?

Michael uses this **decision tree diagram** to sort the fish.

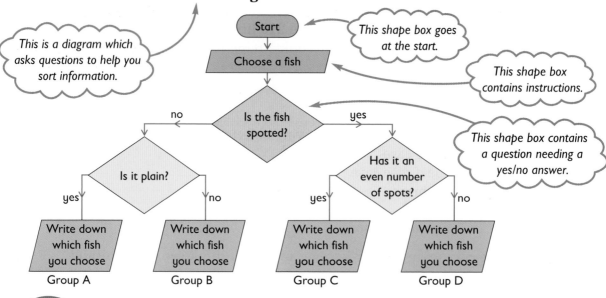

This is a diagram which asks questions to help you sort information.

Start

This shape box goes at the start.

Choose a fish

This shape box contains instructions.

Is the fish spotted?

no   yes

This shape box contains a question needing a yes/no answer.

Is it plain?

Has it an even number of spots?

yes   no   yes   no

Write down which fish you choose — Group A

Write down which fish you choose — Group B

Write down which fish you choose — Group C

Write down which fish you choose — Group D

Task

Use the decision tree diagram to find out which fish go into which group.

? How has Michael sorted the fish?

Exercise

① Look at the fish tank on the opposite page. This time use this decision tree diagram to sort the fish in a different way.

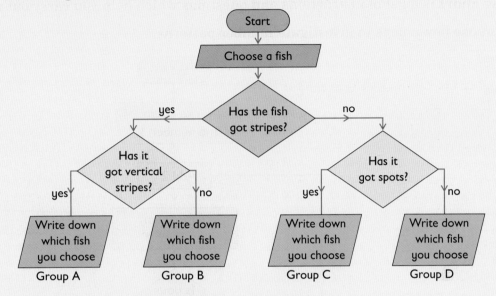

What groups have you sorted the fish into?

② Design a decision tree diagram to sort the fish into:
- blue with stripes
- blue without stripes
- red with stripes
- red without stripes

③ Design a decision tree diagram to sort a set of triangles with known angles into:
- right angled (not isosceles)
- right angled and isosceles
- isosceles (not right angled or equilateral)
- equilateral
- other

Test your diagram using these triangles:

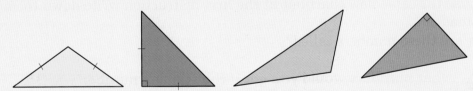

Investigation

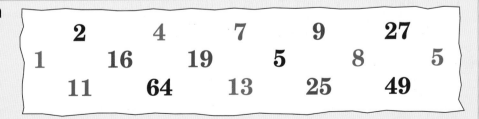

How many different ways can you sort these numbers?
Design two different decision tree diagrams to sort the numbers.

Flow charts and number patterns

A **flow chart** is a list of instructions and questions which help you carry out a task.

We can use flow charts to investigate number patterns.

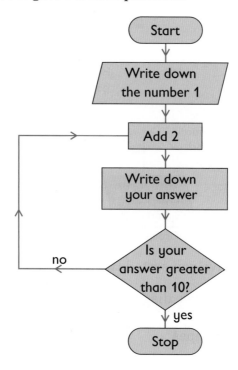

Task

Use the flow chart above to make a 'number chain'.
What are these numbers called?

Now use the same flow chart but at the first instruction write down the number 2 instead of 1.
What are these numbers called?

? **What numbers would you get if the starting number was 3?**

Draw your own flow chart to generate the first 20 odd numbers.

Draw another flow chart to produce the first 5 multiples of 5.

? **How do you know when to stop?**

Task

Design a flow chart to generate the first 10 triangular numbers.

Exercise

1 Design a flow chart to produce the answers to the seven times table.

2 Use the flow chart below to investigate a number pattern.

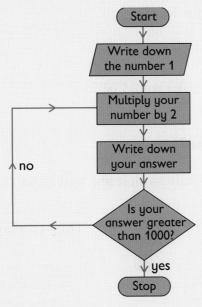

How many numbers do you think you will have to write down before you get to a number greater than 1000?

Use the flow chart to check your answer.

Investigation Work through this flow chart for several different choices of the starting number N.

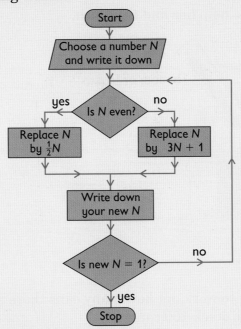

Compare your results with a friend's.

Comment on the lengths of the lists of numbers you get.

(At present no one knows whether *every* N leads to 1 eventually.)

Working systematically with patterns

Tanya is stacking cans at her local supermarket.
She has made a stack which is four layers high.

 How many cans are there in this stack?

Tanya wants to know how many cans would be in a
stack which is 12 layers high.

 How can she work this out?

Tanya decides to work systematically so that she will know that she has found the
right answer.

She starts by looking at one layer:

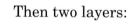

There is 1 can.

Then two layers:

There are 3 cans.

Task

Draw the next three layers in Tanya's stack of cans.
How many cans are there in each?

Tanya makes a table to help her find a pattern.

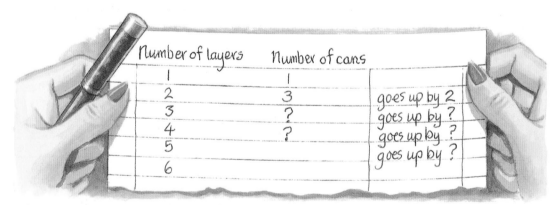

Number of layers	Number of cans	
1	1	
2	3	goes up by 2
3	?	goes up by ?
4	?	goes up by ?
5		goes up by ?
6		

Task

Use Tanya's pattern to work out how many cans there are in 10 layers.
Now work out how to stack 100 cans.

 What are the advantages of working systematically?

Investigation Andy washes up on a Saturday morning in the local cafe.

He stacks the cups and saucers like this:

Andy can put as many saucers on top of each other as he likes.

However he can't put a cup on top of a cup else the pile will fall over.

Andy wants to work out how many different ways he can stack 10 items.

He starts by drawing three different ways:

Andy isn't working systematically.

(a) How will he know that he has found all the different ways possible?

(b) What should Andy do to help him find a pattern?

Andy starts again, this time working systematically.
He looks at stacking 1 item then 2 items and so on.

There are two ways of stacking one item.

This is a quicker way to draw the cups and saucers

There are three ways of stacking two items.

(c) Draw all the ways of stacking 3, 4 and 5 items making sure that you are working logically.

(d) How many ways are there of stacking 6 items?

(e) Predict how many ways there are of stacking 10 items.

(f) Why was it easier to work systematically to solve this problem?

(g) This number pattern has a special name.
Find out what it is called.

Growth patterns

Karen is making growth patterns using match sticks.

Here are the first three stages of the growth pattern:

Karen adds two more matches to make the second stage.

Task

1 What will the next stage in Karen's pattern look like?
Draw the next four stages.

2 How many matches are added to make *each new stage*?

Karen counts how many matches she needs for the first three stages.

? **How many matches are used for the next two stages?**

Karen makes a table for her growth pattern.

> You can write this as
> $1 \rightarrow 3$, $2 \rightarrow 5$
> This is called
> *a* **mapping**.

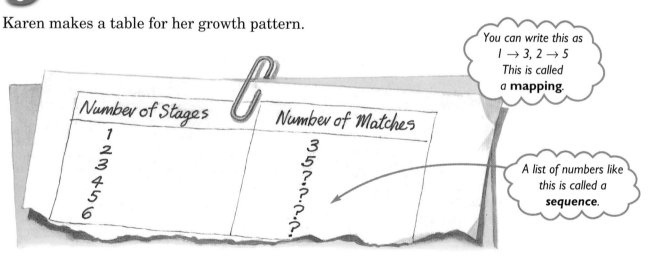

Number of Stages	Number of Matches
1	3
2	5
3	?
4	?
5	?
6	?

> A list of numbers like
> this is called a
> **sequence**.

Task

Complete Karen's table. What patterns do you notice?
How many matches will be used in **(a)** the next stage?
         (b) the 10th stage?

? **How can you check that you are right?**

Exercise

For each question
(a) draw the next three growth patterns
(b) copy and complete the table
(c) predict how many match sticks or squares are needed for the next two stages.

1

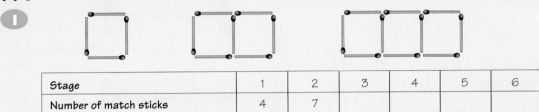

Stage	1	2	3	4	5	6
Number of match sticks	4	7				

2

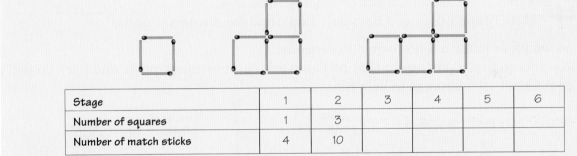

Stage	1	2	3	4	5	6
Number of squares	1	3				
Number of match sticks	4	10				

3

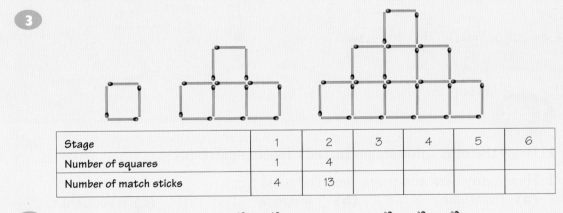

Stage	1	2	3	4	5	6
Number of squares	1	4				
Number of match sticks	4	13				

4

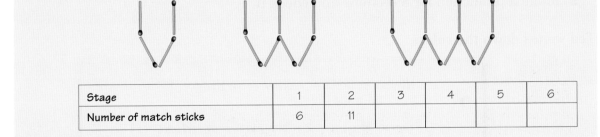

Stage	1	2	3	4	5	6
Number of match sticks	6	11				

Investigation Invent your own growth patterns using match sticks or squares. Show the number of match sticks or squares at each stage in a table.

Number patterns – making predictions

Ted is building a fence.
To make one section Ted needs

>2 upright posts
>and 2 horizontal bars.

Ted now adds another section of fencing.
He now uses

>3 upright posts
>and 4 horizontal bars.

 What will three sections of fencing look like?
How many posts and bars will Ted need for three sections?

Ted wants to make a fence using 20 sections.
He wants to find a pattern so that he can work out how many posts and bars he will need.
Ted makes two mappings to help him.

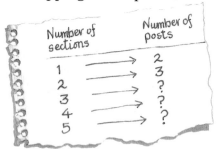
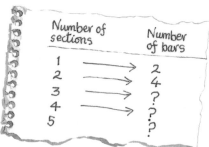

Task

1 Draw the next three stages in Ted's fencing pattern.

2 How many bars and posts does Ted need for:
   (a) 4 sections   **(b)** 5 sections   **(c)** 6 sections?
   What patterns do you notice?

3 Make a prediction for 8 sections and check it.

Ted writes down the rules:

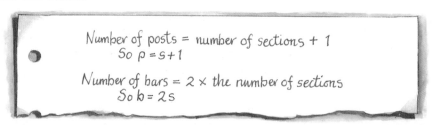

Number of posts = number of sections + 1
        So $p = s + 1$

Number of bars = 2 × the number of sections
        So $b = 2s$

 What do p, s and b stand for?
How many bars and posts are needed for (a) 20 sections (b) 100 sections?

Exercise

1 Mark wants to build a fence around his garden.
This is one section.

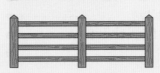

He adds on another section.

(a) Draw what up to five sections would look like.
(b) How many bars and posts need to be added for each section?
(c) Make two mappings like Ted did on the opposite page to show how many posts and bars Mark will need for up to five sections.
(d) Predict how many posts and cross bars Mark will need for
   (i) 10   **(ii)** 20   **(iii)** 50   sections.
(e) Explain how you worked out your answers to part **(d)**.
(f) Write down the rule you are using.

2 Penny is making patterns using hoops.

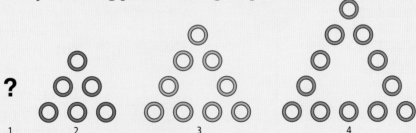

(a) Draw the first pattern.
(b) Draw patterns five and six.
(c) Complete Penny's table for the first 6 patterns.

Pattern	Number of hoops
1	?
2	6
3	?

(d) How many hoops are needed for the
   (i) 7th   **(ii)** 10th   **(iii)** 20th   pattern?
(e) Explain how you worked out your answers to part **(d)**.
(f) Write down the rule you are using.

3 Look at Questions 1, 2 and 3 on page 205. Write down the rules for
(a) the number of squares   **(b)** the number of match sticks.

Finishing off

Now that you have finished this chapter you should be able to:

- continue with a pattern
- work systematically
- use and design a flow chart
- spot patterns

- use and design decision tree diagrams
- draw a table to organise your results
- make predictions and check them
- write down a rule.

Review exercise

1

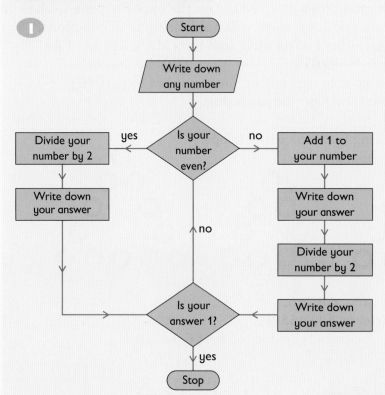

(a) Write down the number chains for 5 different starting numbers.

(b) Why does the flow diagram stop at 1?

(c) Do large numbers have the longest chains?

(d) Which numbers have the shortest chains?

Investigate the number of chains for different starting numbers.

2 Sarah is building a fence.
These are the first two sections:

(a) Draw the next three stages.
(b) Copy and complete the tables.

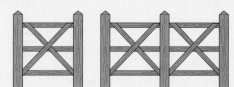

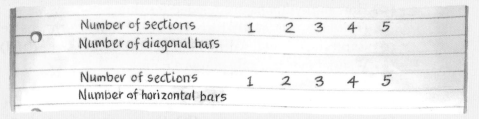

Number of sections	1	2	3	4	5
Number of diagonal bars					

Number of sections	1	2	3	4	5
Number of horizontal bars					

(c) How many diagonal bars and horizontal bars are needed for ten sections?
Write down the rules you used to make your predictions.

3 Joe is building four footpaths at a cross-roads in the local park and filling the corner areas by laying turf.

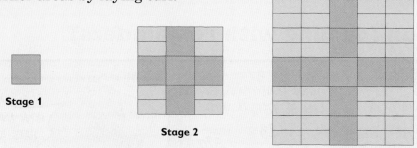

Stage 1

Stage 2

Stage 3

(a) Draw the next three stages. **(b)** Copy and complete the table.

Number of stages	1	2	3	4	5	6	7
Number of paving stones	1	5					
Number of turfs	0	8					

(c) Predict how many paving stones and turfs Joe will need for the 10th stage.

(d) What patterns do you notice? Write down the rules in words, and using the letters s, p and t.

Investigation

If everyone in the class shook hands with everyone else how many handshakes would there be? Start by imagining that there are only two people in the class, then three, and so on.

Nick says this question has something to do with the sides and diagonals of a polygon. Explain what he means.

JMO Question

In a sequence, each term after the first is the sum of the squares of the digits of the previous term. Thus, if the first term were 12, the second term would be $1^2 + 2^2 = 5$, the third term $5^2 = 25$, the fourth term $2^2 + 5^2 = 29$ and so on.

(a) Find the first five terms of the sequence whose first term is 25.

(b) Find the 2001st term of the sequence whose first term is 25.

Division (dealing with remainders)

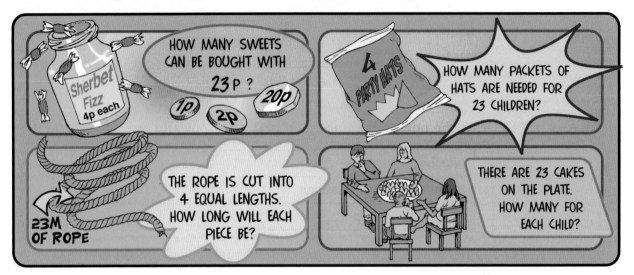

Look at the above.
When 23 is divided by 4 there is a remainder.

Sometimes a sensible answer is found by rounding down, sometimes by rounding up.

Now look carefully at the rope puzzle.
When a remainder can be cut up, the sensible answer is a decimal or fraction.

? **Which of these numbers is the most appropriate answer to each of the puzzles above?**

| 5 | 6 | $5\frac{3}{4}$ | 5.75 |

Task

Make up four questions where the answer is obtained by dividing 37 by 5.

One question should be written so that to get a sensible answer, you round up.

For the second question you will round down, and for the other two questions the sensible answer should be a fraction and a decimal.

When the sensible answer is not a whole number we need to turn the remainder into a decimal or a fraction.

Example 1 The remainder as a fraction

$$23 \div 4 = 5\frac{3}{4}$$

The divisor

When 23 is divided by 4 the remainder is 3

Take the remainder into the next column.

Example 2 The remainder as a decimal

$$
\begin{array}{r}
5.\,7\,5 \\
4\overline{)\,23.^{3}0^{2}0}
\end{array}
$$

Keep dividing after the decimal point.

Add as many noughts as you need.

Exercise

1 Give a sensible answer to the following questions.

(a)

I need 15 eggs. How many boxes should I buy?

(b)

How many 5lb bags of potatoes can be filled?

(c)

The Cola is to be shared between 4 glasses. How much Cola in each glass?

2 A school has 1332 pupils and 92 members of staff. How many buses would be needed to take the whole school on an outing?
(A bus can carry 45 people.)

3 Neeta needs 478 tiles to tile her bathroom.
How many boxes should Neeta buy?
How many spare tiles will there be?

ECONOMY BATHROOM TILES
12 Tiles per pack

4 For each of the following division sums give the answer with the remainder expressed

  (i) as a decimal   (ii) as a fraction.

  (a) 57 ÷ 8   (b) 679 ÷ 25   (c) 532 ÷ 10   (d) 235 ÷ 16

5 For each of the following

  (i) work out the remainder for each of the divisions
  (ii) write the remainder as a fraction.

  (a) 35 ÷ 4   (b) 17 ÷ 5   (c) 102 ÷ 20   (d) 47 ÷ 9   (e) 112 ÷ 7

  (f) 78 ÷ 15   (g) 265 ÷ 27   (h) 352 ÷ 19

6 Give a suitable answer to the following
  (a) £3 ÷ 6   (b) £2.50 ÷ 3   (c) £4.99 ÷ 5   (d) £6.99 ÷ 12

Activity It would be easier to use a calculator for parts (f), (g) and (h) of Question 5.

How can you use a calculator to find the remainder from a division sum?
Write a set of instructions for a friend.

Rounding (giving numbers to a sensible degree of accuracy)

Record Numbers Head for the Coast as Temperatures Soar

The AA reported that 4312 people per hour were heading into the coastal resort of Scarborough

Welcome to Harrisville

Population 253892

? **Why are you unlikely to see information like this displayed so accurately?**

4312 lies between 4300 and 4400.

Which number is 4312 nearest to?
4312 = 4300 (correct to the nearest 100)

253 892 lies between 253 000 and 254 000

Which number is 253 892 nearest to?
253 892 = 254 000 (correct to the nearest 1000)

? **Why has the larger number been chosen in the second example?**

Task

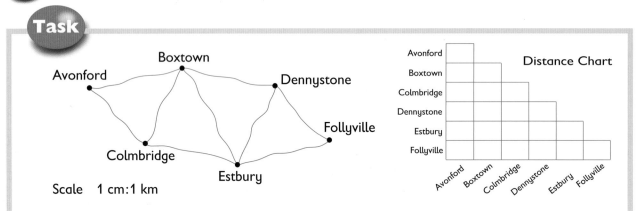

Scale   1 cm:1 km

1 Measure the distances between the towns on the map as accurately as possible.
   How accurate are your measurements?
2 Copy and complete the measurements on the distance chart.
   How accurate are the measurements between towns Avonford and Dennystone and
   Boxtown and Follyville?

The number 23 000 is accurate to the nearest 1000.

23 000 to the nearest 1000 includes
the numbers *from 22 500 to 23 500*.
This is known as the **range**.

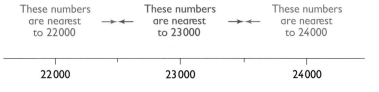

These numbers are nearest to 22000	These numbers are nearest to 23000	These numbers are nearest to 24000
22000	23000	24000

Exercise

1 Give a sensible approximation to the numbers in each of the following statements.
   (a) The number of bacteria in 1 litre of water is 43 659.
   (b) There are 262 pencils in this box.
   (c) I walk 789 metres to school.
   (d) This box of apples weighs 9635 grams.

In each case, state the degree of accuracy you are using.

2 The population of Appleby village is given to the nearest 100.
What is the largest number that this could be?
What is the smallest?

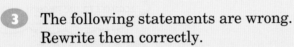

APPLEBY
Population 2300

3 The following statements are wrong.
Rewrite them correctly.
   (a) 8346 = 835 (correct to the nearest 10).
   (b) 7895 = 7900 (correct to the nearest 1000).
   (c) 354 = 350.

LEMON BONBONS
Contents 370

4 What is the highest and lowest possible number of sweets in the jar?

5 Give the range of possible numbers in each of the following.
   (a) 6750 (to the nearest 10)
   (b) 3670 (to the nearest 10)
   (c) 800 (to the nearest 100)
   (d) 2000 (to the nearest 100)
   (e) 2000 (to the nearest 1000).

Activity 1 Look through an atlas or encyclopaedia until you find some numbers that have been rounded.
Record these numbers in a table like this.

Number	Information given	Degree of accuracy
2 175 000 km²	area of Greenland	to the nearest 1000 km²

Activity 2 Collect some packets or boxes that display the number of average contents on the side (e.g. the number of matches in a box).

How accurate are the numbers you have found?
Explain your answers.

To the nearest whole number or whole unit

1

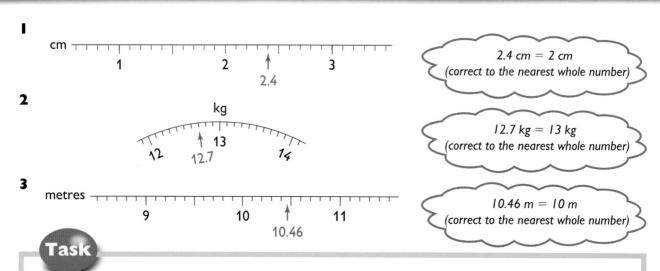

2.4 cm = 2 cm
(correct to the nearest whole number)

2

12.7 kg = 13 kg
(correct to the nearest whole number)

3

10.46 m = 10 m
(correct to the nearest whole number)

Task

1 Make a copy of this number line

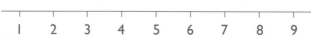

Use arrows to place 8.2, 5.6, 3.41 and 1.72 on the line.
Write each number to the nearest whole number.

2 Draw number lines to help you write these to the nearest whole number:

35.2   11.7   21.34   12.73

3 Write down a rule to explain when to round up to the next whole number and when to round down.
Give your rule to a friend and ask them to use it to write the following numbers to the nearest whole number.

8.75   12.12   29.8   312.49

 A length given as 5 m has been measured to the nearest metre.
What is the lowest possible value for the true measurement? What is the highest?

To the nearest penny

When a division sum involves an amount of money, the answer is not always an exact number of pennies.

The answer must then be rounded to the nearest penny.

34p ÷ 5   = 6.8p   This equals 7p to the nearest penny.

£12.50 ÷ 8   = £1.5625   This equals £1.56 to the nearest penny.

 **Give your answers to the following correct to the nearest penny.**
(a) 69p ÷ 7   (b) £2.95 ÷ 6

Exercise

1 Write the following numbers to the nearest whole number.
    (a) 67.2   **(b)** 345.9   **(c)** 2.95   **(d)** 9.36   **(e)** 9.78
    (f) 12.47   **(g)** 127.37   **(h)** 1.568   **(i)** 10.365   **(j)** 654.931

2 Give the answers to the following to the nearest penny.
    (a) 37p ÷ 4   **(b)** £1.32 ÷ 5   **(c)** 89p ÷ 7   **(d)** £4.80 ÷ 9
    (e) £12.60 ÷ 3   **(f)** £38 ÷ 6   **(g)** £115 ÷ 7   **(h)** £2.75 ÷ 15

3 Round the following to the required accuracy
    (a) 35.4 cm (nearest cm)   **(b)** 15.47 kg (nearest kg)
    (c) 6.98 litres (nearest litre)

4 The following measurements have been taken to the accuracy stated.
In each case give the highest and lowest possible value for
that measurement.
    (a) 12 m (to the nearest m)   **(b)** 78 cm (to the nearest cm)
    (c) 23 kg (to the nearest kg)   **(d)** 4.56 m (to the nearest cm)
    (e) 560 g (to the nearest 10 g)

5 How many minutes is this for
each question? Give your answer to the
nearest minute.
How long will it take to answer all
7 questions?

> ### MATHS EXAM
>
> **Time allowed: 40 minutes**
>
> **This paper contains 7 questions**

6 £20 is to be shared equally between 9 children.
    (a) How much will each child receive?
    (b) How much of the £20 will be left?

7 **(a)** The sides of a rectangle are given as 4 m and 7 m when each is
    measured to the nearest metre. Find the lowest and highest possible
    true measurement for each side.
    (b) Use these to find the lowest and highest possible values of
        (i) the perimeter   **(ii)** the area.

Investigation Numbers can also be rounded to a number of decimal places.
Example 1 56.734 = 56.7 to one decimal place

One number after the decimal point.

No need to round up as this is nearer to 56.7 than 56.8.

Example 2 8.4583 = 8.46 to two decimal places

Two numbers after the decimal point.

This number is rounded up because it is nearer to 8.46 than 8.45.

Write the following numbers (a) correct to one decimal place and
(b) correct to two decimal places.

    2.3647   35.431   456.945   0.1763

Checking your answers

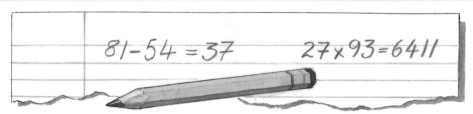

$81 - 54 = 37$ $27 \times 93 = 6411$

? **The calculations above are wrong.**
How can you tell?

Answers can be checked by:

1   Finding an approximate answer

> *Make these numbers as simple as possible so that you can do the calculation in your head.*

> *This means 'approximately equal to'.*

$$322 \times 8.9$$
$$\approx 300 \times 10 = 3000$$

> *Rounded to the nearest 100.*

> *Rounded to the nearest 10.*

? **Find an approximate answer to** $\dfrac{42 \times 112}{2.3}$

> *Adding 34 is the inverse (opposite) of subtracting 34.*

2   Using an inverse operation

$$72 - 34 = 38 \quad \textbf{because} \quad 38 + 34 = 72$$

? **What is the inverse of dividing by 6?**
Use this to check if 480 ÷ 6 = 70 is correct.

Task

Use an approximation or an inverse operation to find which of the following calculations contain a mistake.
For each of the other calculations say whether they are **(i)** definitely correct
or **(ii)** could be correct

1 $27 \times 82 = 2214$ **2** $85 - 47 = 22$ **3** $720 \div 12 = 60$

4 $\dfrac{87 \times 236}{15} = 13\ 688$ **5** $\sqrt{74} = 8.062$ **6** $\sqrt{112} = 13.6$

Look at numbers 5 and 6 in the task.

The inverse of 'find the square root of' is 'square'.

? **Between which two square numbers does 89 lie?**

Explain why it is possible to say that $9 < \sqrt{89} < 10$
Explain why $\sqrt{45} = 5.71$ must be wrong.

Exercise

1 State the inverse operation for each of the following:
    (a) add 7   **(b)** subtract 4   **(c)** divide by 9
    (d) multiply by 8   **(e)** square   **(f)** halve
    (g) treble   **(h)** add 2 and then multiply by 4

2 Work out the following and then use an inverse operation to check your answers.
    (a) $13 + 7$ **(b)** $67 - 45$ **(c)** $84 \div 7$
    (d) $\sqrt{64}$ **(e)** $8 \times 4 - 2$

3 For each of the calculations below there is a choice of possible answers. Use an approximation to help you select the correct answer.
    (a) $3.2 \times 8.9 =$ **(i)** 284.8   **(ii)** 28.48   **(iii)** 54.8

    (b) $72 \div 12.5 =$ **(i)** 9.45   **(ii)** 3.76   **(iii)** 5.76

    (c) $\dfrac{110 \times 94}{88} =$ **(i)** 117.5   **(ii)** 1175   **(iii)** 11.75

    (d) $\sqrt{(37 \times 26)} =$ **(i)** 3.1016   **(ii)** 310.16   **(iii)** 31.016

4 $6 < \sqrt{40} < 7$ because $36 < 40 < 49$
    Write similar statements to show the approximate size of the following square roots.
    (a) $\sqrt{22}$ **(b)** $\sqrt{5}$ **(c)** $\sqrt{104}$ **(d)** $\sqrt{390}$

5 Jane has asked her friend to check her homework.

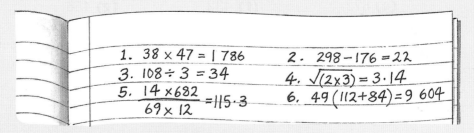

    1. $38 \times 47 = 1\,786$ 2. $298 - 176 = 22$
    3. $108 \div 3 = 34$ 4. $\sqrt{(2 \times 3)} = 3.14$
    5. $\dfrac{14 \times 682}{69 \times 12} = 115.3$ 6. $49(112 + 84) = 9\,604$

    Which of the calculations has Jane got wrong?
    In each case explain Jane's mistake.

Investigation   Only one of the following four numbers is the correct answer to 59×122.

An approximate answer is $60 \times 120 = 7200$.

Choose the correct answer and explain your choice.

    7205   7187   7198   7216

Finishing off

Now that you have finished this chapter you should be able to:

- give a sensible answer when a division sum gives a remainder
- round numbers to the nearest 1000, 100, 10
- give a range of values for a number given to a degree of accuracy
- round to the nearest whole number
- round to the nearest penny, centimetre, kilogram or any other unit of measure
- use an approximation or inverse operation to check your calculations
- place the square root of a number between two consecutive whole numbers.

Review exercise

1 Round the following numbers
   (i) to the nearest whole number   **(ii)** to the nearest 10.

   (a) 23.45   **(b)** 14.76   **(c)** 35.346   **(d)** 19.6
   (e) 135.4678   **(f)** 235   **(g)** 9.7   **(h)** 8.62

2 Give the following numbers
   (i) to the nearest 100   **(ii)** to the nearest 1000.

   (a) 2135   **(b)** 4697   **(c)** 8052   **(d)** 7049
   (e) 872   **(f)** 432   **(g)** 456   **(h)** 1456

3 The map shows the area, in square kilometres, of some countries in Europe. Give each one correct to the nearest thousand square km.

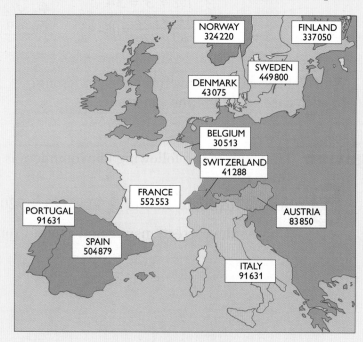

NORWAY 324220
FINLAND 337050
SWEDEN 449800
DENMARK 43075
BELGIUM 30513
SWITZERLAND 41288
FRANCE 552553
PORTUGAL 91631
AUSTRIA 83850
SPAIN 504879
ITALY 91631

4 By rounding the following numbers to a suitable degree of accuracy find an approximate answer to each of the following:
(a) 436×84 **(b)** $1095 \div 540$ **(c)** 8.36×12.7 **(d)** $42(87 + 94)$

5 Calculate to the nearest penny:
(a) £7.83 ÷ 5   **(b)** £25.63 ÷ 4   **(c)** £143 ÷ 6   **(d)** £2.56 ÷ 7.3

6 Round the following numbers
(i) to one decimal place   **(ii)** to two decimal places.
(a) 4.734   **(b)** 35.683   **(c)** 0.1579   **(d)** 0.076

7 4 m to the nearest m covers a range of possible measurements.
This can be shown on a number line.

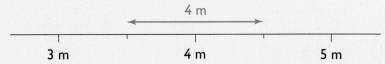

Use a number line to describe the range of the following quantities
(a) 7 m to the nearest m   **(b)** £7 to the nearest £
(c) 250 cm to the nearest cm   **(d)** 89 gm to the nearest gm
(e) 110 degrees to the nearest degree.

8 Find the remainder when
(a) 59 is divided by 7   **(b)** 247 is divided by 15
(c) 658 is divided by 39.

9 Between which two consecutive whole numbers do the following lie?
(a) $\sqrt{72}$ **(b)** $\sqrt{128}$ **(c)** $\sqrt{889}$

10 Rewrite the following sentences giving the numbers to a sensible degree of accuracy.
(a) There were 23 679 people at the match.
(b) The rope is 56.72 cm long.
(c) This week's lottery prize was worth £3 458 216.82.
(d) It takes 3 hr 17 min 45 secs to fly from London to Rome.
(e) The elephant weighs 972.5 kg.

11 The photograph shows part of a crowd of people attending a pop concert.
Estimate the number of people in the crowd in the photograph. Use the square grid to help you.

How accurate is your estimate?

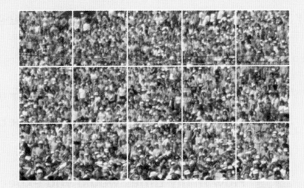

It is very likely to rain again tomorrow.

It is unlikely that England will win the next World Cup.

My piano teacher says that I will probably pass my exam.

People often use words like 'probable', 'likely' and 'unlikely'.
You can use a **probability scale** to show how likely different events are.

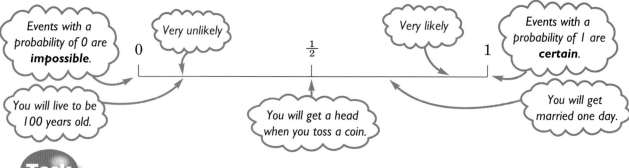

*Events with a probability of 0 are **impossible**.*

Very unlikely

Very likely

*Events with a probability of 1 are **certain**.*

0          $\frac{1}{2}$ 1

You will live to be 100 years old.

You will get a head when you toss a coin.

You will get married one day.

 Task

In pairs, make a list of about 8 more events like the examples above.
Draw a probability scale and put each event on the scale.

Make a probability scale using the examples from the whole class.

When you throw a die, there are six possible outcomes.
The die could show any of the numbers 1, 2, 3, 4, 5 or 6.
These six outcomes are all equally likely.

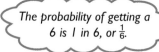
The probability of getting a 6 is 1 in 6, or $\frac{1}{6}$.

? **What is the probability of getting a 1 when throwing a die?**
Is it harder to get a six than any other number?
What is the probability of *not* getting a 1?

If an event has *n* equally likely outcomes, the probability of each outcome is $\frac{1}{n}$.

 Task

Throw a die 60 times. Record the number of times each number comes up.

? **How many times would you expect each number to come up?**

Collect the whole class's results together.

? **How many times would you expect each number to come up in the whole class? How close are your results?**

? **What is the probability of getting a 5 or a 6 with a single throw of a die?**

Exercise

1 Choose one of these words or phrases to describe each of the events below.

certain   very likely   likely   evens   unlikely   very unlikely   impossible

(a) It will snow on Christmas Day.
(b) You will eat chips sometime this week.
(c) The day after Tuesday will be Wednesday.
(d) It will rain tomorrow.
(e) The next baby born in the local hospital will be a girl.
(f) You will get a 7 when you throw an ordinary die.
(g) There will be news on the TV tonight.
(h) You will visit the moon someday.

2 Copy this probability scale and mark each of the events in Question 1 on the scale.

0                               $\frac{1}{2}$ 1

3 Amy picks a card at random from a normal pack of 52 cards.
What is the probability that Amy picks
(a) the Ace of Spades   **(b)** a card which is not the Ace of Spades
(c) a King   **(d)** a Heart
(e) a card which is not a Heart
(f) a picture card (a King, a Queen or a Jack)
(g) a red card
(h) a card with an even number on it?

4 Marie has a box of sweets. The sweets are different shapes and are wrapped in different coloured papers.
Marie chooses a sweet at random. What is the probability that she chooses
(a) a round sweet
(b) a sweet which is not round
(c) a square sweet
(d) a green sweet
(e) a sweet which is not green
(f) a red triangular sweet
(g) a green triangular sweet
(h) a round yellow sweet?

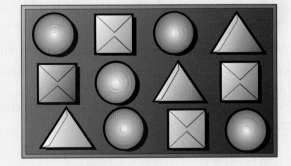

Investigation Toss a coin 20 times and record your results.
How many heads would you expect to get?

Repeat the experiment several times.
Were your results the same each time?

Fair games

Samir and Helen are playing a game with a 10 sided die.
Samir says

 Is the game fair?
Explain your answer.

You win for numbers less than 5,
I win for numbers 5 or more.

Helen wins if the number that
comes up is 1, 2, 3 or 4.

The probability that Helen wins is $\frac{4}{10}$.

Samir wins if the number that
comes up is 5, 6, 7, 8, 9 or 10.

The probability that Samir wins is $\frac{6}{10}$.

Samir is more likely to win the game, so the game is not fair.

 Do you think that Samir will win every time?
How many times do you think Samir will win if they play 10 times?

 Task

With a partner, play Samir and Helen's game 20 times.
(If you don't have a 10 sided die, you can use a set of playing cards.)

Think of a different rule that will make the game fair. Now play your game 20 times.

 Does a fair game mean that each player will always win the same number
of times?

Estimating probabilities

Helen thinks of a different game.
She says

Let's take it in turns to toss a
drawing pin. I win if it lands point up,
and you win if it lands point down.

Do you think *this* game is fair?
Who do you think is more likely to win?

When you toss a coin, it is equally likely to land on heads or tails.
When you toss a drawing pin, it is not equally likely to
land point up or point down.
So you cannot write down a probability that a drawing
pin will land point down.

You can only carry out an experiment
to estimate the probability.

 Task

Toss a drawing pin 50 times. Keep a tally of the results.
Is it more likely to land point up or point down?

 Compare your results with the rest of the class.
How could you use your results to estimate the probability that the
drawing pin lands point up?

Exercise

1 Jamie and Joe are playing a game with an ordinary six-sided die.
Jamie has thought of some different rules which they could use.

For each rule, write down whether the game is fair or unfair.
(a) Jamie wins if an even number comes up.
(b) Jamie wins if a number in the 3 times table comes up.
(c) Jamie wins if a number less than 4 comes up.
(d) Jamie wins if a prime number comes up.
(e) Jamie wins if a number 3 or more comes up.

2 Michelle says

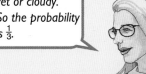

Tomorrow it could be sunny, wet or cloudy. That's three different possibilities. So the probability that it will be sunny is $\frac{1}{3}$.

Is Michelle right?
Explain your answer.

3 Emma and Mark have a bag of coloured balls.
These are the balls that they have.

They take turns to pick a ball out of the bag without looking.
Emma says

I win if I pick out a red or blue ball. You win if you pick out a green or a yellow ball.

(a) What is the probability that Emma wins?
(b) What is the probability that Mark wins?
(c) Is the game fair?
(d) Think of a different rule that would make the game fair.

4 A bag is filled with coloured tickets.
Janice shakes the bag, takes one out, records its colour and puts it back.
She does this several times. Here are her results.

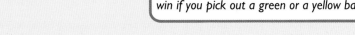

Red	Green	Blue
6	15	4

(a) Use Janice's data to **estimate** the probability of getting each colour.

Later the bag is emptied and the tickets are counted:

Red 50,   Green 150,   Blue 50.

(b) Use these figures to **calculate** the probability of getting each colour.

Combined events

In a game there are two dice, one red and the other blue.
You can show all the possibilities for their total scores on this table of outcomes.

Each square shows one possible outcome (one way the dice fall with the total score this produces).

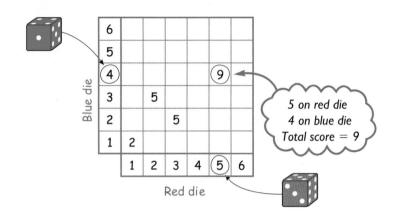

5 on red die
4 on blue die
Total score = 9

Blue die

Red die

Task

Copy and complete the table of outcomes.
Comment on any patterns you notice.

? **How many squares are there in the grid?**

? **How many squares contain the total 5?**

Complete this sentence: The probability of getting total score 5 is $\frac{?}{?}$

which simplifies to $\frac{1}{?}$

? **What are the most likely and least likely total scores? Give their probabilities.**

? **What is the probability of scoring a double when two dice are thrown? How can you see this from your table?**

Task

Throw two dice and record the sum of the scores. Do this sixty times.

? **List all the possible total scores.**

? **From your results, do you think all these scores are equally likely?**

? **Compare your results with someone else's. What do you find?**

Exercise

1 Copy and complete this table of probabilities, simplifying the probabilities where possible.

Total score with two dice	2	3	4	5	6	7	8	9	10	11	12
Probability	$\frac{1}{36}$			$\frac{1}{9}$		$\frac{1}{6}$					$\frac{1}{36}$

Find the probability that the total score is
(a) a multiple of 4   **(b)** greater than 9   **(c)** a prime number.

2 The number of squares a token moves along the board in a game is:

score on green spinner — score on yellow spinner.

(a) Draw a table to show all the possible outcomes.
(b) What are the most likely moves, and what are their probabilities?
(c) What is the probability that the token moves backwards?

3 Two ordinary dice are thrown and their scores are *multiplied* together.
(a) Draw a table of outcomes.
(b) Find the probability that the product of scores is
  (i)   12
  (ii) a perfect square
  (iii) more than half the greatest possible product.

4 A red die and a blue die are painted so that their faces show the following numbers:

  Red 1, 2, 2, 3, 3, 4   Blue 1, 3, 4, 5, 6, 8

Make a table of probabilities (like the one in Question 1) for the total score. What do you notice about this new table?

Investigation Discuss how you could represent the possible outcomes when three ordinary dice are thrown and their scores added together.

Finishing off

Review exercise

1. Choose one of these words or phrases to describe each of the events below.

   certain very likely likely evens unlikely very unlikely impossible

   (a) Someone you know will win the lottery jackpot this week.
   (b) You will watch television tonight.
   (c) You will get a tail when you toss a coin.
   (d) You will get a six when you throw a die.
   (e) The sun will rise tomorrow.
   (f) You will live to be 200 years old.
   (g) You will see a red car on your way home from school.

2. Copy this probability scale and mark each of the events in Question 1 on the scale.

   0                          $\frac{1}{2}$ 1

3. James is playing a game with an 8-sided die.
   The die has the numbers 1 to 8 on it.
   What is the probability that James scores
   (a) 5
   (b) an even number
   (c) 10
   (d) a number less than 4
   (e) a prime number
   (f) a number in the 3 times table?

4 50 tickets are sold for a raffle.
The main prize is a bicycle.

(a) Claire has bought 1 ticket. What is the probability that she wins the bicycle?

(b) John has bought 5 tickets. What is the probability that he wins the bicycle?

A ticket is drawn for the bicycle. Neither Claire nor John wins.
(c) How many tickets are left in the draw?

The second prize is a bottle of wine.
(d) What is the probability that Claire wins the bottle of wine?
(e) What is the probability that John wins the bottle of wine?

5 Natalie and Liam are playing a game with this spinner.

Which of these games is fair?

(a) Natalie wins if she gets red, otherwise Liam wins.
(b) Natalie wins if she gets a 1, otherwise Liam wins.
(c) Liam wins if he gets 2 or 3, otherwise Natalie wins.
(d) Natalie wins if she gets a 2, Liam wins if he gets a 3, otherwise it is a draw.

Think of another fair game they could play with the spinner.

6 In another game with the same spinner Natalie spins before Liam.
Liam wins if he gets the same colour as Natalie, or if he gets blue when she gets red. Use a table of possible outcomes to show that this is a fair game.

Investigation Copy this net onto centimetre squared paper or square dotty paper. Cut out the net and use it to make a die.

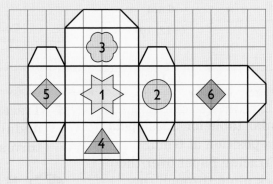

(a) Suppose you play a game with the die. You win if you score 1 or 6, and you lose if you score 2, 3, 4 or 5.
Do you think this is a fair game? Why?

(b) Play the game 50 times and keep a tally of your results. Is the game fair?

(c) Can you find a fairer way of playing the game?

This photograph of the night sky was taken by a camera with the shutter left open. Each line is the trail of a star as it moves round the sky during the hour.

? **What shape is the path of each star?**
Which stars move the most?

This kind of movement is called **rotation**.
Each trail you can see is part of a circle, called an **arc**.
All the circles have the same centre – the **centre of rotation**.

The bright star near the centre of the picture is the Pole Star. It has hardly moved at all because it is almost at the centre of rotation.

You can plot the movement of the stars on a co-ordinate grid.
Here we can see how the Plough rotates in six hours.
The centre of rotation is the origin.
Each shape rotates a **quarter of a turn** (90°) in an **anticlockwise** direction.

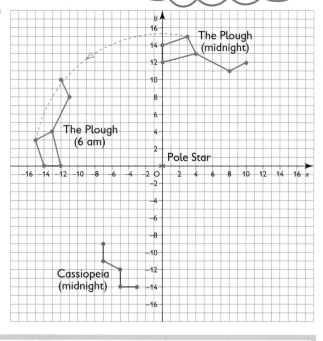

Task

1 Ask your teacher for a copy of the diagram above or copy it on to squared paper.
2 Copy and complete this table to show how the co-ordinates of the Plough have rotated.

The Plough		
midnight	→	**6 am**
(10, 12)		(−12, 10)
(8, 11)		
(6, 12)		
(4, 11)		
(3, 15)		(−15,3)
(0, 12)		
(0, 14)		(−14, 0)

3 Make a similar table for Cassiopeia and draw its position at 6 am.
4 Place some tracing paper over the grid and stick a pin through the centre of rotation.

5 Trace the Plough and Cassiopeia at midnight then rotate them a $\frac{1}{4}$ of a turn anticlockwise.

? **Have you plotted Cassiopeia's 6 am position correctly?**

To describe a rotation accurately you must give the centre of rotation, the angle *and* the direction of turning.

Although the constellations have moved their *size* and *shape* have not changed. We say that the two outlines of the Plough are **congruent**.

Exercise

1 Draw and label a set of axes like the ones opposite.
Plot the following co-ordinates joining them *as you go along*.

$$(-16, 4) \quad (-13, 4) \quad (-10, 3) \quad (-7, 0) \quad (-10, 0) \quad (-13, -2)$$

You have drawn the constellation called *Camelopardalis* at 6 pm.
Plot and label the Pole Star at the origin.

(a) Draw and label the position of *Camelopardalis* at midnight when it
has rotated a quarter of a turn in an anticlockwise direction.
Use tracing paper if you wish.

(b) Draw and label the position of *Camelopardalis* after another six hours.
Describe fully the transformation which takes *Camelopardalis* from
its 6 pm position to its 6 am position. What do you notice about the
co-ordinates of *Camelopardalis* at 6 pm and 6 am?

2 Copy these grids and shapes on to squared paper.

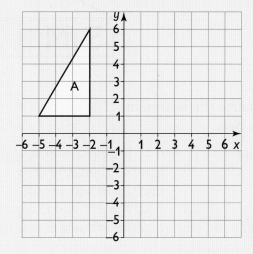 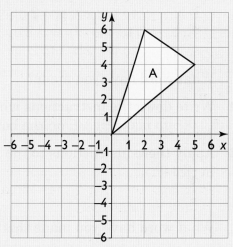

(a) For each one, rotate Shape A by a $\frac{1}{4}$ of a turn *in a clockwise direction*,
centre (0, 0). Label the resulting image B.

(b) For each one rotate Shape A by $\frac{1}{2}$ a turn around the origin.
Label the resulting image C.
Why does the direction not matter for this rotation?

3 Draw a pair of axes like those in Question 2.
Plot the following points and join them to form a letter L.

$$(0, 0) \quad (-5, 0) \quad (-5, 6) \quad (-3, 6) \quad (-3, 2) \quad (0, 2)$$

Rotate the L by $\frac{1}{4}$ of a turn *clockwise* and also by $\frac{1}{4}$ of a turn *anticlockwise*
about the origin. Label each image.
Describe *fully* the movement which would take one image to the other.

4 Why do the stars appear to move?
How long was the shutter open for the photograph opposite?

Translation

The movement of a shape in mathematics is called a **transformation**.
Rotation is one kind of transformation.
In the puzzle below the letter tiles slide to new positions in a different kind of way.

Ask your teacher for a copy of the puzzle or copy it on to squared paper.

The S has been moved 4 to the right and 2 up.

I Draw the remaining tiles after you have followed these instructions:

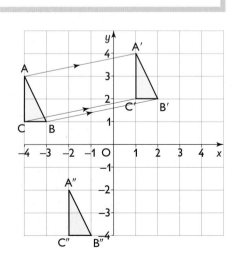

> M   1 to the right and 2 up
> I   1 to the left and 2 up
> L   3 to the left and 2 up
> E   1 to the left and 2 up

What word have you made?

2 Write down the instructions which move the letters in LIMES to make SLIME on the bottom row.

3 Apply these instructions to the letters in SLIME.

> S   4 to the right and 6 up
> L   1 to the right and 6 up
> I   1 to the left and 6 up
> M   3 to the left and 6 up
> E   1 to the left and 6 up

What word have you made this time?

What instruction moves the S in SMILE to the S in SLIME?
Write down the instructions which move the letters in SMILE to make SLIME on the bottom row.

The letter tiles in the puzzle move *without* turning.
This type of transformation is called **translation**.

When an **object** is translated, every point moves the *same distance* in a *parallel direction*.

Object ABC is translated 5 squares to the right and 1 square up to become **image** A' B' C'.
A maps to A', B maps to B' and C maps to C'.

What translation takes A' B' C' to A" B" C"?
What translation takes A' B' C' to ABC?

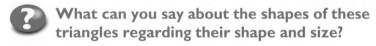
What can you say about the shapes of these triangles regarding their shape and size?

Exercise

1 Describe the following transformations.
In each case say how many right or left and how many up or down

(a) from C to B

(b) from A to B

(c) from D to A

(d) from C to D

(e) from D to C

(f) from B to D

(g) from B to C.

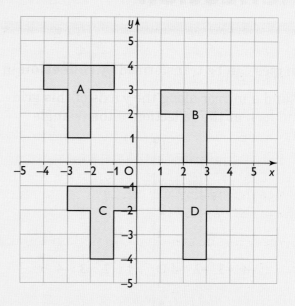

2 Draw x and y axes from -5 to $+5$ on centimetre squared paper.
Plot the following co-ordinates and join them to make a rectangle.

(1, 2) (1, 5) (3, 5) (3, 2)

Label this rectangle P.

(a) Translate rectangle P 5 to the left and 3 down.
Label the new rectangle Q.

(b) Translate rectangle P 1 to the left and 5 down.
Label the new rectangle R.

(c) Translate rectangle R 2 to the right and 4 up.
Label the new rectangle S.

(d) Describe the translation which takes P to S.

(e) Translate rectangle Q 0 along and 3 up.
Label the new rectangle T.

(f) Describe the translation which takes T to P.

3 Draw and label x and y axes from -9 to $+9$.
Plot the following points and join them to make a triangle.

$(-8, 2)$ $(-6, 7)$ $(-3, 2)$

Label this triangle W.

(a) Translate triangle W 11 to the right and 2 up.
Label the new triangle X.

(b) Rotate triangle X by $\frac{1}{2}$ a turn about the origin.
Label the new triangle Y.

(c) Rotate triangle W by $\frac{1}{2}$ a turn about the origin.
Label the new triangle Z.

(d) What transformation takes Y to Z?
What do you notice about this transformation?

Reflection

Shapes can be transformed by **reflection** in a mirror.

Stand a mirror along the y axis of this grid and look at the reflection of the triangle.

You will see this:

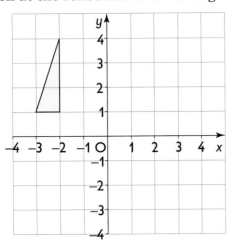 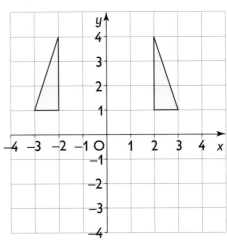

The shape on the left has been reflected in the y axis to form the shape on the right.

? **Are the two triangles congruent?**
What happens to writing when you read it in a mirror?

Task

1 Copy the grid above with the single triangle on to squared paper.
   Draw where the triangle would be if you reflected it in the x axis.
   Check with a mirror.

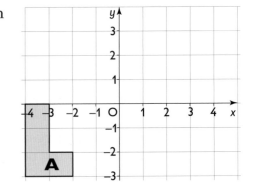

2 Copy this grid including Shape A.
   (a) Reflect Shape A in the y axis.
      Label the result B.
   (b) Reflect B in the x axis.
      Label the result C.
   (c) Describe two transformations, one after the other, which would take C back to A.
      Does it matter what order the transformations are in?
   (d) Can you think of a *single* transformation which would take C to A?

   ? **What happens to points on the mirror line in a reflection?**

   ? **Shapes A, B and C are congruent.**
      Are they identical? Explain your answer.

To describe a reflection you *must* say where the mirror line is.

Exercise

1 **(a)** Copy this letter Y on to a
co-ordinate grid as shown.

(b) Reflect the shape in the y axis.
What can you say about the image?

(c) Reflect the new image in the x axis.
Look carefully at the result.
Is it 'back to front'?

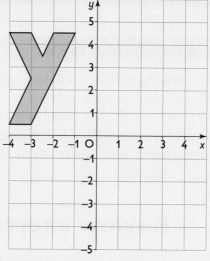

2 **(a)** Copy this letter A on to a
co-ordinate grid as shown.

(b) Reflect the shape in the y axis.
What can you say about the
image?

(c) Reflect the new image in the x
axis.
Look carefully at the result.
Is it 'back to front'?

(d) Why is the letter A always the
'right way round' but not the Y?

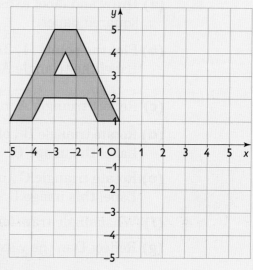

3 Draw x and y axes from -8 to $+8$. Plot the points $(-7, -2)$, $(-2, -3)$,
$(-5, -6)$ and join them to form a triangle labelled A.

Reflect triangle A in the x axis and label the image B.
Reflect triangle B in the y axis and label the new image C.
What single transformation would take A to C?

4 In part 2 of the Task on the opposite page, you reflected Shape A in first
the y axis and then the x axis. What happens if, instead, the second
reflection (in part **(b)**) is in the line $y = x$? Give new answers to parts **(c)**
and **(d)**.

Activity Make a banner which says AMBULANCE when read in a mirror.

 Why do you see this sort of writing on the front of emergency vehicles?

Finishing off

Now that you have finished this chapter you should:

- be able to rotate, translate and reflect shapes on a co-ordinate grid
- know that these are types of transformation
- know that shapes which are the same size and shape as each other are congruent
- know that rotation, translation and reflection all produce images which are congruent with the original shape.

Review exercise

1 **(a)** Draw and label axes from -8 to $+8$ on centimetre squared paper.

(b) Plot the points $(1, 2)$, $(3, 7)$, $(6, 1)$ and join them to form a triangle. Label the triangle A.

(c) Reflect triangle A in the x axis and label the image B.

(d) Rotate triangle B $\frac{1}{4}$ of a turn clockwise about centre of rotation $(0, 0)$. Label the image C.

(e) Rotate triangle C $\frac{3}{4}$ of a turn anticlockwise about the origin. Label this image D.

(f) What single transformation would have taken B straight to D?

(g) Reflect D in the y axis. Where has D landed?

2 **(a)** Draw and label axes from -10 to $+10$.

(b) Draw a shape on the grid which is not symmetrical.

(c) Reflect the shape in the x axis.

(d) Transform the image using a translation.

(e) Is it possible to move the final image back to the original shape using a single transformation?

If it is, can you describe the transformation which would do this?

3 **(a)** Draw triangle A of Question 1 again.

(b) Reflect triangle A in the diagonal line $y = -x$. Label the image E.

(c) Reflect triangle A in the diagonal line $x + y = 3$. Label the image F.

(d) Describe the transformation which moves triangle E to triangle F.

4 All the shapes on this grid are congruent.

(a) For each of the following describe *fully* the transformation which takes the first shape on to the second.
  (i)   C to D
  (ii) G to C
  (iii) D to G
  (iv) E to G

(b) Think of a different transformation which takes C to D besides your answer to (a) part (i).
Why can both transformations work?

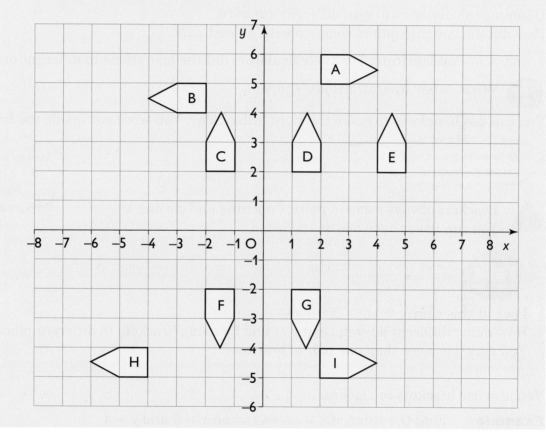

Investigation I Find as many new transformations between pairs of shapes on the grid above as you can.
Beware – some of them are not easy to describe!

Investigation 2 Draw this shape and reflect it in the y axis.

(a) What sort of triangle have you drawn?

(b) What can you say about its base angles?

(c) What happens if angle A is 60°?

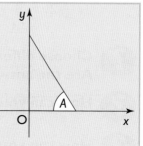

Brackets

Amber and Rhodri both enter $2 + 3 \times 5$ into their calculators.

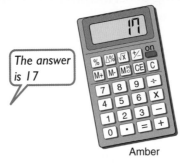

The answer is 17

No it's not. The answer is 25. My calculator says so, and calculators are never wrong.

Amber   Rhodri

Different calculators will give different answers.
How did the two calculators come up with 17 and 25?

$+$ and $\times$ are **operations**. The two calculators did the operations in different orders.

 What other operations are there?

You can use **brackets** to make the right order clear. You work out inside the brackets first.

Start by working out $6 + 8$ inside the brackets.

$(6 + 8) \div 2$
$14 \div 2$
7

$6 + (8 \div 2)$
$6 + 4$
10

Start by working out $8 \div 2$ inside the brackets.

! Brackets always come in pairs: (opening and closing).
You can never have one on its own.

Task

Look at this sum: $7 + 2 \times 3 - 1$
How many different answers can you find by using brackets in different places?
You may use more than one pair of brackets.

You also use brackets in algebra.

Example   Find the value of $2 \times (x + y)$ when $x = 3$ and $y = 4$.

$2 \times (3 + 4)$
2×7
14

You would usually leave out the $\times$ sign in algebra and write this $2(x + y)$.

Another way of writing $2(x + y)$ is $2x + 2y$.

When $x = 3$ and $y = 4$
$2x + 2y = 6 + 8$
$= 14.$

This is the same answer as you got for $2(x + y)$.

 Choose different values for x and y. Use them to work out $2(x + y)$ and $2x + 2y$. Are the answers always the same? Is $2x - 2y$ the same as $2(x - y)$?

 How can you write $12x + 12y$ using brackets?

 How can you work out $2 \times (3 + 4)$ on your calculator?

Exercise

1 Work out the following:
- **(a)** $(2 + 3) \times 5$
- **(b)** $(3 - 2) \times 100$
- **(c)** $(2 + 1) \times 10$
- **(d)** $(9 + 1) \times 10$
- **(e)** $(12 - 2) \times 4$
- **(f)** $(6 + 6) \times 3$
- **(g)** $5 \times (8 - 4)$
- **(h)** $(10 + 2) \div 3$
- **(i)** $(7 + 3) \div 2$
- **(j)** $9 \times (11 - 10)$
- **(k)** $(5 + 2) \div 7$
- **(l)** $(16 - 2) \div 7$
- **(m)** $(4 - 1) \div 3$
- **(n)** $(10 + 10) \times 5$
- **(o)** $(6 \div 3) \times 5$

2 Work out the following:
- **(a)** $(5 + 4) \times (9 - 7)$
- **(b)** $(9 - 1) \times (8 - 1)$
- **(c)** $(100 - 10) \div (2 + 1)$
- **(d)** $(3 + 2) \times (2 + 3)$
- **(e)** $(5 - 4) \times (9 - 8)$
- **(f)** $(6 + 6) \times (5 + 5)$
- **(g)** $(3 - 2) \times (4 + 1)$
- **(h)** $(6 - 2) \times (8 - 3)$
- **(i)** $(9 - 4) \times (8 - 6)$
- **(j)** $(7 - 1) - (8 - 6)$
- **(k)** $(36 \div 3) \div (18 \div 9)$
- **(l)** $(17 + 3) \div (8 - 3)$
- **(m)** $(12 - 6) - (6 - 4)$
- **(n)** $(12 \div 6) \div (6 \div 3)$
- **(o)** $(9 \div 3) \times (5 - 2)$

3 Find the values of the following:
- **(a)** $3(x + y)$ when
  - **(i)** $x = 2$ and $y = 8$
  - **(ii)** $x = 4$ and $y = 1$
  - **(iii)** $x = 2$ and $y = 0$
  - **(iv)** $x = 5$ and $y = -1$
- **(b)** $5(x - y)$ when
  - **(i)** $x = 10$ and $y = 8$
  - **(ii)** $x = 10$ and $y = 9$
  - **(iii)** $x = 10$ and $y = 0$
  - **(iv)** $x = 5$ and $y = 5$
- **(c)** $(x + y) \times (x - y)$ when
  - **(i)** $x = 5$ and $y = 2$
  - **(ii)** $x = 4$ and $y = 3$
  - **(iii)** $x = 6$ and $y = 0$
  - **(iv)** $x = 4$ and $y = 1$
- **(d)** $(a + b + c) \div 3$ when
  - **(i)** $a = 5$, $b = 6$ and $c = 7$
  - **(ii)** $a = 1$, $b = 1$ and $c = 1$
  - **(iii)** $a = 2$, $b = 1$ and $c = 0$
  - **(iv)** $a = 9$, $b = 6$ and $c = -6$

4 Write the following without brackets:
- **(a)** $4(x + y)$
- **(b)** $3(p + 2q)$
- **(c)** $2(x + 2y + 3z)$
- **(d)** $7(2a + 3b)$
- **(e)** $4(5l - 2m)$
- **(f)** $3(4a - 3b - 2c + d)$

5 Write the following using brackets:
- **(a)** $2x + 2y$
- **(b)** $5a + 5b$
- **(c)** $6c + 6d$
- **(d)** $4p + 4q$
- **(e)** $99l - 99m$
- **(f)** $9x + 9y - 9z$

6 Check that you can use brackets on your calculator. Use it to check your answers to Question 1.

Investigation Sometimes you meet brackets inside brackets.
Work through

$$(2 + (4 - 3) \times 5) \times 6 - 1$$

to get the answer 41.
Copy and complete this rule:
    'Start with the ... brackets and work ...'.

BIDMAS

Look at this picture.

It contains squares of various sizes.

 How does the picture show you that
$4 \times 3^2 + 5 \times 2^2 + 8 \times 1^2 = 64$?

In the last lesson you learnt about brackets.
You always work out inside brackets first.

There are 3 operations in $4 \times 3^2 + 5 \times 2^2 + 8 \times 1^2$.
They are $\times$, $+$ and square.

Square can also be called 'to the power 2' or 'Index 2'.
To get the answer 64, you must carry out the operations in the right order.

	4×3^2	$+$	5×2^2	$+$	8×1^2
Index (square)	4×9	$+$	5×4	$+$	8×1
Multiply	36	$+$	20	$+$	8
Add		$= 64$			

You will find the word BIDMAS helpful.
It tells you the right order to carry out the operations.

B rackets
I ndex
D ivide
M ultiply
A dd
S ubtract

 Task

Copy and complete this crossnumber:

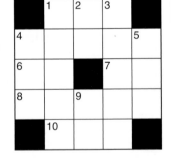

Across
1   $120 \times 2 + 14$
4   $3 \times (11 \times 1000 + 1)$
6   3×2^2
7   $(2 + 2)^3$
8   $(21 \times 10 - 9)^2$
10 $1000 \div 5 - 9$

Down
1   $2 \times 10^4 + 3 \times 10^3 + 2 \times 10^2 + 1$
2   $(50 + 50) \div 2$
3   $200^2 + 3 \times 200 + 1$
4   $(1000 - 58) \div 3$
5   $(3 \times 10 + 1) \times (12 - 1)$
9   $(4 + 3 \times 2) \times 5 - 1$

Now make a crossnumber of your own with clues like these.
Ask a friend to test it. Then write it on a poster.

 How do you write   (a) $x \times x \times x$
(b) $x + x + x$
(c) $x \times x + x$?

Exercise

1 Work out the following
(a) $3 \times 10 + 4$ (b) $5 \times 10 + 9$ (c) $8 + 10 + 1$
(d) 4×10^2 (e) 5×10^3 (f) 2×10^4
(g) $4 \times 10^2 + 5 \times 10 + 1$ (h) $4 \times 10^2 + 5 \times 10$ (i) $4 + 10^2 + 1$
(j) $3 \times 10^3 + 4 \times 10^2 + 6 \times 10 + 9$ (k) $3 \times 10^3 + 6 \times 10 + 9$
(l) $3 \times 10^3 + 4 \times 10^2 + 9$ (m) $3 \times 10^3 + 9$
(n) $3 \times 10^3 + 4 \times 10^2 + 6 \times 10$ (o) $3 \times 10^3 + 4 \times 10^2$

2 Write out the following
(a) $1 + 3 \times 5$ (b) $12 + 8 \div 4$ (c) $(17 - 2) \div 3$
(d) $6 + 2^3$ (e) $10^3 - 1$ (f) $2^3 + 3^2$
(g) $3^2 - 2^3$ (h) $10^3 + 10^2 + 10 + 1$ (i) $(2 \times 8 + 4)^2$
(j) $(29 - 4) \div 5$ (k) $3 \times 2^2 + 8$ (l) $(7 + 2 \times 2 - 1)^2$

3 Find the values of the following
(a) $x^2 + y$ when   (i) $x = 2$ and $y = 3$ (ii) $x = 4$ and $y = 3$
                   (iii) $x = 1$ and $y = 1$ (iv) $x = 5$ and $y = 2$
(b) $x + y^2$ when   (i) $x = 2$ and $y = 3$ (ii) $x = 4$ and $y = 3$
                   (iii) $x = 1$ and $y = 1$ (iv) $x = 5$ and $y = 2$
(c) $(x + y)^2$ when   (i) $x = 2$ and $y = 3$ (ii) $x = 4$ and $y = 3$
                   (iii) $x = 1$ and $y = 1$ (iv) $x = 5$ and $y = 2$
(d) $(x + y) \times 2$ when   (i) $x = 2$ and $y = 3$ (ii) $x = 4$ and $y = 3$
                   (iii) $x = 1$ and $y = 1$ (iv) $x = 5$ and $y = 2$

Activity   Here is a message in code. You will need to work out the code.
What does it say?

$3 + 5 \times 4$	$(5 + 5) \div 2$	$(2 + 1) \times (2 + 2)$
$2^2 \times 3$	$3 \times 2 - 6$	$2^4 \div 4$
$3 \times (4 + 1)$	$(4 + 3) \times (14 \div 7)$	$3^2 - 2^2$

JMO
Question Observe that $49 = 4 \times 9 + 4 + 9$.

(a) Find all other 2-digit numbers which are equal to the product of
their digits plus the sum of their digits.

(b) Prove that there are no 3-digit numbers which are equal to the
product of their digits plus the sum of their digits.

Collecting like terms

Liz is organising an evening at the Spotted Dragon for people at work.
She has written the cost of tickets as £*f* and £*d*.

 Why does Liz not know the values of *f* and *d*?

	Cutting Room	Sewing room	Despatch	Office
The total cost, in £, is	$2f + 4d$	$+$ $3f + 5d$	$+$ $2f + 3d$	$+$ $6f + d$

Tidy this up. Collect all
like items together:
$$2f + 3f + 2f + 6f + 4d + 5d + 3d + d$$
$$= 13f + 13d$$
$$= 13(f + d)$$

This is called an expression

In this case you can use brackets.

*All the f terms are **like** each other. All the d terms are **like** each other. The f terms are **unlike** the d terms*

Task

The Spotted Dragon say the costs will be £15 (full evening) and £5 (disco only).
What is the total cost?

How many different ways can you find to work out the total cost?

Which is the easiest to work out? Which is the hardest?

Sometimes there are numbers and minus terms.

Example   Tidy up $3x - 4 - 8x + 5 + 12x - 3 - 2x + 11$

Collect the +x terms, then the −x terms, then the + numbers and then the − numbers.

$3x + 12x$	$-8x - 2x$	$+5 + 11$	$-4 - 3$
+x terms	−x terms	+ numbers	− numbers
15x	−10x	+16	−7

This is the answer. It cannot be tidied up any more.

$5x + 9$

This is another expression.

Exercise

1 Group the like terms together in these lists. The answer to part (a) is already there.

(a) $+3x, +4y, +2x, -2y$ Answer $+3x, +2x$ and $+4y, -2y$

(b) $+5x, +6y, -7x, -7y$　　　　(c) $+8x, +5, -7, -2x, +3x, -5$

(d) $+8, -6, -2x, -3, +2y, -8$ (e) $+a, +2a, +3b, +4, +5, +6b, +7a$

2 Tidy up the following:

(a) $5a + 3a$ 　　　　　(b) $4b + 7b$ 　　　　　(c) $3c - 2c + 4c$

(d) $4d - 3d + d$ 　　　(e) $4e - 3e - e$ 　　　(f) $2f - f - f + 3f$

(g) $3g - 2g - 8g + 11g$ (h) $6h + 2h - 9h + 11h$ (i) $i + 2i - 3i - 4i + 6i$

(j) $2x + y + 3x + 2y$ 　(k) $5x + 2y + 6x + 9y$ 　(l) $5x - 4y - 4x + 6y$

(m) $2x - 4y + 3x + 5x - 8y + 15y$

(n) $3a + 2b - 4c + 5a - 3b - 2a + 5c - 2b + c$

(o) $p - q - r + 2p + 3q - 3r + 4q - 5r + 6p - 7r + 2q$

3 Miranda keeps a record of the first and second class letters leaving her office. A first class letter cost fp to send. A second class letter cost sp.

	First Class fp	Second Class sp
Monday	3	5
Tuesday	2	11
Wednesday	5	1
Thursday	20	12
Friday	10	11

(a) What is the cost of the letters on each day of the week? Your answers will include the letters f and s.

(b) What is the total cost?

(c) At the time, $f = 29$ and $s = 21$. What is the total cost?

4 Tidy up the following. Use brackets in your answers where you can.

(a) $2x + 3x + 10y - 5y$ 　　　　(b) $3a + 5 + 4a + 2$

(c) $2x + 6y + 8x - 3y$ 　　　　(d) $7p - q + 3p - 1$

(e) $8l + 6m - l + m$ 　　　　　(f) $8m + 25n + 7m - 15n - 5n$

(g) $5x + 8 + 2x - 7$ 　　　　　(h) $5p + 7q + 5p - 7q$

(i) $2(x + y) + x + 5y$ 　　　　(j) $3(2x + y) + x + 10y$

(k) $2(p + q) + 4p + q - 3p$ 　　(l) $5(a + 2b) + 2(a + 2b) - 7b$

(m) $2(x + 2y) + 3(x + 3y) + 2(x - 3y)$ (n) $3(x - y) + 2(x + y) + 5(x + 2y)$

JMO Question

AOC is a straight line and angle $AOB = 42°$. OP and OQ trisect angle AOB (which means they divide the angle into three equal parts). OR and OS trisect angle BOC.

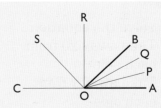

(a) Showing all working, calculate angle QOR and angle POS.

(b) Calculate angle QOR when angle $AOB = x°$.

Inverse operations

Look at Kwame's game.
Try it with several different numbers.

 **Does Kwame's game always work?
Try starting with a minus number,
or a fraction.**

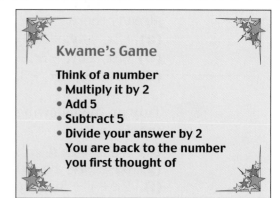

> **Kwame's Game**
>
> **Think of a number**
> • **Multiply it by 2**
> • **Add 5**
> • **Subtract 5**
> • **Divide your answer by 2**
>   **You are back to the number
>   you first thought of**

Take any starting number. Call it x.

- Multiply by 2 $2 \times x$ or $2x$
- Add 5 $2x + 5$
- Subtract 5 $2x + 5 - 5 = 2x$
- Divide by 2 $2 \times x \div 2 = x$

These two cancel each other out.

These two steps cancel each other out as well.

This is the number you first thought of. So, yes, it always works.

You can see that -5 cancelled out $+5$
                 $\div 2$ cancelled out $\times 2$.
We say that $-$ is the **inverse** operation of $+$
               $\div$ is the **inverse** operation of $\times$.

Operation	Inverse operation
$+$	$-$
$-$	$+$
$\times$	$\div$
$\div$	$\times$

 What is the inverse operation of 'square'?

 Task

Make up a 'Think of a number' game of your own and try it with a friend.

You use inverse operations when you solve equations.
Look at this balance.

Each coin weighs x grams.

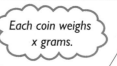

 How does it give the equation $4x + 20 = x + 80$?

To solve the equation
1 Take away 20 from $4x + 20 - 20 = x + 80 - 20$
   each side $4x \quad\quad\quad\quad = x + 60$
2 Take away x from $4x - x \quad\quad\quad = +x - x + 60$
   each side $3x \quad\quad\quad\quad = 60$
3 Divide each side $3x \div 3 \quad\quad\quad = 60 \div 3$
   by 3 $x \quad\quad\quad\quad = 20$

$-$ is the inverse of $+$

$-$ is the inverse of $+$

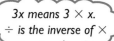

*$3x$ means $3 \times x$.
$\div$ is the inverse of $\times$*

So each coin weighs 20 grams.

Exercise

1 The diagram shows a journey made by a beetle. It starts at O and ends at O.

(a) Describe each stage of the journey. For example OA is 4 metres right.

(b) State which stages are the inverses of each other.

(c) What is the inverse of Left? What is the inverse of Down?

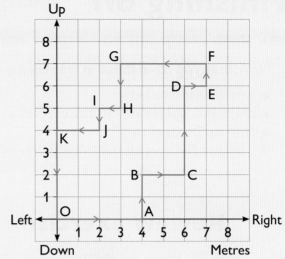

2 A soldier is on parade doing drill. He can be ordered 'Left Turn', 'Right Turn' or 'About Turn'.

(a) What is the inverse of the order 'Left Turn'?

(b) What is the inverse of the order 'Right Turn'?

(c) What is the inverse of the order 'About Turn'?

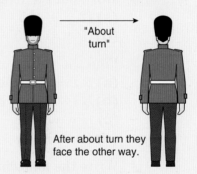

"About turn"

After about turn they face the other way.

3 Solve the following equations. Set out the various steps in full.

(a) $x + 5 = 7$ (b) $x - 6 = 1$

(c) $3x + 2 = 8$ (d) $5x + 8 = 18$

(e) $2x - 6 = 4$ (f) $2x - 2 = 12$

(g) $8x - 3 = 5$ (h) $5x - 2 = 18$

(i) $3x + 1 = 16$ (j) $4x + 2 = 14$

(k) $2 + 6x = 14$ (l) $7 + 2x = 17$

4 Solve the following equations. Set out the various steps in full.

(a) $12x + 5 = 10x + 9$ (b) $8x - 7 = 3x + 8$

(c) $4x + 2 = x + 8$ (d) $11x - 4 = 9x + 4$

(e) $16x - 7 = 9x + 42$ (f) $3x - 2 = 2x - 1$

(g) $4x + 1 = 2x + 21$ (h) $6x - 2 = 2x + 14$

(i) $3x + 8 = 19 - 8x$ (j) $16 - 7x = 18 - 9x$

(k) $3x + 2 + 2x - 3 = x + 7$ (l) $9x + 5 = 2x + 40 + 2x - 20$

5 Kwame thinks that solving $5x + 3 = 3x + 9$ gives $x = 3$.

He checks this by substituting $x = 3$ into both sides of the equation.

Left hand side: $5 \times 3 + 3 = 18$ Right hand side: $3 \times 3 + 9 = 18$

The answers are the same so he is right.

Use this method to check all your answers to Question 3.

Finishing off

Now that you have finished this chapter you should know how to:

- work with brackets
- carry out operations in the correct order (BIDMAS)
- tidy up in algebra
- use inverse operations to help you solve equations.

Review exercise

1 Work out the following.
(a) $(2 + 3) \times 5$ **(b)** $(9 - 1) \div 4$ **(c)** $2 \times (4 - 1)$
(d) $(5 + 4) \times (5 - 4)$ **(e)** $(10 + 2) \times (14 - 2)$ **(f)** $(6 \times 2) \div (4 - 1)$

2 Find the values of the following.
(a) $5(x + y)$ when $x = 2$ and $y = 4$
(b) $3(x + 2y)$ when $x = 4$ and $y = 1$
(c) $(x + y) \times (x - y)$ when $x = 5$ and $y = 1$
(d) $(x + 1) \times (y + 1)$ when $x = 1$ and $y = 3$

3 Write the following using brackets.
(a) $2x + 2y$ **(b)** $4x + 4y$ **(c)** $6f + 6g$
(d) $12p + 12q$ **(e)** $6l - 6m$ **(f)** $6s - 6t$

4 Work out the following.
(a) $10^3 + 10^2 + 10 + 1$ **(b)** $2 \times 10^3 + 3 \times 10^2 + 4 \times 10 + 5$
(c) $2 + 3 \times 6$ **(d)** $(2 + 3) \times 4 + 1$
(e) $(2 + 3) \times (4 + 1)$ **(f)** $2 + 3 \times (4 + 1)$

5 Work out the following.
(a) $2^2 \times 3 \times 5$ **(b)** $2 \times 3^2 \times 5$ **(c)** $2 \times 3 \times 5^2$
(d) $2^2 \times 3^2 \times 5$ **(e)** $2 \times 3^2 \times 5^2$ **(f)** $2^2 \times 3^2 \times 5^2$

6 Tidy up the following. Use brackets in your answers where you can.
(a) $5a + b + 3a + 2b$ **(b)** $4c + 5d + 3c + 2d$
(c) $6x + 5 + 5x + 6$ **(d)** $12x + 6y - 10x - 4y$
(e) $6p + 3q + 4q + 2p + 10p + 11q$ **(f)** $3x - 4 - 2 - x + 6x + 8 + x$
(g) $5x + 4 + 2y - 2x - 6y - 3 + 6x + 8 + 9y - 3x$

7 Solve the following equations.
(a) $3x + 1 = 7$ **(b)** $4x + 5 = 25$ **(c)** $5x + 6 = 16$
(d) $3x - 2 = 4$ **(e)** $4x + 2 = 2x + 6$ **(f)** $11x - 1 = 10x + 5$
(g) $7x + 2 = 5x + 8$ **(h)** $12x + 8 = 9x + 11$ **(i)** $3x - 2 = 2 - x$
(j) $2 - x = 8 - 2x$

8 Check your answers to Question 7. Substitute the answers in both sides of the equation. You should get the same numbers.

9 Explain why this 'Think of a number' game works.
Start by calling your number x.

> Think of a number
> Multiply it by 3
> Add 4
> Add 2
> Subtract 6
> Divide by 3
> You are left with the
> number you first thought of.

10 Use your calculator to find $\sqrt{2}$.
Now find $(\sqrt{2})^2$ on your calculator. Explain your answer.

Investigation Magic squares

In a magic square you get the same answer when you add up the numbers in each of the
rows, in each of the columns *and* in each diagonal.

1 Show that Square 1 is a magic square.

13	8	9
6	10	14
11	12	7

Square 1

2 Now look at Square 2. It is given in algebra.
Show that Square 2 is a magic square.

$m + a$	$m - a + b$	$m - b$
$m - a - b$	m	$m + a + b$
$m + b$	$m + a - b$	$m - a$

Square 2

3 Find the values of m, a and b in Square 2 which give
   (a) Square 1 values
   (b) a magic square containing the numbers 1, 2, 3, 4, 5, 6, 7, 8 and 9.

4 Now complete this magic triangle by putting the
numbers 1, 2, 3, 4, 5, 6 in the circles so that the sums of
the numbers along the three sides are equal.

How many different magic triangles can you make using
these numbers? (Two triangles are not counted as
different if one can be changed into the other by
reflection or rotation.)

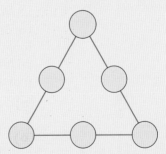

In this chapter there are 8 short investigations. You must decide for yourself how to go about them and which topics in mathematics you need to use. When you answer an investigation you must always give a clear explanation of what you have done. Make sure that your arguments are correct. Just giving a number is not enough, even if it is correct.

The questions are taken from past JMO papers. You are not allowed to use calculators or measuring instruments.

JMO Questions

1 How many different solutions are there to the letter sum on the right? Different letters stand for different digits, and no number begins with a zero.

$$\begin{array}{r} \text{JMC} \\ + \text{JMO} \\ \hline \text{SUMS} \end{array}$$

2 **(a)** Explain why the sum of three consecutive integers is always divisible by 3.

(b) Is it true that the sum of four consecutive integers is always divisible by 4?

(c) For which k is it true that the sum of k consecutive integers is always divisible by k?

3 **(a)** Find all the 2-digit numbers which are increased by 75% when their digits are reversed.

(b) Find all the 3-digit numbers which are increased by 75% when their digits are reversed.

4 Kate has 90 identical building blocks. She uses all of the blocks to build this four step 'staircase' in which each step, apart from the top one, is the same length.

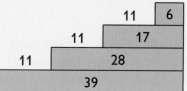

(a) Show that there are exactly two different ways in which it is possible to use all 90 blocks to build a six step 'staircase'.

(b) Explain fully why it is impossible to use all 90 blocks to build a seven step 'staircase'.

5  A counter.

Two players, X and Y, play a game on a board which consists of a narrow strip which is one square wide and n squares long. They take turns at placing counters, which are one square wide and two squares long, on unoccupied squares on the board. The first player who cannot go loses. X always plays first and both players make the best available move.

(a) Who wins the game on a 4×1 board? Explain how they must play to win and why they are then certain to win.

(b) Who wins on a 5×1 board? Explain why. So who wins on a 7×1 board? Explain.

(c) Who wins the game on a 6×1 board? How?

(d) Who wins the game on an 8×1 board? How?

6   Alice, the March Hare and the Mock Turtle were the only three competitors at the Wonderland sports day, and all three of them competed in each event. The scoring system was exactly the same for each event: the points scored for first, second and third were all positive integers and (even in Wonderland) more points were awarded for the first place than for second and more points for second place than for third.

Of course, the March Hare won the Sack Race. At the end of the day, Alice had scored 18 points while the Mock Turtle had 9 points and the March Hare had 8 points.

Can you decide how many events there were?

And can you tell who came last in the Egg and Spoon Race?

7   This question is about ways of placing square tiles on a square grid, all the squares being the same size. Each tile is divided by a diagonal into two regions, one black and one white. Such a tile can be placed on the grid in one of four positions as shown here.

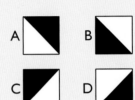

When two tiles meet along an edge (side by side or one below the other) the two regions which touch must be of different types (i.e. one black and one white).

(a)   A 2 × 2 grid of squares is to be covered by four tiles.

    (i)   If the top left square is covered by a tile in position A, find all the possible ways in which the other three squares may be covered.

    (ii)   In how many different ways can a 2 × 2 grid be covered by four tiles?

(b)   In how many different ways can a 3 × 3 grid be covered by nine tiles?

(c)   Explaining your reasoning, find a formula for the number of different ways in which a square grid measuring $n \times n$ can be covered by n^2 tiles.

8   X and Y play a game in which X starts by choosing a number, which must be either 1 or 2. Y then adds either 1 or 2 and states the total of the two numbers chosen so far. X does likewise, adding either 1 or 2 and stating the total, and so on. The winner is the first player to make the total reach (or exceed) 20.

(a)   Explain how X can always win.

(b)   The game is now modified so that at each stage the number chosen must be 1 or 2 or 4. Which of X or Y can now always win and how?

Answers

Here are the answers to the Review exercises to enable you to check your progress. All other answers are supplied in the Teacher's Resource accompanying this book. Full solutions to the JMO questions can be found in recent UKMT Yearbooks: see their website www.ukmt.org.uk.

1 How our numbers work (pages 8–9)
1 10^4, 40×1000, 45 678, 54 678, 10^5, 1 million
2 (a) Seven hundred and seventy eight million, three hundred thousand
   (b) Two million, one hundred and seventy five thousand
   (c) Eight thousand, eight hundred and forty eight
   (d) One hundred and sixty seven million
   (e) Thirty one million, five hundred and thirty six thousand
   (f) Two hundred and ninety nine million, seven hundred and ninety two thousand, five hundred
3 (a) 1 250 726   (b) 10 353 705 024
4 (a) 60 000   (b) 6 400 000
   (c) 72 000   (d) 20
   (e) 30   (f) 30 000
5 (a) 337 500 000 km   (b) 78 300 000 km
   (c) 1 654 900 000 km   (d) No, they are elliptical
   1 191 100 000 km
6 (a) 100 (b) 10 000 (c) 1 000 000
7 (a) 10^3 (b) 10^6 (c) 10^9 (d) 10^{12}, 10^{15}, 10^{18}, 34th

2 Position (pages 14–15)
1 (a) Trainers (b) Chair (c) A1, A2 (d) D2, D3
2 (a) 12 (b) 9 (c) 4 (d) 3 (e) 4 (f) G1, G14, F1, F13
   (g) C1 & C2, D1 & D2, E1 & E2, C11 & C12, D12 & D13,
   E13 & E14, H1& H2, H3 & H4
3 (a) due south   (b) 7 km
4 (a) 2A is the grid reference, 52 is the page number
   (b) Covent Garden 1A 52, Temple 1B 52, Charing Cross
   2A 52, Embankment 2A 52, Westminster 3A 52,
   Waterloo 3C 52, Lambeth Nth. 4C 52
   (c) (i) 3A (ii) 1A (iii) 4A
5 (a) 25 (b) 34 (c) A8 (d) Because cell D8 is highlighted
   (e) Means find the sum of cells D1 to D6 (f) In cell B8
   (g) B2, B6, D2, D5, D6, D8, F4, F8

3 Basic number (pages 26–27)
1

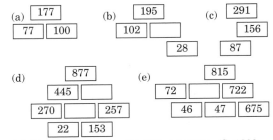

2 (a) 72 (b) 36 (c) 74 (d) 296 (e) 2664 (f) 1332
   (g) 13 320 (h) 666 000
3 (a) 32 (b) 130 (c) 2080 (d) 4160 (e) 325 (f) 32 500
4 (a) 99 999, 4 855 851 (b) 9 150 625, 4 855 851, 7 272 727
   (c) 4 855 851
5 (a) 2, 6 (b) 1, 4, 7 (c) 6 (d) 1, 5, 9 (e) 8

Activity
1 103 2 282 3 1087 4 941 5 11 6 33 7 39 8 362
9 2418 10 4123 11 20 601 12 45 408 13 35 14 413
15 104 16 52 17 216 18 432 19 196 20 49

Investigation
21 538, 21 835, 23 518, 23 815, 51 832, 53 218, 53 812,
81 235, 81 532, 83 215, 83 512

4 Angles (pages 36–37)
1 (a) F, B, D, A, E, C
   (b) (i) A (ii) B, D, F (iii) C
2 A = 113°, B = 49°, C = 343°
3 Ask your teacher to check your angles.
4 3°, 53°, right angle, obtuse angle, straight line, 240°, 300°
5 A = 34°, B = 146°, C = 120°, D = 133°, E = 121°, opposite
   sides of the quadrilateral are parallel and equal.

Investigation
Statement true.

5 Displaying data (pages 46–47)
1 (a)

Drink	Tally	Frequency
Cola	|||	10
Lemon	|||	5
Coffee	|||	3
Orange	||||	4
Tea	|||	6
	Total	28

   (b) 28 (c) Ask your teacher to check your pictogram
2 (a)

Grade	A	B	C	D	E
7T	4	10	8	5	3
7X	3	8	7	7	4

   (b) 30 (c) 29 (d) 7T
3 (a) $\frac{1}{4}$ (b) Dog (c) Dog, cat, guinea pig, rabbit, hamster
4 (a) People are less likely to be at work or school
   (b) 22nd July
   (c)

Number of visitors	Tally	Frequency
0–49	||	2
50–99	|||	8
100–149	|||	5
150–199		0
200–249	|||	3
250–299	|||	8
300–349	||||	4
350–399			1
	Total	31

   (d) Ask your teacher to check your bar chart.
5

	Frequency	Angle of slice
France	25	100°
Switzerland	23	92°
Austria	20	80°
Italy	16	64°
Scotland	6	24°

Ask your teacher to check your pie chart.
90 bookings.

6 Symmetry (pages 54–55)

1. (a) yes (b) no (c) yes (d) yes (e) no (f) yes (g) no (h) no (i) yes
2. (a) Denmark (1), Jamaica (2), Japan (2), Norway (1), Bangladesh (1), Botswana (2)
   (b) Jamaica (2), Japan (2), Trinidad and Tobago (2), Botswana (2)
3. Statues above entrance, window blinds, weathervane
4. (a) B (b) E (c) none (d) D

Investigation
(a) Yes (b) No (c) Yes

7 Decimal notation (pages 62–63)

1. (a) $\frac{1}{10}$ or $\frac{10}{100}$ (b) $\frac{3}{10}$ or $\frac{30}{100}$ (c) $\frac{13}{100}$ (d) $\frac{21}{100}$ (e) $\frac{37}{100}$
   (f) 0.1, 0.3, 0.13, 0.21, 0.37
2. 4.6, 15.03, 0.009, 301.207, 0.059
3. (a) A = 10.2, B = 11.4, C = 12.8, D = 13.6
   (b) W = 50, X = 58, Y = 64, Z = 76
   (c) L = 16.3, M = 16.8, N = 17.5
   (d) F = 88, G = 72, H = 52
4. (a) > (b) = (c) < (d) <
5. (a) £3.92 (b) £1.08
6. (a) £27.32 (b) £2.68
7. (a) £17.03 (b) £8.53 (c) £4.55
8. (a) (i) Altogether £179.97 (ii) He has £20.03 left
   (b) £16.96

Activity

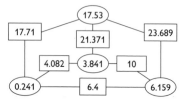

8 Co-ordinates (pages 70–71)

1. (a) (i) (0, 10) (ii) (20, 15)
   (b) (i) 15 km (ii) 25 km
   (c) (i) 15 km (ii) 20 km
2. (a) (−2, 4), (2, −4) (b) (−5, −3), (5, 3)
3. Ask your teacher to check your graph.
   Add point (−3.5, −3.5) to make shape symmetrical
4. Because it is 4 away from his first guess.

9 Fractions (pages 82–83)

1. (a) $\frac{3}{4}$ (b) $\frac{4}{5}$ (c) $\frac{5}{6}$ (d) $\frac{3}{4}$ (e) $\frac{3}{5}$ (f) $\frac{3}{4}$ (g) $\frac{3}{5}$ (h) $\frac{2}{3}$ (i) $\frac{8}{9}$ (j) $\frac{1}{2}$
2. (a) $\frac{11}{100}$ (b) $\frac{3}{100}$ (c) $\frac{79}{100}$ (d) $\frac{91}{100}$
3. (a) $\frac{3}{25}$ (b) $\frac{1}{25}$ (c) $\frac{4}{5}$ (d) $\frac{23}{25}$ (e) $\frac{9}{20}$ (f) $\frac{9}{50}$ (g) $\frac{8}{25}$ (h) $\frac{3}{4}$
4. (a) £8 (b) 440 yards (c) 10 ozs (d) £12
5. (a) £28 (b) £32 (c) £36 (d) £20 (e) £12 (f) £4
6. (a) £195 (b) $2 (c) 27 Euros (d) 36 kg (e) 2 m (f) 44 km
7. (a) $\frac{1}{12}$ (b) $\frac{2}{21}$ (c) $\frac{4}{13}$ (d) $\frac{1}{4}$ (e) $\frac{8}{55}$ (f) $\frac{2}{33}$
8. (a) $\frac{3}{8}$ (b) $\frac{1}{2}$ (c) $\frac{3}{14}$ (d) $\frac{12}{187}$ (e) $\frac{1}{63}$ (f) $\frac{7}{18}$
9. (a) $\frac{7}{12}$ (b) $\frac{42}{55}$ (c) $\frac{3}{26}$ (d) $\frac{13}{56}$ (e) $\frac{7}{24}$ (f) $\frac{16}{55}$
10. (a) 4 : 5 (b) 5 : 1 (c) 4 : 3 (d) 4 : 2 : 3 (e) 3 : 5 : 6
    (f) 8 : 5 : 6
11. (a) 3 kg lime and $1\frac{1}{2}$ kg potash
    (b) 8 kg hoof and horn, 8 kg lime, and 4 kg potash

Activity
3. (2, 1), (4, 2), (6, 3), (8, 4), (10, 5) $\frac{1}{2} = \frac{2}{4} = \frac{3}{6} = \frac{4}{8} = \frac{5}{10}$
4. (a) $\frac{4}{6}, \frac{6}{9}, \frac{8}{12}$ (b) $\frac{8}{10}$ (c) $\frac{6}{8}, \frac{9}{12}$

10 Number patterns (pages 94–95)

1. (a) 3,6,9,12,15 (b) 7,14,21,28,35 (c) 12,24,36,48,60
   (d) 11,22,33,44,55 (e) 9,18,27,36,45 (f) 30,60,90,120,150
2. (a) 1,3,5,15 (b) 1,2,3,4,6,8,12,24 (c) 1,19 (d) 1,3,9,27
   (e) 1,2,4,8,16 (f) 1,13
   13 and 19 are prime
3. (a) 21,42,63 (b) 7,9,13,17,21,25,27,29,63
   (c) 9,16,25,64,100 (d) 8,27,64 (e) 7,13,17,29 (f) 8,16,64
4. (a) 28
5. (a) 1, 2, 4, 5, 10, 11, 20, 22, 44, 55, 110, 220 (c) 1184
6. (a) $2^3 \times 3 \times 13^2$ (b) 6, 156 (c) 117, 78
7. (a) (i) 3 (ii) 7 (iii) 31 (iv) 127 (v) 2047 = 23 × 89

Investigation 1
(b) 10, 15, 21 (c) 3 + 6, 10 + 15, 21 + 15 ... (d) 36

11 Everyday measures (pages 102–103)

1. 86 400
2. Elephant – 1 ton
   Feather – 3 gm
   Baby – 4.5 kg
   Potatoes – 5 lb
   Sweets – 8 oz
3. (a) Longest river: Nile 6669 km
   (b) tallest woman: 2.48 m (8 ft $1\frac{3}{4}$ in), a Zeng Jinlian
   (c) record for 100 metres: 9.79 sec (set in 1999 by Maurice Greene)
   (d) 5 litres in an average human man
   (e) heaviest man: 635 kg (100 stone), a Jon Minnoch
4. (a) 20 mins (b) 3 buses per hour
   (c) (i) 19:25 (ii) 10 mins
   (d) yes – the last bus leaves at 8.25 p.m.
5. (a) 2 000 ml (b) 18 ft (c) 48 ounces
6. 170 cm
7. (a) Monday and Thursday (b) No (c) 40 hrs
   (d) Friday – $6\frac{1}{2}$ hrs
8. 15 people

12 Flat shapes (pages 114–115)

1. Ask your teacher to check your drawing.
2. Ask your teacher to check your drawings.
   (c) Corresponding angles are equal.
   Each triangle contains a right angle.
   Angles inside each triangle add up to 180°.
3. Ask your teacher to check your answer.
4. Ask your teacher to check your drawing.
   Other two angles are 77° each.
5. 23.3 m
6. Ask your teacher to check your drawing.
7. Ask your teacher to check your drawing.
   ABC and XYZ are parallel.
8. Ask your teacher to check your drawing.

Investigation
(b) 360°

JMO Question (see JMO 2000)
80°

13 Multiplying and dividing decimals (pages 124–125)

1. £17.85 2. £47.36 3. £112.50
4. (a) 7.04 (b) 6.1488 (c) 0.9614 (d) 1.3485 (e) 0.167778
   (f) 143.82
5. (a) 1.75 (b) 0.12 (c) 0.85 (d) 0.65 (e) 8.9 (f) 1.6̇3̇
6. (a) 20.5 (b) 0.6 (c) 12.2 (d) 215 (e) 720 (f) 6
7. (a) £0.12 (b) £0.11 Second set
8. No, 26 × 0.7 = 18.2 cm
9. (a) 17.28 (b) 0.137 62 (c) 219.342 (d) 0.017 (e) 1 029.031
   (f) 0.001 12 (g) 2.34 (h) 0.356 (i) 3.2 (j) 0.0141
10. (a) 0.375 (b) 0.6 (c) 0.4 (d) 0.625 (e) 0.875 (f) 0.16
    (g) 0.8̇3̇ (h) 0.58̇3̇
11. (a) 44% (b) 40% (c) $37\frac{1}{2}$% (d) 45% (e) 11% (f) 7%
    (g) 60% (h) 75%
    7%, 11%, $37\frac{1}{2}$%, 40%, 44%, 45%, 60%, 75%
12. (a) $\frac{3}{5}$ (b) $\frac{3}{20}$ (c) $\frac{7}{25}$ (d) $\frac{1}{50}$
13. (a) 0.9 (b) 0.12 (c) 0.85 (d) 0.5̇
14. (a) $\frac{17}{100}$ (b) $\frac{3}{50}$ (c) $\frac{3}{10}$ (d) $\frac{1}{8}$
15. Consistently good. Best: English, worst: Geography.

Activity
(a) 0.06 (b) 4180 (c) 0.006 (d) 1.673 (e) 0.9 (f) 0.021
(g) 3 (h) 0.13 (i) 0.01 (j) 0.0013 (k) 0.4 (l) 0.72 (m) 7
(n) 0.00018 (o) 0.00004

14 Number machines (pages 132–133)

1. (a) 2 (b) 3 (c) 50 (d) 0
2. (a)

Micro Mobiles	time in mins → ×4 →+20 → Cost of call
Lo-Calls	time in mins → ×6 →+10 → Cost of call

   (b) Micro Mobiles (c) Lo-Call
   (d) Micro Mobiles – 11 mins, Lo-Calls – 9 mins
3. (a) 2 (b) 12 (c) 5 (d) 10

4 (a) e.g.

4	→	×6	→	−3	→	21
4	→	×2	→	+13	→	21
4	→	÷4	→	+20	→	21
4	→	×4	→	+5	→	21

(b) (i) 6 (ii) 26 (iii) 31 (iv) 101
(c) input → ×5 → +1 → output
(d) (i) 8 (ii) 10 (iii) 15 (iv) 25

5 (a) (i) 14, 13 (ii) 86, 85
(b) E = 2n, O = 2n − 1

Investigation
(a) (i) $C \to \boxed{\times 9} \to \boxed{\div 5} \to \boxed{+32} \to F$ (ii) $F = \frac{9}{5}C + 32$
(b) (i) $F \to \boxed{-32} \to \boxed{\times 5} \to \boxed{\div 9} \to C$ (ii) $C = \frac{5}{9}(F - 32)$

15 Scale (pages 140–141)

1

Object	Real length	Model length
Engine	20 m	10 cm
Level crossing	20 m	10 cm
Signals	8 m	4 cm
Station	100 m	50 cm
Tree	5 m	2.5 cm
Suitcase	100 cm or 1 m	5 mm
Station cat	40 cm	2 mm

2 (a) 1 : 300 (b) 1 : 20 (c) 1 : 100 000 (d) 1 : 50 000
(e) 1 : 500 000 (f) 1 : 20 (g) 1 : 50 (h) 1 : 2.5
3 (a) 1 cm to 0.25 km (b) 1 cm to 0.5 km (c) 1 km to 1 km
4 (a) 1 cm to 5 m (b) 4 cm to 1 m or 1 cm to 0.25 m
(c) 2 cm to 1 m or 1 cm to 0.5 m
5 (a) 2 miles (b) 3.5 miles (c) 4.75 miles
6 1 to 25
7 Ask your teacher to check your drawing. 5.3 m
8 (a) 400 m (b) 1700 m

16 Averages (pages 148–149)

1 (a) 2 (b) 2.2 (c) 2 (d) 6
2 (a) Mean for boys = 6.5
   Mean for girls = 5.4
(b) Median for boys = 3.5
   Median for girls = 5
(c) Range for boys = 41
(d) Range for girls = 9
(e) The boys' data is more spread out than the girls'.
3 11, 13, 15, 16, 16 years
4 (a) £3.25 (b) £4.225 or £4.23 (c) Mean (d) £3.40
5 (a)

46	47	48	49	50	51	52	53
1	2	3	5	9	6	3	1

(b) Mode = 50 (c) Mean = 49.8 (d) Median = 50
6 (a) Batch A   mean = 1.688   Batch B   mean = 1.8
         median = 1.7   median = 1.7
         range = 2   range = 3.4

Height in cm	Batch A	Batch B
0–0.9	3	4
1.0–1.9	14	10
2.0–2.9	8	5
3.0–3.9	0	3

Ask your teacher to check your bar charts.
Modal class is 1.0–1.9 for each batch.

17 Formulae (pages 154–155)

1 (a) A – adults C – children P – price
(b) (i) £14 (ii) £6 (iii) £29
(c) 4 (d) 3 (e) P = 3A + 2C (f) 6 children, 4 adults

2 (a) 20 (b) 5 (c) 13 (d) 30 (e) 25 (f) 12 (g) 20
(h) 5000 (i) 0
3 (a) C = 80(w + h) + 50wh (b) (i) £430 (ii) £81
4 (a) Cost = 2 × £3 + 4 × £4 = £22 (b) C = 3h + 4g
(c) £50 (d) 0 hamsters and 6 gerbils, or 3 gerbils and
   4 hamsters, or 6 hamsters and 0 gerbils 3 ways
5 (a) Cost = 5 × 25 + 3 × 15 = £170 (b) Cost = 25l + 15s
(c) £145 (d) 5 small (e) 2 large and 3 small

Investigation
1 p = price, a = adults, s = students, c = children
2 2 adults, 1 student and 2 children; 1 adult and 4 students

18 Negative numbers (pages 162–163)

1
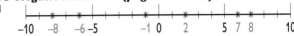

2 −6, −3, −1, 0, +1, +5
3 (a) −1 (b) −1 (c) −3 (d) +3 (e) −6 (f) −1 (g) −8
(h) +7 (i) −4 (j) −36 (k) −24 (l) +8
4 (a) −2 (b) −7 (c) 2   (d) 0   (e) 4   (f) −4 (g) −3
(h) 2 (i) 6 (j) −9 (k) 3 (l) 9
5 (a) +10 (b) −8 (c) −11 (d) +7 (e) −3 (f) +7 (g) −4
(h) −15 (i) −2 (j) +33 (k) −28 (l) +22
6 (a) −8 (b) −15 (c) +42 (d) +36 (e) +30 (f) 0   (g) +1
(h) +9 (i) −8 (j) +625 (k) +16
(l) 4 × (−243) = −972
7 (a) −6 (b) +4 (c) +5   (d) −7 (e) +4 (f) +16
(g) −6 (h) −9 (i) −19 (j) +7 (k) −8 (l) −25
8

−4	10	1	−5
−1	−3	2	4
3	1	2	−4
4	−6	−3	7

9

2	−9	−12
−36	6	−1
−3	−4	18

Activity
(a) −3 (b) −8 (c) 9 (d) −8 (e) 0 (f) +4 (g) +28
(h) −30 (i) −24 (j) −4 (k) −7 (l) 0 (m) 16 (n) −27

19 Equations (pages 170–171)

1 (a) A-5 B-10 C-20 (b) D-0.5 E-0.5 F-1 G-1
2 (a) 4 (b) 2 (c) 4 (d) 3
3 (a) 4 (b) 1 (c) 4 (d) 10 (e) 32 (f) 4 (g) 6 (h) 30 (i) 1
4 (a) 1 (b) 2 (c) 3 (d) 3 (e) 2 (f) 1 (g) 2 (h) 8 (i) 0
5 (a) 5 (b) 1 (c) 10 (d) 2 (e) 8 (f) 10 (g) 3 (h) 2 (i) 1
6 (a) 4n + 6 = 30 (b) 6
7 (a) 24 + 4b = 84 (b) 15p
8 26°, 64°
9 (a) (i) £15, £20, £30 (ii) £8, £13, £16
(b) At least £45 is needed.

Investigation
Leah x = 3, Ryan x = 3

20 Solid shapes (pages 178–179)

1 (a) cylinder (b) triangular prism (c) cuboid
(d) hexagonal prism (e) cuboid
2 A Isosceles triangular prism
B Irregular prism
C Cylinder
D Hexagonal prism
E Cuboid
F Equilateral triangle prism
3 Ask your teacher to check your drawing.
4 All elevations are identical.
Ask your teacher to check your drawing.

21 Graphs (pages 186–187)

1 (a) 63 miles (b) 134 km (c) 106 miles (d) 84 km
2 (a)

Length of call (in mins)	1	2	3	4	5	6	7	8
Cost (in pence)	16	22	28	34	40	46	52	58

(b) Ask your teacher to check your graph.

3 (i)

x	-4	-3	-2	-1	0	1	2	3	4
$y = x + 6$	2	3	4	5	6	7	8	9	10

(ii)

x	-4	-3	-2	-1	0	1	2	3	4
$y = 2x$	-8	-6	-4	-2	0	2	4	6	8

Ask your teacher to check your graphs.

4 (i) $(-3, -4), (-2, -3), (-1, -2), (0, -1), (1, 0), (2, 1), (3, 2)$ $y = x - 1$
(ii) $(-3, -2), (-2, 1), (-1, 0), (0, -1), (1, -2), (2, -3), (3, -4)$ $y = -x - 1$
(iii) $(-3, -4), (-3, -3), (-3, -2), (-3, -1), (-3, 0), (-3, 1), (-3, 2)$ $x = -3$
(iv) $(3, -4), (3, -3), (3, -2), (3, -1), (3, 0), (3, 1), (3, 2)$ $x = 3$
(v) $(-3, -4), (-2, -2), (-1, 0), (0, 2)$ $y = 2x + 2$
(vi) $(0, 2), (1, 0), (2, -2), (3, -4)$ $y = -2x + 2$

Investigation
(a) (i) 20.5 cm   (ii) 1.6 years
(b) Ask your teacher to check your graph   (i) 115 g   (ii) 1.6 years
(c) Yes

22 Measuring (pages 196–197)
1 (a) 20 cm, 24 cm^2 (b) 22 m, 24 m^2
    (c) 17 inches, 15 inches^2 (d) 19 yards, 22 yards^2
    (e) 4 miles, 1 mile^2
2 approx 19 miles^2
3 (a) 54 m^3 (b) 13.5 cm^3 **4**   5940 cm^3

Investigation 1
1000 cm^3; 1 ml = 1 cm^3; total volume of cylinders in which fuel is burnt.

Investigation 2
Cheapest design (cube) costs £52.92

Activity
Approximate volumes: cassette case 122 cm^3; CD case 176 cm^3; imperial house brick 118 inches^3; metric house brick $1397\frac{1}{2}$ cm^3; this book 648 cm^3; one page of this book 2.57 cm^3.

JMO Question (see JMO 2001)
122, 28 cm by 122 cm or 12, 18 cm by 132 cm

23 Flow diagrams and number patterns (pages 208–209)
1 (a) Ask your teacher to check your answers
    (b) Because $(1 + 1) \div 2 = 1$
    (c) Not necessarily
    (d) Shortest chains are the powers of 2 i.e. 2, 4, 8, 16, 32 ...
2 (a)

Stage	1	2	3	4	5
Number of diagonal bars	2	4	6	8	10

(b)

Stage	1	2	3	4	5
Number of horizontal bars	3	6	9	12	15

    (c) 20 diagonal bars and 30 horizontal bars
       diagonal bars = 2 × number of sections   or D = 2S
       cross bars = 3 × number of sections   or B = 3S
3 (a) Ask your teacher to check your diagrams.
    (b)

Stage	1	2	3	4	5	6	7
Number of paving stones	1	5	9	13	17	21	25
Number of turfs	0	8	32	72	128	200	288

    (c) 37, 648
    (d) Number of stones = 4 × stage -3, $p = 4s - 3$
       Number of turfs = 8 × square of (stage $-$ 1), $t = 8(s - 1)^2$

Investigation
$1 + 2 + \ldots (n - 1)$ where n = number in class. This is the same formula for the number of diagonals in a polygon with n vertices.

JMO Question (see JMO 2001)
(a) 25, 29, 85, 89, 145   (b) 16 (sequence repeats every 14 terms)

24 Accuracy (pages 218–219)
1 (a) 23   20   (b) 15   10   (c) 35   40   (d) 20   20
    (e) 135   140   (f) 235   240   (g) 10   10   (h) 9   10
2 (a) 2100   2000   (b) 4700   5000   (c) 8100   8000
    (d) 7000   7000   (e) 900   1000   (f) 400   0
    (g) 500   0   (h) 1500   1000

3

France	553 000	Spain	505 000	Portugal	92 000
Belgium	31 000	Switzerland	41 000	Italy	92 000
Denmark	43 000	Sweden	450 000	Austria	84 000
Norway	324 000	Finland	337 000		

4 (a) 400 × 80 = 32 000 (or 400 × 100 = 40 000)
    (b) 1000 ÷ 500 = 2   (c) 8 × 12 = 96 (or 8 × 10 = 80)
    (d) 40 (90 + 90) ≈ 40 × 200 = 8000
5 (a) £1.57   (b) £6.41   (c) £23.83   (d) 35p
6 (a) (i) 4.7   (ii) 4.73   (b) (i) 35.7   (ii) 35.68
    (c) (i) 0.16   (ii) 0.158   (d) (i) 0.1   (ii) 0.08
7 Ask your teacher to check your number lines.
8 (a) 3   (b) 7   (c) 34
9 (a) 8 and 9   (b) 11 and 12   (c) 29 and 30
10 Possible answers are:
    (a) 24 000 (to the nearest 1000)
    (b) 57 cm (to the nearest cm)
    (c) £3 500 000 (to the nearest £100 000)
    (d) 3 hr 20 min (to the nearest 10 min)
    (e) 1000 kg (to the nearest 10 kg)
    If you have given a different degree of accuracy, ask your teacher to check your answers.
11 Ask your teacher to check your answer.

25 Probability (pages 226–227)
1 Ask your teacher to check your answers.
2 Ask your teacher to check your answers.
3 (a) $\frac{1}{8}$ (b) $\frac{2}{8}$ or $\frac{1}{4}$ (c) 0   (d) $\frac{3}{8}$ (e) $\frac{4}{8}$ or $\frac{1}{2}$ (f) $\frac{2}{8}$ or $\frac{1}{4}$
4 (a) $\frac{1}{50}$ (b) $\frac{5}{50}$ or $\frac{1}{10}$ (c) 49   (d) $\frac{1}{49}$ (e) $\frac{5}{49}$
5 (a) fair   (b) unfair   (c) fair   (d) fair
6 Ask your teacher to check your method.

26 Transformations (pages 234–235)
1 Ask your teacher to check your diagrams.
    (f) Rotation of $\frac{1}{2}$ turn about the origin.   (g) On A.
2 Ask your teacher to check your diagrams.
    (e) This may be done by a reflection in a horizontal axis, but only if the translation in (d) involved no left or right movement.
3 Ask your teacher to check your diagram.
    (d) Translation 3 to right, 3 up.
4 (a) (i) Reflection in y axis.
       (ii) Rotation by $\frac{1}{2}$ turn about the origin.
       (iii) Reflection in x axis.
       (iv) Rotation by $\frac{1}{2}$ turn about (3, 0).
    (b) Translation 3 to right, 0 up.   C and D are symmetrical.

Investigation 1
72 transformations in total, some of which can be done in more than one way, due to the symmetry of the shape.
E.g. A → F is a rotation by $\frac{1}{4}$ turn clockwise about $(-3\frac{1}{2}, 3\frac{1}{2})$.

Investigation 2
(a) Isosceles   (b) Equal   (c) The triangle is equilateral.

27 Operations in algebra (pages 244–245)
1 (a) 25   (b) 2   (c) 6   (d) 9   (e) 144   (f) 4
2 (a) 30   (b) 18   (c) 24   (d) 8
3 (a) $2(x + y)$ (b) $4(x + y)$ (c) $6(f + g)$ (d) $12(p + q)$
    (e) $6(l - m)$ (f) $6(s - t)$
4 (a) 1 111   (b) 2 345   (c) 20   (d) 21   (e) 25   (g) 17
5 (a) 60   (b) 90   (c) 150   (d) 180   (e) 450   (f) 900
6 (a) $8a + 3b$ (b) $7(c + d)$ (c) $11(x + 1)$ (d) $2(x + y)$
    (e) $18(p + q)$ (f) $9x + 2$ (g) $6x + 5y + 9$
7 (a) 2   (b) 5   (c) 2   (d) 2   (e) 2   (f) 6   (g) 3   (h) 1   (i) 1   (j) 6
8 (a) 7 = 7   (b) 25 = 25   (c) 16 = 16   (d) 4 = 4
    (e) 10 = 10   (f) 65 = 65   (g) 23 = 23   (h) 20 = 20
    (i) 1 = 1   (j) $-4 = -4$
9 Steps are: x; $3x$; $3x + 4$; $3x + 6$; $3x$; x
10 $(\sqrt{2})^2 = 2$ ✓   and square are inverse operations

Investigation
1 All rows, columns and diagonals add to 30
2 All rows, columns and diagonals add to $3m$
3 (a) $m = 10, a = 3, b = 1$
    (b) $m = 5, a = 3, b = 1$ or $m = 5, a = 1, b = 3$
4 Four possible arrangements (round the triangle, starting at a corner): 1, 5, 3, 4, 2, 6   or   1, 6, 3, 2, 5, 4   or
              2, 5, 4, 1, 6, 3   or   4, 3, 5, 1, 6, 2.